HUMAN DIGNITY
AND GENETIC HERITAGE

Protection of Life Series

Table of Contents

Introduction

The advent of the year 2000, and of the next millennium, portends tremendous promise in the science of human genetics. Like the discovery of the atom and, more recently, the ability to conceive human life *in vitro*, advances in human genetics harbour the potential for good and for evil. The very essence of humankind is at stake. At the same time, the potential of this science lies in the knowledge it provides, knowledge that will finally force to the forefront a discussion of the nature, uniqueness and potential for change of the human species. Indeed, the era of genetics will provide us with the opportunity and the duty to give meaning to the inherent dignity of the human person.[1]

The lack of precise knowledge about where human genetics might take us raises false hopes in some and leads others to make wholesale denunciations. The latter group has applied such terms as "interfering with nature," "playing God" and the "slippery slope" to genetic engineering.[2] There is no doubt that the new tools of human genetics do, and will, affect the human being in the ultimate substratum, namely, the gene. Whether the result will be "good" or "evil" will depend on whether individuals, scientists and governments seek and apply genetic knowledge responsibly and discriminately. In order to understand the potential of this knowledge, we must understand first how the progress in molecular genetics has changed the practice of medical genetics (Chapter One).

In 1982, the Council of Europe, in its recommendation on Genetic Engineering, advocated that the right to life and to human dignity implied the right to an unaltered genetic pattern – one that had not been artificially altered.[3] It also proposed that this right should be made explicit in the European *Convention for the Protection of Human Rights and Fundamental Freedoms*.[4] However, no guidance was provided as to what was meant by a genetic pattern or heritage or how it could be protected from change by means of law.

---

1. *Universal Declaration of Human Rights*, G.A. Res. 217/A, Off. Doc. G.A., 3rd Session at 71, U.N. Doc. A/810 (1948):

   > *Whereas* recognition of the inherent dignity and of the equal and inalienable rights of all members of the human family is the foundation of freedom, justice and peace in the world . . .
   >
   > *Whereas* the peoples of the United Nations have in the Charter reaffirmed their faith in fundamental human rights, in the dignity and worth of the human person and in the equal rights of men and women . . . (Preamble).

2. Keith Boone, "Bad Axioms in Genetic Engineering" (1988) 18:4 Hast. Cent. Rep. 9.
3. Council of Europe, P.A., 33rd Sess., Pt III, *Texts Adopted, Recommendation 934 (1982) on Genetic Engineering*, s. 4(i).
4. (1955) 213 U.N.T.S. 221 [hereinafter European Convention on Human Rights].

Considering the advances in molecular biology affecting human genetics since that 1982 recommendation, we must now determine what genetic heritage is. Does it mean the collective gene pool or the individual genome?[5] Answers to this question are necessary to decide what is inherent to human dignity that merits legal protection (Chapter Two).

Even though the inherent dignity of the human person is seen as fundamental, its interpretation in a human rights context is not yet clear. However, there is no doubt that respect for the human body, for one's genetic make-up and origins, is indivisible from respect for the person. Human cells, with their genetic information, are more than a temporary substrate for the existence of the human body; they are a constituent of human dignity. The Council of Europe linked the right to protection of the genetic heritage to the right to life and to human dignity. However, it did not exclude therapeutic interventions. In fact, its preliminary report contains the startling suggestion that reproductive freedom of those persons at risk of transmitting certain serious genetic illnesses might be linked to their consenting to genetic therapy to reduce the probability of transmitting those illnesses to subsequent generations. Thus, assigning a right to a "healthy" genetic heritage to protect human dignity may do as much to undermine that human dignity by restricting freedom (Chapter Three).

While the meaning of human dignity in international human rights law is not fully developed, the notion can serve as the foundation for the interpretation of human rights in the context of constitutional law. In particular, under the *Canadian Charter of Rights and Freedoms*, the rights to life, liberty and security of the person, the right to be free from unreasonable search and seizure and the right to equality and protection from discrimination have been seen as based on the recognition of that inherent dignity.[6] We may then ask whether such constitutional guarantees are directly applicable to the issues raised by the new human genetics in a free and democratic society such as Canada. Some examples of issues that may arise are: compulsory testing for disease or carrier status in particular groups of individuals; the obligation of parents to have their children tested for treatable diseases; and the use of DNA samples for unauthorized purposes (Chapter Four).

Improving the capability to treat or alter the genome of an individual and genetic testing to identify the risk of future diseases may result in stigmatization. Indeed, "[f]rom a societal perspective, a gene probe for manic depression may be seen as akin to AIDS antibody testing: in both instances, testing leads to the uncovering of a marker."[7] The marker could predict (with varying degrees of accuracy) the onset of the disease. But attached to this prediction is a substantial risk of social stigmatization.

---

5. See the Glossary, *infra* at 77 for the definitions of technical terms.

6. Part I of the *Constitution Act, 1982*, being Schedule B of the *Canada Act 1982* (U.K.), 1982, c. 11, ss. 7, 8 and 15.

7. Marc Lappé, "The Limits of Genetic Inquiry" (1987) 17:4 Hast. Cent. Rep. 5 at 7.

Such stigmatization and our reactions to the new genetics may be shaped by our view of human nature. If one sees genetic consequences as inevitable and certain, one may be inclined to look to the elimination of the genetically disabled rather than to the finding of ways to accommodate such persons within society. By adopting this view we are deciding what is "normal" and acceptable. We may, for example, screen workers and exclude them on the basis of their susceptibility genes, rather than looking to reduce the risk of disease by cleaning up the workplace. We may fail to examine our political system, which leaves those with genetic disabilities less insured than those without. We may exert pressure on individuals to control their reproductive outcome according to our view of normality, and promote the elimination of the handicapped by abortion rather than making the world a better place for them. If, on the other hand, we see the diversity of our genetic constitution as natural and as the essence of humanity, we may resist genetic intervention regardless of its moral justification (Chapter Five).

Three ethical principles may be considered in an evaluation of the impact of modern science on the human being: autonomy, beneficence and non-maleficence. In the context of modern molecular biology and predictive genetics, as in medicine generally, the principle of autonomy may conflict with the principles of beneficence and non-maleficence. What framework do these principles provide for future legislative policy?

On a governmental level, the use of a cost-benefit analysis with its utilitarian rationale could lead to considerable pressure to test or be tested. It could force individuals to know about their genetic predispositions, to tell others and to act, so that the "proper choices" of those individuals would save society the long-term costs of disabling diseases. Such economic incentives could lead to a new eugenics based, not on undesirable characteristics, but rather on cost-saving, a form of economic social justice rather than "genetic justice." Considering those choices, genetic justice will require both greater communication of knowledge within the protection of the physician-patient relationship and civic responsibility on the part of the participant to share knowledge that will benefit his or her family (Chapter Six).

The development of a theory of genetic justice will require an in-depth examination of human rights in the workplace, in matters of insurability and in the physician-patient relationship. Other issues that will need full elaboration in the future are: the individual's control of bodily tissues or cells and of the genetic information contained therein; control of the diffusion of genetic information to family members; and the availability and adequacy of genetic counselling services and genetic education.[8] However, the values and policy issues underlying such specific subjects require delineation now.

---

8. See generally Neil A. Holtzman, *Proceed with Caution: Predicting Genetic Risks in the Recombinant DNA Era* (Baltimore: Johns Hopkins University Press, 1989); Lori B. Andrews, *Medical Genetics: A Legal Frontier* (Chicago: American Bar Foundation, 1987).

This study attempts to establish the basic, yet changing, philosophical and scientific knowledge underlying new developments in the science of human genetics. It looks at the impact that this understanding will have on the definition and legal protection of the human genetic heritage. The concept of genetic heritage and the legal means to protect it must be situated within an analysis of what is meant by the inherent dignity of the person. This will allow us to envisage a revised concept of genetic ''abnormality'' within a new concept of genetic justice.

The new genetics affects us individually and collectively, in our social, political and economic fabric. However, the inherent dignity of the human person, as recognized in the international covenants and national constitutions, has not yet been fully interpreted by the courts. It will be argued that the recognition of the dignity of each person, and of humanity as a whole, requires an approach to the protection of our genetic heritage that is based on medically oriented principles of respect for human life. It will be shown that human life in the genetic sense is not fixed in time, nor can it be reduced to one immutable gene pool. This study proposes that respect for the complexity, variability and uniqueness of the human being, and the recognition of equality through genetic difference, may be accomplished through the widespread genetic education of both the public and the medical profession. The failure to so educate could lead to the misuse of genetic knowledge for discriminatory purposes. It could also lead to the dangerous language of ''genetic rights'' with its accompanying legal claims and obligations. In short, the purpose of this study is to attach some meaning to the inherent human dignity of the person in the context of the new choices of human genetics, and to propose interpretations of human dignity that ensure the indivisible genetic nature of the human person within a common social ethic, that of genetic justice.

CHAPTER ONE

Genetics Overview

I. Introduction

Humankind has had an intuitive understanding of the inheritance of physical characteristics for thousands of years. Farmers have, over the centuries, improved the characteristics of domestic animals and crops by selecting those with superior characteristics for breeding purposes. But it was only a little more than a century ago that the biological basis of inheritance began to come to light with the work of the Austrian monk, Gregor Mendel. He was able to establish that there are units of inheritance that are transmitted from generation to generation, according to simple mathematical rules. In other words, genetic heritage can be predicted.

The early part of the twentieth century saw an explosion of genetic research that elaborated on Mendel's work. First, it was established that the units of inheritance described by Mendel are carried on the chromosomes. In the 1940s the composition of the hereditary material was discovered. This substance, called deoxyribonucleic acid (DNA), carries the genetic information of every cell. The next step was to discover how this information could be passed on from one cell to another. In 1953, James Watson and Francis Crick discovered that the DNA is arranged in a way that accomplishes this — in the famous double helix. That discovery won them the Nobel prize.

Since then, human genetics has been revolutionized by advances in what is called molecular biology.[9] Some of those technological advances will be described. But first we summarize how our genetic differences arise, and what kinds of differences lead to changes in the appearance or function of the human organism. Next is an examination of how advances in molecular biology have changed the practice of clinical genetics.

---

9. Claude Laberge, "La révolution biologique" in Jacques Dufresne, Fernand Dumont and Yves Martin, eds, *Traité d'anthropologie médicale* (Quebec: Presses de l'Université du Québec, 1985) at 201.

II. The Structural Basis of Genetic Differences[10]

Inherited characteristics are transmitted by genes. The genes are arranged on thread-like chromosomes. Twenty-three pairs of chromosomes are found in each of the body's cells.[11] One chromosome of each pair comes from the mother via the egg, and the other comes from the father via the sperm. The egg and the sperm (also called germ cells or gametes) are formed in the ovaries of the female and the testes of the male, respectively, by a process called meiosis. During meiosis the pairs of chromosomes become aligned side by side. There is a crossing over of genetic information between the pairs. Then the pairs separate. The result is that the germ cells have 23 chromosomes each instead of 23 pairs, and each germ cell bears a mixture of genetic material from the parental chromosomes.

Germ cells contain 22 autosomal chromosomes. These are the chromosomes found in both sexes. There is also a sex chromosome in each germ cell. In the egg it is always an X-chromosome, and in the sperm it can be an X- or a Y-chromosome. Union of the egg with an X-bearing sperm results in a female, and with a Y-bearing sperm, a male. After this union — the fertilization — cell division gives rise to the body cells called somatic cells which, as we have said, have two sets of chromosomes.

The unit of inheritance is the gene and the chemical composition of the gene is the DNA, which consists of two strands wrapped into a double helix. The strands are linked together by bases or nucleotides[12] as in the rungs of a twisted rope ladder. This structure is the double helix.

The sequence of bases in each strand can be deduced from that of the other. This complementarity between the two strands of DNA is the key to its information-bearing capabilities. The sequence of nucleotides in the gene is transcribed into a messenger molecule: messenger ribonucleic acid (mRNA). The mRNA moves from the nucleus of the cell out into its cytoplasm. Here, the sequence of nucleotides in the mRNA serves as a template to assemble amino acids into the protein. Thus, the DNA determines the sequence of mRNA bases, which determines the sequence of amino acids, which in turn determines the structure of the protein. That is, every protein has a specific gene that determines its structure.

However, not all of the DNA in the nucleus codes for proteins. A significant amount of the remaining DNA is dispersed within or between the protein-producing

---

10. Holtzman, *supra*, note 8.

11. Except for the sperm and the egg, which have 23 unpaired chromosomes each.

12. There are four types of nucleotides in DNA: adenosine (A), guanosine (G), cytidine (C) and thymine (T). Adenosine will only link with thymine and guanosine with cytidine. The nucleotides in the messenger ribonucleic acid (mRNA) are complementary to the DNA except that RNA contains uracil (U) instead of thymine.

genes. Some of this non-coding DNA is involved in regulating the activity of the genes. In others, the function of non-coding DNA is unknown.[13]

The complete set of genes of an individual is its genome. A gene is located at a particular locus on one of the chromosomes. Each of us has two genes at each locus, one on each paired chromosome (except in the male, where the sex chromosomes are XY).

The pair of genes at a particular locus may be identical or they may differ in the information they carry. Different forms of genes are called alleles. Alleles arise from a spontaneous change (called a mutation) in the DNA which, in the simplest situation, is a change in a single nucleotide pair. This may result in a different amino acid in the protein. When a mutation occurs in a germ cell, the change may be transmitted to the offspring and in turn to future generations. Mutations provide for genetic variation in a species, and this allows for evolution. Through evolution, the most advantageous allele will be selected. Some mutations appear to be neutral — that is, they do not seem to be more or less advantageous than others. Neutral genes may have several alleles at a given locus, none of which is rare. These kinds of alleles are called polymorphic. Polymorphisms also occur in the DNA between genes and, as we will see, constitute an important tool in mapping the genome.

Although some mutations are advantageous to the organism, and some are neutral, most will be deleterious. It is the deleterious genes which may result in disease or dysfunction.

III. Genetic Disorders

It is estimated that at least one in ten Canadians will die, or be impaired, disabled or handicapped at some time in their lives, as a result of deleterious genes. Diseases with a genetic component account for 30 to 50 per cent of admissions to paediatric hospitals.[14] Yet our understanding of the pathogenesis of these disorders and their treatment is limited, and the gene locus is known in only 3 per cent of them.[15]

Genetic disorders can be divided into three categories: chromosomal, single gene and multifactorial.[16]

---

13. See Arno G. Motulsky, "Medical Genetics" (1989) 261:19 JAMA 2855.

14. See generally, Government of Canada, *A New Perspective on the Health of Canadians* (Lalonde report) (Ottawa, 1974). See also the contrasting figures in Alan E.H. Emery and David L. Rimoin, "Nature and Incidence of Genetic Disease" in Alan E.H. Emery and David L. Rimoin, eds, *Principles and Practice of Medical Genetics*, vol. 1 (Edinburgh: Churchill Livingstone, 1983) at 1-3.

15. National Research Council, *Mapping and Sequencing the Human Genome* (Washington, D.C.: National Academy Press, 1988) at 28.

16. See James J. Nora and F. Clarke Fraser, *Medical Genetics: Principles and Practice*, 3d ed. (Philadelphia: Lea & Febiger, 1989) for a more detailed discussion of genetic disorders.

A. Chromosomal Disorders

In 1959 it was discovered that children with Down syndrome have 47 instead of the normal 46 chromosomes (trisomy 21). Soon after, other disorders were found to be associated with too much or too little chromosome material. In the 1970s, new histological staining techniques improved the ability to study chromosomes under the microscope, and brought to light even more chromosomal disorders.

The absence or excess of chromosomal material may involve all or part of a whole chromosome. Most disorders arise from errors in the separation of the chromosomes at meiosis. Chromosomal disorders occur in about one of 200 live-born individuals. Most of those people are mentally and physically disordered, and are often malformed.

Chromosome disorders can be detected prenatally. Testing is generally offered where a woman is 35 years of age or older,[17] a couple has had a previous child with a chromosomal disorder or one member of a couple is known to have a balanced chromosomal rearrangement.

B. Single Gene Disorders

The second category of genetic disorders is often referred to as Mendelian because their inheritance follows the rules of inheritance established by Gregor Mendel. We now know of more than 4,000 Mendelian traits of which about 3,000 may cause disease or dysfunction.[18] If the disorder is expressed when only one of a pair of alleles is defective, it is said to be dominant. Such disorders may be expressed to differing degrees in different people (variable expressivity). In some individuals, the disease may not be expressed at all (reduced penetrance). These phenomena, and the fact that a disorder may not appear until late in life, make it difficult to predict the severity and age of onset of the disorder in a particular individual.

Where both alleles must be defective for the disorder to be expressed, it is said to be recessive. The parents, who each carry the mutant allele, may be outwardly normal. With some recessive disorders it is possible to detect carriers (for example, for sickle cell anaemia), making it possible to identify who in a population carries the gene. Where it is not possible to detect carriers, parents only know that they are carrying the defective allele after the mother gives birth to an affected child.

For some genetic disorders, the consequences of the abnormal gene may be prevented by environmental manipulation. For example, in phenylketonuria (PKU), the defective gene results in a defective enzyme that would normally convert phenylalanine

17. There is an increasing risk that a woman will have a child with Down syndrome the older she is.

18. Victor A. McKusick, *Mendelian Inheritance in Man: Catalogs of Autosomal Dominant, Autosomal Recessive and X-linked Phenotypes*, 9th ed. (Baltimore: Johns Hopkins University Press, 1990).

to tyrosine. The resulting accumulation of phenylalanine causes a mental disorder. However, this accumulation can be prevented if the dietary intake of phenylalanine is carefully controlled from the newborn period and at least throughout early childhood, and in this way the long-term effects of PKU can be minimized.

The last type of single gene disorder is the so-called X-linked recessive disorder. Like autosomal recessive disorders, this type is not expressed when there is a normal allele on the other chromosome. Thus, a female with only one defective X-chromosome will be normal. However, if her son inherits the defective X-chromosome, as in haemophilia, he will have the disorder because he has no second X-chromosome to protect him.

There are over 50 single gene disorders that are detectable prenatally, by the use of biochemical tests on foetal cells obtained from the pregnant woman's amniotic fluid.

C. Multifactorial Disorders

The final category of genetic disorders to be discussed consists of multifactorial disorders. It is somewhat arbitrary to classify them as genetic since environmental factors may be as important as the defective genes in their causation and expression.

Multifactorial disorders include common diseases such as hypertension, coronary heart disease, atherosclerosis and diabetes and common birth defects such as spina bifida. A genetic component may be deduced from family studies, as in spina bifida. In other cases, a gene may have been identified that increases susceptibility to a disorder.[19] Most common genetic disorders are complex and heterogeneous. A disease or malformation may have a different set of causal factors in different families or in different individuals.

IV. Technological Advances in Molecular Biology

The importance of the technological advances in molecular biology relates to their use in mapping the human genome. Mapping means finding the position of the gene that causes a genetic disorder on a particular chromosome, and finding its position in relation to other, adjacent genes.

19. Lappé, *supra*, note 7 at 10. *E.g.*, ankylosing spondylitis (spinal fusion) is associated with the B-27 allele at the gene locus for human leucocyte antigen (HLA). However, not all individuals with the susceptibility gene will develop the disorder, while some individuals without the gene will.

A project to determine the sequence of the entire genome, approved by the United States Congress,[20] has expanded into an international collaborative project (HUGO).[21] It will provide information that could lead to the avoidance or prevention of genetic disorders and eventually to their treatment and even cure.[22] The following discussion highlights some of the technological advances that have made that project feasible.[23]

A major advance in mapping came in the 1980s with the use of "restriction fragment length polymorphisms" (RFLPs). Restriction enzymes, of which there are hundreds now known, cut the DNA into fragments at both ends of specific nucleotide sequences. The length of the fragments is specific for each enzyme. If a mutation occurs at a particular cutting site, the enzyme will not cut the DNA at that site, and the length of the resulting DNA fragment will change. Thus, when the particular fragment is labelled with a probe, and fragments are separated on a gel according to length, the particular fragment from the individual with the mutant allele will appear at a different position on the gel than the fragments from normal DNA. The resulting variation in length of a specific fragment is called a restriction fragment length polymorphism.

These polymorphic alleles are inherited in a Mendelian fashion. Since there are many RFLPs and many of them are common, RFLPs are very useful for mapping loci for genetic disorders.

Where an RFLP can be shown to be closely linked to the locus for a genetic disorder, the marker can then be used in a particular family to determine the probability that an individual actually has the gene for that disorder. Thus, where the likelihood for an autosomal dominant disorder is 50 per cent by Mendelian rules, the probability of a person actually having the gene can be revised downward or upward according to which linked polymorphism is present. Occasionally an RFLP will be within the gene and will predict the presence of the gene with virtual certainty.

---

20. Joseph Palca, "National Research Council Endorses Genome Project" (1988) 331:6156 Nature 467.

21. Joseph Palca, "Human Genome Organization Is Launched with a Flourish" (1988) 335:6188 Nature 286; G. Christopher Anderson, "Genome Project: Howard Hughes Gets HUGO off the Ground" (1990) 345:6271 Nature 100. It is interesting to note that as printed information, these three billion base pairs of the human genome sequence would fill "200 volumes the size of the Manhattan telephone book," "New Tools for Genome Study Being Made" (1988) 24:32 Medical Post 28.

22. As of 1988 the chromosomal location of over 1,215 human genes was known (of the approximately 100,000 estimated to exist). Congress of the United States, Office of Technology Assessment [hereinafter OTA], *Mapping Our Genes: Genome Projects — How Big, How Fast?* (Baltimore: Johns Hopkins University Press, 1988) at 4.

23. See Thomas D. Gelehrter and Francis S. Collins, *Principles of Medical Genetics* (Baltimore: Williams & Wilkins, 1990) for details.

V. The Changing Practice of Medical Genetics

Information from mapping can be used in a number of situations. For Mendelian disorders, it can be used prenatally to determine whether a foetus has the disorder.[24] After birth, it can confirm a diagnosis or detect the presence of a disease before signs are evident (pre-symptomatic testing). An example of the latter is its use in Huntington's disease[25] where, if the person inherits the gene and lives long enough, he or she will develop the disease. Testing may also be done to detect normal couples of which both individuals are carriers for recessive disorders. They may use this information to make reproductive decisions. Lastly, testing may be used to determine whether an individual has a genetic marker for a multifactorial disease that influences the probability of the individual's getting the disease.

In the past, there were few disorders having a known gene product that could confirm the presence of a mutant gene. Thus, disorders were first established as Mendelian on the basis of family studies. Then one could predict, from Mendelian principles, the chance that an affected person or two carrier parents would have an affected child. Now, the capacity to locate a gene or a marker close to the gene for the disease will greatly improve the precision of these predictions, depending on how close the linked marker is to the gene. What will be profoundly changed in medical genetics is that many more genetic loci will be discovered that can be used in prenatal and pre-symptomatic testing and in population screening. Some of these disorders will not be serious. Furthermore, some of the same sources of uncertainty remain, that is, those that are due to variable expressivity, to reduced penetrance and to the general complexity of common multifactorial disorders.

VI. Gene Therapy

Where the sequence of DNA bases is known, it is possible to change it in a directed way. This will eventually provide us with the means to treat or cure genetic disease. Genes can be isolated, together with their adjacent DNA containing the important regulatory information. It will then be possible to insert "normal" genes into cells taken from a patient who lacks the genes or who has them in an abnormal form. Gene therapy at present is done only in somatic cells. Unlike germ-cell modification, somatic-cell modification is not passed on to future generations.[26] Even

---

24. The purpose of prenatal diagnosis is to permit couples or individuals, who are at risk for the transmission of genetic diseases, to undertake having children. With respect to cystic fibrosis, see S. Blakeslee, "New Techniques Help Researchers Track Gene Defects," *International Herald Tribune* (14 September 1989) 7; P.N. Goodfellow, "Cystic Fibrosis: Steady Steps Lead to the Gene" (1989) 341:6238 Nature 102.

25. See J.-G. A., "Chorée de Huntington: test prédictif offert" (1989) 24:7 Le médecin du Québec 87.

26. OTA, *Human Gene Therapy: Background Paper* (Washington, D.C.: OTA, 1984) at 6.

though at present germ cell-line alteration is not possible in humans, there is a remote possibility of inadvertently affecting the germ line during somatic therapy which, we must remember, is still in the experimental stages of clinical application. It is being considered only for treatment of individuals with one of a few disorders that seem particularly amenable to this approach.[27] It may eventually be possible (although not practical) to apply gene therapy to the treatment of embryos at the pre-implantation stage (during the fourteen-day period following fertilization).[28]

In April 1988, delegates of the seven industrialized nations attended the Fifth International Summit Conference on Bioethics on the mapping of the human genome. They agreed that "there are no intrinsic limitations to the acquisition of knowledge of the human genome and that research in this area should be strongly encouraged."[29] They also held that gene therapy of somatic cells should be judged on the same basis as other experimental medical treatments. However, they stated that there were neither medical nor ethical justifications for the intentional genetic manipulation of human germ-line cells at this time. The Medical Research Council of Canada, in its report, recognizes the specificity of these scientific endeavours as being distinct from research in human beings generally. The Council adopted the following position on research protocols in human somatic gene therapy: "gene transfer should only be considered for diseases which meet all the following criteria: they are caused by a defect in a single gene; they cause a liveborn human being to suffer severe debilitation or early death; [and] they cannot be treated successfully by any other means."[30] The Council committee studying this issue agreed that there is no indication, presently, for germ cell-line therapy or for any types of gene transfer to enhance functions, as opposed to curing severe debilitative diseases.[31] This position is consistent with that of United States commissions studying human gene therapy[32] and with that taken by the 1982 President's Commission for the Study of Ethical Problems in Medicine and Biomedical

---

27. Joseph Palca, "Gene Transfer to Humans Approved in the Face of Advice" (1988) 335:6191 Nature 577; Joanne Silberner, "Finally, Putting Genes into Humans" US News and World Report (17 October 1988) 66, where it was reported that terminal cancer patients may soon receive altered versions of their tumour-fighting cells. See also Jean L. Marx, "Gene Transfer Is Coming on Target" (1988) 242:4876 Science 191; Diane Gershon, "Genetic Engineering: Transfer Study Expands" (1990) 344:6266 Nature 483.

28. See generally "Preimplantation and Early Post-Implantation Diagnosis" (1987) 2:5 Human Reprod. 399; R.G. Edwards, "Diagnostic Methods for Human Gametes and Embryos" (1987) 2:5 Human Reprod. 415.

29. Alexander M. Capron, "The Rome Bioethics Summit" (1988) 18:4 Hast. Cent. Rep. 11 at 12. See also International Conference on Bioethics, *The Human Genome Sequencing: Ethical Issues* (Brescia, Italy: Clas International, 1989) at 291.

30. Medical Research Council of Canada, *Guidelines for Research on Somatic Cell Gene Therapy in Humans* (Ottawa: Supply and Services Canada, 1990) at 12.

31. *Ibid.*

32. *Supra*, notes 15 and 26.

and Behavioral Research, in the United States[33] More recently, the Science Council of Canada constituted a multidisciplinary group of experts to study advances in human genetics and their implications with the goal of developing a national health policy in genetic medicine.[34]

The continental European countries are much more cautious in their attitudes to gene alteration. The European Medical Research Councils have approved somatic gene therapy.[35] Nevertheless, as will be seen in the following study of human dignity and of the notion of genetic "normality,"[36] European countries such as France,[37] Switzerland[38] and West Germany[39] favour a more restrictive application of the new human genetics.

---

33. President's Commission for the Study of Ethical Problems in Medicine and Biomedical and Behavioral Research [hereinafter President's Commission], *Splicing Life* (Washington, D.C.: The Commission, 1982); see also President's Commission, *Screening and Counseling for Genetic Conditions* (Washington, D.C.: The Commission, 1983).

34. Science Council of Canada, *Genetics in Canadian Health Care* (Ottawa: Supply and Services Canada, 1990).

35. See "Gene Therapy in Man: Recommendations of the European Medical Research Councils" (1988) 11:8597 Lancet 1271 at 1272: "Only somatic cell gene therapy, resulting in non-heritable changes to particular body tissues, should be contemplated. Germline therapy, for introduction of heritable genetic modifications, is not acceptable."; *Contra*: Commission of the European Communities, *Modified Proposal for a Council Decision*: *Human Genome Analysis*, COM (89) 532 final, 13 November 1989 at s. 4.4.4: "That the development and the application of somatic gene therapy are not provided for within the framework of the present programme." Not only will no monies be provided for somatic therapy but "the contracting parties undertake to abstain from all research seeking to modify the genetic constitution of human beings by alteration of germ cells or of any stage of embryo development which may make these alterations hereditary" (s. 4.4.2).

36. Below, Chapter Five.

37. Conseil d'État, *Science de la vie: De l'éthique au droit*, 2d ed. (Paris: La Documentation française, 1988) at 84, takes the position that all germ-line alterations should be prohibited. It also recommends prohibiting genetic diagnosis of preimplantation embryos by embryo biopsy. This position is similar to that taken by the Comité National d'Éthique in its *Opinion relative to research work on human embryos in vitro and use thereof for medical and scientific purposes* of December 1986 (reproduced in Comité consultatif national d'éthique pour les sciences de la vie et de la santé, *Avis de recherches sur l'embryon* (Vendome, France: Actes du Sud et Inserm, 1987) at 73). See also G. Huber, *Patrimoine génétique et droits de l'humanité* (Livre blanc des recommandations) (Paris: Osiris, 1990).

38. Commission d'experts pour la génétique humaine et la médecine de la reproduction [hereinafter Commission d'experts], *Rapport au Département fédéral de l'intérieur et au Département de la justice et police* (Berne, 19 August 1988) at 97, takes the position that somatic cell therapy should be limited to cases of grave hereditary disorders. Germ-line therapy on gametes or embryos and non-therapeutic genetic manipulations will be prohibited. This opinion is particularly interesting as it is based on the Council of Europe's equation between the right to dignity and genetic heritage (see below, Chapter Three).

39. *Fécondation in vitro, analyse du génome et thérapie génétique* (Benda report) (Paris: La Documentation française, 1987) considered that somatic cell therapy is still experimental and thus subject to the mandatory rules and protocols on human experimentation. Because germ-line research would involve the use of embryos and their possible destruction in experiments, it was not justified. The Commission recommended prohibiting germ-line experiments or treatments. This position was reaffirmed in the recent Report of the Enquete Commission to the Bundestag of the Federal Republic of Germany [hereinafter Enquete Commission], *Prospects and Risks of Gene Technology*, in "A Report from Germany" (1988) 2:3 Bioethics 254, which, at 257, considers that the natural development of human beings is a measure of their humanity. Like the proposed *Embryo Protection Law* of 1986, it would totally prohibit even therapeutic experimentation on human germ lines (at 261); see also Hans-Martin Sass, "A Critique of the Enquete Commission's Report on Gene Technology" (1988) 2:3 Bioethics 264 at 273.

VII. Conclusion

The foregoing overview demonstrates that the application of molecular biology to the investigation of genetic disorders not only provides us with new options but also creates uncertainty. The explosion of knowledge has widened the gap between our ability to identify and our ability to understand and treat genetic disorders.

The number of disorders for which prenatal and presymptomatic testing can be done is rapidly increasing. The ability to test for genetic loci that increase our susceptibility to developing common disorders, or to having children that develop them, could bring most of the human population under genetic scrutiny. Education of both health care professionals and the public is urgent if we are to avoid the detrimental fall-out of this scrutiny.[40]

---

40. Neil A. Holtzman, "Recombinant DNA Technology, Genetic Tests, and Public Policy" (1988) 42:4 Am. J. Hum. Genet. 624.

CHAPTER TWO

The Genome and the Gene Pool

I. Introduction

As mentioned earlier,[41] the Parliamentary Assembly of the Council of Europe recommended in 1982 that the Committee of Ministers "provide for explicit recognition in the European Convention on Human Rights of the right to a genetic inheritance which has not been artificially interfered with, except in accordance with certain principles which are recognised as being fully compatible with respect for human rights."[42] Neither the report of the hearing,[43] which preceded the drafting of the recommendation, nor the recommendation itself elaborated on the meaning of genetic heritage, that is, whether it referred to the genome (an individual's genetic material) or the gene pool (the sum of the genomes in the population). What then are the common, scientific and legal notions of genetic heritage?

---

41. *Recommendation 934*, *supra*, note 3.

42. *Ibid.* s. 7(*b*). An exception to non-interference was for prevention and therapy where there were clear and scientific reasons. See the discussion in Chapter Three. Similarly, His Holiness Pope John Paul II in his *Instruction* of 1987, while condemning most forms of research and the clinical applications of reproductive technologies and of genetic engineering, specifically approved the possibility of treating genetic disease *in utero* if it is in the interest of the child to be born. Congregation for the Doctrine of the Faith, *Instruction on Respect for Human Life in Its Origin and on the Dignity of Procreation* (Vatican City: Vatican Polyglot Press, 1987) at 14 (prenatal diagnosis):

> Such diagnosis is permissible, with the consent of the parents after they have been adequately informed, if the methods employed safeguard the life and integrity of the embryo and the mother, without subjecting them to disproportionate risks.

At 15-16 (human embryo):

> A strictly therapeutic intervention whose explicit objective is the healing of various maladies such as those stemming from chromosomal defects will, in principle, be considered desirable, provided it is directed to the true promotion of the personal well-being of the individual without doing harm to his integrity or worsening his conditions of life. Such an intervention would indeed fall within the logic of the Christian moral tradition.

43. Council of Europe, P.A., *Genetic Engineering: Risks and Chances for Human Rights*, European Parliamentary Hearing, Copenhagen, 25 and 26 May 1981 (Strasbourg: The Council, 1981).

II. Common Usage of Heritage

In popular usage, heritage is seen as an estate, a right of endowment inherited from one's ancestors. This individualistic notion of heritage as property is the most commonly known concept. Nevertheless, the etymological origins of the word encompass a figurative meaning that includes the notion of a common heritage of humankind, such as discoveries in science, or the culture or economy of a nation. Even in common usage, there is a biological interpretation of heritage, defined as the inherited characteristics as expressed in the outward appearance of an individual (the phenotype).[44]

III. Scientific Usage

Because the population gene pool is made up of individual genomes, heritage is, for the biologist, both a collective and an individual notion. There is also a time element connecting the gene pool and the genome. Diversity in the gene pool arises over time through the process of mutation. Furthermore, in each generation the diversity between individuals is increased by the process of crossing over during meiosis. Recall that the egg or the sperm, produced by meiosis, contains a mixture of the chromosomal material of that person's parental chromosomes.[45] As a result of the biological processes of mutation and meiosis, each individual is unique and each offspring is different from his or her parents.

Yet, there is both a spatial and temporal connection between the genome and the gene pool. This universal, ancestral filiation makes the human gene pool both individual in expression and supranational in origin.[46] This is important in understanding the effects of germ-line and somatic-cell gene therapy.[47] Germ-line therapy would lead to

---

44. See generally *Webster's Third New International Dictionary of the English Language unabridged* (Springfield, Mass.: Meriam-Webster, 1986): "[1]b: anything derived from one's father or ancestors: Heritage c: an inheritance from the past" at 1656; *Larousse de la langue française: lexis* (Paris: Librairie Larousse, 1979, 1989): "2. Ce qui est transmis par les parents, par la génération antérieure" at 896; Paul Robert, *Petit Robert I: dictionnaire alphabétique et analogique de la langue française* (Paris: Le Robert, 1988): "Biol. *Le patrimoine héréditaire de l'individu*, l'ensemble des caractères hérités" at 1378.

45. See above, Chapter One.

46. André Langaney, "La diversité génétique humaine: considérable et mal connue" in *Génétique, procréation et droit* (Paris: Actes Sud, 1985) at 349; see also C.B. Stringer and P. Andrews, "Genetic and Fossil Evidence for the Origin of Modern Humans" (1988) 239:4845 Science 1263.

47. *Human Gene Therapy*, *supra*, note 26 at 31.

inherited changes and could therefore have an impact on the future population.[48] As mentioned earlier,[49] somatic-gene therapy affects only the individual concerned and would have no immediate, direct effect on the mix of genes in the human population. Yet, ultimately, the success of somatic therapy would lead to the survival of patients who would otherwise die. It would allow such individuals to transmit their genes to the next generation, thus increasing the frequency of the mutant gene.[50] Where descendants of such individuals develop the same disorder as their ancestors, they would also require treatment. In this way, while germ-line therapy would change the gene pool in a direct way, somatic-cell therapy would change it indirectly.

IV. Legal Notions of Heritage

The legal notions of heritage also reflect a diversity of interpretations. They traditionally restrict the scope of heritage in the private law domain to property of economic value, and in the public law domain to property of common interest. More recently, the notion of the public domain has been extended to a more universal form. In international law it includes property that is the common heritage of humankind.

A. Private Law

Beginning with the private law domain, the Roman law protected the family *patrimonium*. While the Quebec and French Civil Codes do not explicitly define *patrimoine*, it is seen as a universality of rights or property with an economic value whose assets and liabilities cannot be disassociated. It cannot be divided, nor can it be transmitted to another during a person's life. Every person can have only one *patrimoine* whose character is principally seen as pecuniary in nature. Moreover, rights of *patrimoine* often denote possession or ownership in the physical sense, as opposed to extra-patrimonial rights such as personal rights, innate rights and legal actions in relation to civil status.[51]

---

48. *Ibid.* This could lead to loss of genetic diversity, but such an effect would be insignificant. This is because most disease is multifactorial and gene therapy could only be applied to some single gene disorders, which are rare. The loss of genetic diversity in the gene pool would more likely be the result of "relaxing historic selection pressures on the human population through changes in the environment, sanitation, and health care" (at 31) than from deliberate intervention on an individual level.

49. See above, Chapter One.

50. Of course, the same is true of conventional therapy for diseases with a genetic basis.

51. See generally, Quebec Research Centre of Private and Comparative Law, *Private Law Dictionary and Bilingual Lexicons* (Montreal, Que.: The Centre, 1988); Henry Campbell Black, ed., *Black's Law Dictionary*, 5th ed. (St. Paul, Minn.: West Publishing, 1979) at 1015: "Patrimonium: that which is capable of being inherited. The private and exclusive ownership or dominion of an individual . . . ."

Yet, like the notion of real or personal property in the common law, the legal notion of heritage is no longer necessarily restricted to inherited property or to property in its economic sense. Nor is it so clearly distinct from personal rights as witnessed by the emergence, in both systems, of mixed rights such as those pertaining to intellectual property (for example, patents and copyright). Nevertheless, we shall see that the adoption of a private law approach mandating a property interest or a right in one's genome is problematic.

B. Public Law

The traditional legal notion of public property is: that which is in the public domain or is subject to public trust, *res nullius* (things without an owner) and *res communis* (things belonging to all). In particular, the air, the sea and outer space have historically been considered as *res communis* — incapable of individual ownership, and therefore inappropriable, indivisible, imprescriptible and inalienable.[52] State regulation has severely curtailed the ambit of these traditional notions.[53] As with a private law approach, it will be argued that a strictly public law approach to genetic material or information is also problematic.

C. International Law

Another legal interpretation of property in public law is found in an international concept that emerged during the nineteenth century. It proposed the notion of common ownership or public interest in the "common heritage of mankind." Inspired by the work of Grotius, the first recognition of this common heritage of humankind was in relation to the sea. The sea was considered *res communis*, so that countries with shorelines had rights of servitude only over their own territorial waters. In modern international law, this respect for the common heritage of humankind requires a sharing between nations and a safeguarding of resources for future generations.[54]

The common factors are that: utilization must be peaceful; access must be open to those who have that right who, in turn, must respect the rights of others; sharing must be equal; and, owing to its indivisible character, administration of that which is *res*

---

52. OTA, *New Developments in Biotechnology: Ownership of Human Tissues and Cells* (Washington, D.C.: U.S. Government Printing Office, 1987); Marie-Angèle Hermitte, "Histoires juridiques extravagantes: la reproduction végétale" at 40 and "Le concept de diversité biologique et la création d'un statut de la nature" at 238, as well as Catherine Labrusse-Riou, "Servitude, servitudes" at 308, all three texts found in Bernard Edelman and Marie-Angèle Hermitte, eds, *L'homme, la nature et le droit* (Paris: Christian Bourgois, 1988).

53. See generally Henri Lepage, *Pourquoi la propriété?* (Paris: Hachette, 1985); "Destins du droit de propriété" (1985) Droits (Revue française de théorie juridique) (Paris: P.U.F., 1985).

54. Alexandre-Charles Kiss, "La notion de patrimoine commun de l'humanité" (1982) II, 175 RCADI 99.

nullius must be in the interest of the common welfare.[55] This international concept stems from the need to prevent the private ownership of things of communal interest and to preserve for the future things that are of international interest. Like the concept of the trust in private law (once limited to "things" [*res*] and now extended to interests and rights), the concept is akin to that of the "public" trust. This trust serves to assist in the transmission of property or other interests from one generation to another.

The international conventions on the Law of the Sea,[56] or of the cultural or natural heritage of humankind,[57] have recognized the common contribution and interests of peoples or countries and the common need to share and preserve these heritages. While such "capital" can remain in public or private hands, the state has an obligation to define, identify, protect and conserve such property for future generations.[58] Thus, even such a vague notion as the "cultural property belonging to any people"[59] has been considered as included in the cultural heritage of humankind. In Europe, the Parliamentary Assembly of the Council of Europe has called on the "governments of member states to recognise that the European cultural heritage belongs to all Europeans."[60] According to UNESCO, "[a]s the testimony of the creative genius and the history of peoples, cultural property is a basic element of their identity and full enjoyment of this heritage is for each people an indispensable condition for its self-realisation."[61] Yet, in practice, the concept is often limited to national legal protection of the cultural heritage.[62] Even so, the obvious lack of clarity about what actually falls within the definition of such a heritage makes definitive legal obligations between nations extremely problematic. The concept on an international level remains largely a "political" one.[63]

Although initially restricted to the protection of flora and fauna,[64] the international concept of the common heritage of humankind could be extended to include human "genetic heritage." Traditionally, plants and animals were considered as *res nullius*, appropriable by all and susceptible to destruction. This mandated their protection and

---

55. *Ibid.*; see also K. De Jager, "Claims to Cultural Property under International Law" (1988) 1 Leiden J. Int'l L. 183.

56. *United Nations Convention on the Law of the Sea*, U.N. Doc. A/Conf.62/122 (1982).

57. De Jager, *supra*, note 55.

58. Kiss, *supra*, note 54 at 129ff.

59. *Convention for the Protection of Cultural Property in the Event of Armed Conflict* (The Hague, 1954) (1956) 249 U.N.T.S. 240.

60. Council of Europe, P.A., 35th Sess., Pt II, *Text Adopted, Resolution 808 (1983) on the Return of Works of Art*, s. 10.

61. UNESCO Committee of Experts to Study the Question of the Restitution of Works of Art, Venice, 1976, SHC-76/CONF.615/5, s. 19.

62. See, *e.g.*, *Cultural Property Act*, R.S.Q., c. B-4.

63. See De Jager , *supra*, note 55, quoting Larschan and Brennan at 191.

64. The protection of the flora and fauna was based on the fear that the creation of new micro-organisms, of hybrids or of synthetically based organisms could lead to the disappearance of "original" stock whose genetic value had not as yet been realized.

management in the common interest.[65] Humanity, in the global sense then, is the trustee of those resources, although international organizations may set the principles to be implemented by adhering states. Such protection against degradation, exploitation and waste of the natural heritage is both "transspatial" and "transtemporal" since it is not limited by geographic or political borders and it concerns future generations.[66]

The 1982 Council of Europe recommendation on genetic engineering of micro-organisms of plant and animal species extended this concept to human beings. Could the protection of the *human* genetic heritage be possible through the application of this international legal notion of common heritage or through that of private or public law?

D. An Integrated Approach

It may be difficult to apply this particular international law notion of the common heritage of humankind to human genetics, since the human genome (individual) or the gene pool (communal), would first have to be considered as *res communis* (owned by all) or as *res nullius* (not owned by anyone). Secondly, there are certain conceptual and political problems associated with the notion of common participation in the stewardship of the heritage, all the more evident in the absence of shared ownership. Integration is the natural genetic way; apartheid is cultural ignorance. Finally, the determination of what would be considered as peaceful use and what would constitute abuse requires the delineation of societal goals with respect to human genetics.[67] Therefore, the question involves a determination of "the extent to which our collective gene pool is public property, which we hold in trust for the future, and the extent to which the very personalized packages into which it is subdivided precludes treating it as a public resource."[68]

In 1987, the American Office of Technology Assessment alluded to the possibility of congressional action recognizing "that any cell line be presumed to be in the public domain,"[69] thus barring anyone from claiming property rights to those products. Similarly, the Committee on Mapping and Sequencing the Human Genome of the United States National Research Council recommended in 1988 "that human genome

65. See generally Marie-Angèle Hermitte, *Le droit du génie génétique végétal* (Paris: Librairies Techniques, 1987) and, *e.g.*, the *Environmental Quality Act*, R.S.Q., c. Q-2.

66. *Convention for the Protection of Cultural Property in the Event of Armed Conflict, supra*, note 59 at 240.

67. Below, Chapters Five and Six. See also (Sept. 1988) Forum (Council of Europe) for a special issue on genetics (Animal, vegetable, environmental and medical).

68. James V. Neel, "Social and Scientific Priorities in the Use of Genetic Knowledge" in Bruce Hilton et al., *Ethical Issues in Human Genetics: Genetic Counseling and the Use of Genetic Knowledge* (New York: Plenum Press, 1973) 353 at 358.

69. *New Developments in Biotechnology*, *supra*, note 52 at 17.

sequences should be a public trust and therefore should not be subject to copyright.''[70] This possibility was also raised by the Committee on Mapping and Sequencing of the American Society of Human Genetics when it solicited comments from its members on the public trust position, namely, ''an expression of belief that the human genome sequences should be a public trust and therefore not be subject to copyright.''[71] On the other hand, the Ad Hoc Committee on DNA Technology of the Society held that ''[b]anked DNA is the property of the depositor unless otherwise stipulated.''[72] The two approaches from the same Society need not be seen as contradictory. In fact, it could be argued that one's individual control over the uses of his or her tissues and cells is not incompatible with the notion of the human genome itself being considered a public trust. It should be possible to balance the notions of individual ''genetic control'' together with public stewardship of the larger ''gene pool'' or human genome without recourse to property law. Such an approach would parallel the actual biological reunion of the individual pattern and gene pool source found in the human person.

V. Conclusion

The difficulties and shortcomings of applying the private, public or even international law concept of the common heritage of humankind to human genetics stem from the fact that such notions are rooted in their own historical and cultural contexts. The implications of human genetics affect the personal, the public and, with the mapping of the genome, the international domain. Thus, a more innovative approach to the concept of heritage is necessary — one that respects the person in the totality of his or her being and as a member of society.

The choice must be integrated at both the provincial and the national level. Moreover, individual control and public trust concepts must conform to internationally shared principles. In this way, the notion of the human genetic heritage may acquire the necessary specificity for adequate and real protection.

As mentioned earlier in this chapter, the Parliamentary Assembly of the Council of Europe recommended that genetic heritage be protected. We have explored the concept of genetic heritage and have seen that it is both an individual and a collective notion, consisting of the genome and the gene pool.

Our next task is to examine the question of why the genetic heritage needs protection. The Parliamentary Assembly of the Council of Europe considered it

---

70. *Supra*, note 15 at 100.

71. Elizabeth M. Short, ''Proposed ASHG Position on Mapping/Sequencing the Human Genome'' (1988) 43:1 Am. J. Hum. Genet. 101 at 102.

72. Ad Hoc Committee on DNA Technology, American Society of Human Genetics, ''DNA Banking and DNA Analysis: Points to Consider'' (1988) 42:5 Am. J. Hum. Genet. 781 at 782.

necessary to protect human dignity. In the next two chapters we will explore the meaning of human dignity in the context of human genetics, first from the perspective of international law, and then from a constitutional point of view.

CHAPTER THREE

Human Dignity and Genetics – The International Context

I. Introduction

''*Whereas* recognition of the inherent dignity and of the equal and inalienable rights of all members of the human family is the foundation of freedom, justice and peace in the world . . . .'' With these majestic and inspiring ideals, the *Universal Declaration of Human Rights* was proclaimed by the United Nations General Assembly on December 10, 1948. Article 1 of that same text affirms that ''[a]ll human beings are born free and equal in dignity and rights'' and article 27 that ''[e]veryone has the right freely to . . . share in scientific advancement and its benefits.''[73] Similarly, the Preamble to the European Convention on Human Rights of 1950 and the *International Covenant on Economic, Social and Cultural Rights*[74] of 1966 recognize this foundation. The latter states that all legal rights derive from the inherent dignity of human beings.[75] While Canada is a party to those two international covenants, the *Canadian Charter of Rights and Freedoms* does not adopt their terminology, nor does it explicitly refer to the notion of human dignity. In contrast, section 4 of the Quebec *Charter of Human Rights and Freedoms* guarantees that ''[e]very person has a right to the safeguard of his dignity,''[76] without further qualification.

Those provisions concerning human dignity have not been authoritatively interpreted or applied by any of the competent, independent, international institutions.[77] In fact, as is evident from the very wording of the foregoing international texts, a respect for human dignity is seen as a *sine qua non* for the elaboration and construction of all other fundamental human rights. Human dignity being so basic in nature and the

---

73. *Supra*, note 1.

74. (1976) 993 U.N.T.S. 4.

75. See also the similar preamble to the 1966 *International Covenant on Civil and Political Rights* (1976) 999 U.N.T.S. 172 (''*Recognizing* that these rights derive from the inherent dignity of the human person''); *American Convention on Human Rights* (1969), art. 11(1): ''Everyone has the right to have his honour respected and his dignity recognised''; *African Charter on Human and Peoples' Rights* (1981), art. 5: ''Every individual shall have the right to the respect of the dignity inherent in a human being.'' Both the American Convention and the African Charter are reproduced in Council of Europe, *Human Rights in International law: Basic Texts* (Strasbourg: The Council, 1985) at 176 and 207.

76. R.S.Q., c. C-12. For a study of Canadian constitutional law, see below, Chapter Four.

77. Paul Sieghart, *The International Law of Human Rights* (Oxford: Clarendon Press, 1983) at 309. As regards the Quebec Charter, see Jean-Maurice Brisson, *Texte annoté de la Charte des droits et libertés de la personne du Québec* (Montreal: SOQUIJ, 1986).

source of all human rights, perhaps it is not deemed necessary to guarantee or limit that notion.[78] All human rights derive from respect for this inherent dignity.

That interpretation is supported in the literature which, in defining the basic policies for an international law on human dignity, maintains that the relevant perspective "rests on a conception of the universe in which the moral personality of man and his dignity and rights stand in the center."[79]

Moreover, the strength of human rights, framed as they are in general terms, comes from their ethical and moral dimensions as distinct from other legal rules of a technical nature. Human rights function to mediate between the juridical, ethical and political domains, the result being a form of natural law. This natural law provides the principal framework for such mediation. The realization of the concept of human dignity is therefore variable in its content, depending on national and cultural needs and on differences in interpretation.[80]

Finally, human rights exist in national and international constitutions not only to provide "some private immunity in relation to the authorities or to oblige the authorities to offer us protection against action of other citizens"[81] or organizations of citizens, but also "to bring about certain positive conditions for the actual enjoyment of human rights."[82]

In the medical context, the third General Assembly of the World Medical Association adopted an *International Code of Medical Ethics* in 1949.[83] The Assembly held that one of the imperative duties of the physician is to provide competent medical services "with compassion and respect for human dignity."[84] The 1981 *Declaration of*

---

78. Note, however, that respect for inherent dignity of the human person was specifically linked to protection of persons deprived of their liberty under art. 10(1) of the *International Covenant on Civil and Political Rights*, *supra*, note 75.

79. Myres S. McDougal, Harold D. Lasswell and Lung-Chu Chen, *Human Rights and World Public Order: The Basic Policies of an International Law of Human Dignity* (New Haven, Conn.: Yale University Press, 1980) citing M. Muskowitz at 373.

80. Mireille Delmas-Marty, "Un nouvel usage des droits de l'homme" in *Éthique médicale et droits de l'homme* (Paris: Actes Sud/INSERM, 1988) 313.

81. B. Elmquist, "Genetic Engineering: Risks and Chances for Human Rights — Legal Aspects: Possibilities of New Legislative Steps at National and International Level" in Council of Europe, *supra*, note 43, 203 at 207.

82. P. Leuprecht, intervention at Parliamentary Hearing in Council of Europe, *supra*, note 43 at 115. Such positive conditions are evident in the creation by a given state, for example, of the office of the ombudsman or of affirmative action programs.

83. Reprinted in "Medical Ethics Declarations" (1984) 31:3 World Medical Journal [back cover]. This Code was based on the 1948 *Declaration of Geneva* and revised at the 35th Assembly of the World Medical Association, in Venice in 1983.

84. *Ibid.* See a similar provision of the American Medical Association, *Principles of Medical Ethics* (Chicago: The Association, 1980).

Lisbon on the rights of the patient speaks of the right to die in dignity.[85] The revised *Declaration of Helsinki*[86] on biomedical research involving human subjects makes no explicit reference to a right to dignity. However, like the more specific Council for International Organizations of Medical Sciences (CIOMS) guidelines that followed in 1982,[87] the very foundation for elaborating the protection of human subjects is built on the inherent dignity of the human person.

Under the principles of international human rights law, human dignity and genetic heritage concern the status, protection and uses of, and access to, human genetic material. Thus, issues concerning the right to self-determination, to marry and to found a family, to life, to health, to be free from inhuman and degrading treatment and to respect for privacy and for family life could arise. These human rights have been extensively interpreted with respect to abortion.[88] But, as is evident with regard to reproductive technologies and the protection of human genetic material such as gametes or embryos, recourse to the protection offered by these rights in public international law would be indirect, incomplete and, in all likelihood, inadequate.[89] Indeed, as we shall now see, some of the arguments raised by the Parliamentary Assembly of the Council of Europe point to the need for precision in the delineation of human rights specific to reproductive technologies and to human genetics.[90]

II. Rights in Genetic Heritage

The 1982 recommendation of the Parliamentary Assembly of the Council of Europe was the first to situate the notion of the inherent dignity of the human person specifically in the context of human genetic engineering.[91] It considered that "the

---

85. Reprinted in "WMA's Declarations and Statements" (1982) 29:6 World Medical Journal 91. The Declaration was adopted at the 34th World Medical Assembly, Lisbon, Portugal, 1981. See also Canadian Medical Association, *Code of Ethics* (Ottawa: The Association, 1990), s. 18.

86. Recommendations Guiding Physicians in Biomedical Research Involving Human Subjects, adopted 1964 (am. Tokyo, 1975; am. Venice, 1983; am. Hong Kong, 1989). The text is reproduced in "World Medical Association Adopts Amended Version of the Declaration of Helsinki" (1990) 41:3 Int'l Dig. Health Leg. 530.

87. World Health Organization and Council for International Organizations of Medical Sciences, *Proposed International Guidelines for Biomedical Research Involving Human Subjects* (Geneva: CIOMS, 1982); see also Medical Research Council of Canada, *Towards an International Ethic for Research with Human Beings* (Ottawa: Supply and Services Canada, 1988) at 66, on the need for greater surveillance over the protection of dignity and privacy in epidemiological studies.

88. See *infra*, note 129, Chapter Four.

89. See Bartha M. Knoppers, "Reproductive Technology and International Mechanisms of Protection of the Human Person" (1987) 32 McGill L.J. 336 at 350-56 and its continuation by the same author in "L'adoption d'un code de conduite international en matière de technologies de la reproduction," in International Law Association, *Report of the Sixty-third Conference* (Warsaw, Poland: The Association 1988) at 879.

90. See *infra*, notes 103-108.

91. *Recommendation 934, supra*, note 3, s. 4(i). See also Knoppers, "Reproductive Technology," *supra*,

rights to life and to human dignity protected by Articles 2 and 3 of the European Convention on Human Rights imply the right to inherit a genetic pattern which has not been artificially changed."[92] To avoid any ambiguity, the Parliamentary Assembly recommended that "this right should be made explicit in the context of the European Convention on Human Rights."[93]

At the Parliamentary Hearings preceding the recommendation, there was a general acceptance of the notion that all rights derive from this inherent dignity and contribute to its meaning. The report of those hearings states as follows.

> Among the fundamental human rights embodied in this convention, absolute priority is given to the right to life (Article 2) and to integrity of persons (Article 3); these rights, together with all the regulations contained in the convention and in its protocol signed in Paris on 20 March 1952, provide a highly refined concept of human dignity which has inspired the member states which have committed themselves under this, an international instrument, to respecting them and participating actively in their development.[94]

The extensive advances in, and potential applications of, human genetics and DNA technology apparently inspired the Parliamentary Assembly to propose a more specific delineation of inherent dignity as a human right in Recommendation 934.[95]

In 1986, in line with most national reports on the need to respect human embryos,[96] the Assembly passed Recommendation 1046 on the use of human embryos and foetuses for diagnostic, therapeutic, scientific, industrial and commercial purposes. It recommended that human embryos and foetuses be treated with the respect that is due to human dignity,[97] irrespective of their legal status. Furthermore, the first article of Recommendation 1046 reiterated the need to recognize "the right to a genetic inheritance which should not be artificially interfered with except for therapeutic purposes."[98] Finally, in 1989, in Recommendation 1100 on the use of human embryos

---

note 89, where, while not referring to a right to inherit a genetic pattern, we argued that the rights to life, to integrity and to the inviolability of the human person have been recognized in international texts. See also Bartha M. Knoppers and Claude M. Laberge, "DNA Sampling and Informed Consent" (1989) 140:9 C.M.A.J. 1023, where we presented our position that the advent of somatic cell or of germ-line therapy does not change the necessity of protecting inviolability or of respecting integrity by obtaining informed consent from an individual prior to therapy or prior to any uses of a person's genetic material. In fact, the use of molecular biology techniques in human genetics expands the scope of the need for informed consent.

92. *Recommendation 934, supra*, note 3, s. 4(i).

93. *Ibid.*, s. 4(ii).

94. D. Cucchiara, intervention at the Parliamentary Hearing, in Council of Europe, *supra*, note 43 at 81.

95. *Supra*, note 3.

96. See Knoppers, *supra*, note 89.

97. Council of Europe, P.A., 38th Sess., Pt II, *Text Adopted, Recommendation 1046 (1986) on the Use of Human Embryos and Foetuses for Diagnostic, Therapeutic, Scientific, Industrial and Commercial Purposes*, s. 10.

98. *Ibid.*, s. 1.

and foetuses for research purposes, the Parliamentary Assembly repeated its support of the former proposals in those earlier recommendations.[99]

The Council of Europe, in Recommendation 1046, specified that there is a need for a legislative prohibition of abuses of human genetic engineering. Such abuses include the cloning of individuals, sex selection, the creation of chimeras, interspecies fertilization and other non-therapeutic genetic manipulations.[100] That recommendation has been unanimously supported by other European governmental commissions studying reproductive technologies and human genetic engineering.[101]

III. Consequences of Rights in Genetic Heritage

The Parliamentary Assembly, in its 1989 recommendations, supported its earlier proposals that there should be a right to an unaltered genetic heritage.[102] It was specified at the hearings preceding the 1981 recommendation that this right would belong to "future generations,"[103] presumably including children already conceived but not yet born, to those embryos or gametes *in vitro* or in storage or to those children not yet conceived.

Who would be entitled to bring such a non-existing person's right to an unaltered genetic heritage before the courts? According to the rapporteur of the report, "perhaps [this would fall to] the authorities and in any case the persons themselves when once they have been born and if they felt themselves that they had been genetically engineered in an illegal manner."[104]

In their 1982 recommendation on genetic engineering, the Council of Europe specifically recognized an exception to the generally recommended prohibition on

---

99. Council of Europe, P.A., 40th Sess., Pt III, *Text Adopted, Recommendation 1100 (1989) on the Use of Human Embryos and Foetuses in Scientific Research*, s. 2: "Noting the contents of the Council of Europe's Parliamentary Assembly Recommendation 934 (1982) and its proposals for the application of genetic engineering on the basis of respect for the genetic heritage of mankind, which shall not be interfered with in individuals save for clearly and scientifically demonstrated preventive and therapeutic purposes; . . . ."

100. *Ibid.*, s. 14(iv).

101. Benda report, *supra*, note 39 at 48: "L'utilisation des méthodes qui viennent d'être décrites constitue une atteinte particulièrement grave à la dignité de l'être humain. Résolution: Quelle que soit la méthode employée, le clonage d'êtres humains est inadmissible. L'est également la création de chimères et d'hybrides d'homme et d'animal." See also *supra*, note 35 and below, Chapter Five.

102. See *Recommendation 1100*, *supra*, note 99.

103. Elmquist, *supra*, note 81 at 208. That is to say, gametes in storage *ex utero* or in the gonads.

104. *Ibid.* at 209.

human genetic engineering. This was for prevention and therapy where a need was "clearly and scientifically demonstrated."[105]

Such an exception called for criteria to decide what kinds of disorders would fall within its ambit. The 1986 Recommendation 1046 proposed drawing up a list for "those illnesses where therapy can be based on reliable means of diagnosis and reasonable guarantees of success. This list would be periodically updated to take account of new discoveries and scientific progress."[106]

The rapporteur of the 1981 report preceding the adoption of Recommendation 934 specified that there would need to be general agreement for an illness to be included on the list.[107] The rapporteur also suggested that for diseases on the list, "authorised enforced genetic engineering should perhaps be considered. . . . A compromise might be a demand that the person in question accepted genetic engineering as a pre-condition for being allowed to have children."[108]

Thus, there are two aspects to the proposals. The first is to prevent genetic manipulation that ought not to be done, and the second is to ensure that genetic manipulation is done only where not doing so would result in the passing on of genes that could produce a serious illness.

Undoubtedly, there is a need to establish legal limits to deter possible abuses of genetic engineering. Such is the case presently with the recommendation of the Parliamentary Assembly to prohibit certain forms of non-therapeutic genetic experimentation.[109] Nevertheless, the promotion of such protection as a legal "right" not to inherit certain genes could lead to horrific consequences. If one were to adopt the interpretation suggested in the 1981 report, the ensuing consequences could include scientific or personal lobbying with respect to the inclusion or exclusion of certain diseases on the list, pre-conception screening for genetic suitability, enforced treatment for listed diseases and suits against actual or potential parents. What types of illnesses could be considered sufficiently serious so as to require genetic engineering? Should the willingness to use genetic engineering be a pre-condition for the "privilege" of conception? Could one claim against one's parents or against the state for failing to act in the interests of the child by not having chosen to make use of genetic engineering?[110] The right to inherit an intact genome, the inherent dignity of the human person and the framing of some form of legal protection are issues that cannot be disassociated.

---

105. *Recommendation 1100*, *supra*, note 99, s. 2. This recommendation was approved in the 1986 recommendation on the use of human embryos and foetuses.

106. *Supra*, note 97, Appendix, B(iv).

107. Elmquist, *supra*, note 81, by reference from s. 10 of *Recommendation 1046* to the Appendix, B(iv).

108. Elmquist, *supra*, note 81 at 208.

109. *Recommendation 1046*, *supra*, note 97.

110. This would seem to be the logical conclusion from the 1981 report, Council of Europe, *supra*, note 43. It is also a position held by certain American authors such as Margery W. Shaw, "Conditional Prospective Rights of the Fetus" (1984) 5 J. Legal Med. 63.

IV. Critique of Genetic Rights

Currently, pre-conception choices are left to couples within the limits of state regulation and available medical services and information.[111] During pregnancy, recourse to abortion and medical treatment and the choice of personal life-style have, on the whole, been seen as falling within the right of the woman to liberty and personal privacy.[112] State interest in protecting potential "persons" is balanced against those rights. A result of this interest is an increasing gradation of state surveillance over the woman and protection of the foetus as the foetus becomes viable.[113] Finally, where fertilization occurs *in vitro*, direct state intervention to protect the embryo by legislation is still the object of discussion.[114]

While certain forms of non-therapeutic genetic experimentation have been universally condemned,[115] prior to Recommendations 934 and 1046 of the Parliamentary Assembly, a right to dignity in relation to the inheritance of a particular genome had not been mentioned. The possible interpretations to which the adoption of such a right may lead having been seen, its rationale should be questioned. A more profound discussion and analysis are required before that right becomes enshrined.

Any future recommendation should consider the following points as well. First, there are relatively few disorders to which somatic gene therapy, or one day perhaps

111. Bartha M. Knoppers, "Modern Birth Technology and Human Rights" (1985) 33 Am. J. Comp. L. 1, Knoppers, *supra*, note 89 and Bartha M. Knoppers, *Conception artificielle et responsabilité médicale: une étude de droit comparé* (Cowansville, Que.: Yvon Blais, 1986).

112. Sanda Rodgers, "Fetal Rights and Maternal Rights: Is There a Conflict?" (1986) 1 C.J.W.L. 456; see also Chapter Five, below.

113. Rodgers, *supra*, note 112; see also Jean-Louis Baudouin and Catherine Labrusse-Riou, *Produire l'homme: de quel droit?* (Paris: P.U.F., 1987) and Law Reform Commission of Canada, *Crimes against the Foetus*, Working Paper 58 (Ottawa: The Commission, 1989). The foetus is also protected indirectly in private law. Thus, where health care workers negligently fail to inform parents of reproductive risk, or misinform them, they or their disabled child born as a result may bring a suit in "wrongful birth" or "wrongful life." See below, Chapter Five, and Knoppers, supra, note 111.

114. Knoppers, *supra*, note 89.

115. *Supra*, notes 94, 97; see also J. Dausset, "Éditorial: Les droits de l'Homme face à la science" (1989) 3:3 Cahiers du M.U.R.S. at article X. [U.M.S.R. (Universal Movement for Scientific Responsibility) proposes to add a new article to the *Universal Declaration of Human Rights*] "Scientific knowledge should be used only to promote dignity and preserve the integrity and the future of man. No-one can hinder the acquisition of scientific knowledge." U.M.S.R. also proposes the adoption by the United Nations Organization of the following principles:

  — Sources of energy should be used only for the benefit of mankind, without damaging the biosphere.

  — Human genetic inheritance, given our present level of knowledge, should not be modified.*

  — The human body — cells, tissues or organs — has no price, and thus cannot be a source of profit.

  * This does not exclude the treatment of genetic diseases by introducing genes into those cells of the patient which are involved in sexual reproduction.

germ-line therapy, will be applicable, because gene therapy is only applicable to single gene disorders where the gene locus has been identified. Most diseases are not due to a single gene. Second, when direct intervention does become possible, it may instead take the form of pre-fertilization, pre-implantation or *in utero* genetic selection, rather than gene therapy. Thus, the areas in which respect for the inherent dignity of the human person will be important are the diffusion, communication and handling of genetic information, the freedom of procreative choices, the safeguards to be placed on DNA banking and, only rarely, genetic manipulation *per se*. These important areas involve choice and the provision of information to make such choice. In order to ensure the individuality of the person as well as the continuity of the human species, freedom of genetic choice needs to be legally protected, because individual choice is the basis of human dignity.[116]

Finally, respecting the dignity of the person in its substrate — the human gene — means respect for the person.[117] The human person can be seen as having the following dimensions: organic, psychic and symbolic.[118] These dimensions of body, mind and soul imply the need for reciprocity and sharing — a need that is specific to human beings. The obligation of reciprocity is a construct of the solidarity of human kinship in the Family of Man. These three dimensions of human dignity are inherent in the person and should be valued as priceless and ageless.

V. Conclusion

In the international context, we have seen the dangers of the interpretation of human dignity that concerns the "rights" to an unaltered genetic heritage.[119] Under the guise of protection, such an interpretation would lead to the screening and selection of those individuals suitable to reproduce and, ultimately, to lawsuits within families and between generations. A new approach to defining dignity as the basic principle for human rights in the context of human genetics is called for. Dignity cannot exist independent of the individual. If we assume that the human gene, including the information it contains, is more than a substrate for the existence of the human person, then the individual's freedom to control its expression during his or her life span will become the core of human dignity.

---

116. Oscar Schachter, "Human Dignity As a Normative Concept" (1983) 77 Am. J. Int'l L. 848.

117. Congregation for the Doctrine of the Faith, *supra*, note 42 at 8-9.

118. Jean-François Malherbe, *Pour une éthique de la médecine* (Paris: Larousse, 1987); Mary Warnock, "Do Human Cells Have Rights?" (1987) 1:1 Bioethics 1; Lucien Sève, *Recherche biomédicale et respect de la personne humaine: Explication d'une démarche* (Paris: La Documentation française, 1987); see also below, Chapter Six.

119. For an interpretation of international law and human rights in the context of human procreation and reproductive technology generally, see Knoppers, *supra*, note 89.

In Canada, the concept of human dignity has not been specifically studied by the courts in relation to human genetics. It has, however, been interpreted in the larger context of human rights under Canadian constitutional law. An examination of this interpretation in relation to those human rights may shed some light on alternative approaches.

CHAPTER FOUR

Human Dignity and Genetics — The *Canadian Charter of Rights and Freedoms*

I. Introduction

As we have seen, public policy recommendations in genetics can have profound implications for the individual in his or her most intimate self. There is no doubt of the need to legislate in the future to protect the inherent dignity and self-worth of individuals with respect to their genetic heritage. But any such legislation must conform to the *Canadian Charter of Rights and Freedoms*. What guidance can be gleaned from the structure of the *Charter* and from Supreme Court of Canada decisions relevant to our subject? Let us examine the possible impact of the *Charter* on future legislative policies on human genetics by first discussing its scope.

Legal recourse under the *Charter* is possible when legislation or other governmental action has violated a protected right. Under section 32, the *Charter* prohibits unconstitutional actions by federal, provincial and territorial governments or government entities. In other words, it protects Canadians from government interference with the rights and liberties enunciated therein.[120] The *Charter* does not apply to non-governmental organizations. Where an infringement of human rights is alleged by an individual against another individual, or against a corporation or employer, provincial human rights codes would generally apply.

The Canadian *Charter* does not explicitly refer to the notion of human dignity. However, it is the fundamental theme that underlies the *Charter*. An important component of the inherent dignity of the person is freedom of choice in decision making. The corollary is that the state must respect individual choice.[121]

The theme of human dignity can be found in the sections of the *Charter* guaranteeing various rights and liberties. We will look at several of these: freedom of conscience and religion, and of association (section 2), the right to life, liberty and security of the person and the right not to be deprived thereof except in accordance with the principles of fundamental justice (section 7), the right to be secure against

---

120. *RWDSU* v. *Dolphin Delivery Ltd.*, [1986] 2 S.C.R. 573.

121. Luc Huppé, "La dignité humaine comme fondement des droits et libertés garantis par la Charte" (1988) 48 R. du B. 724.

unreasonable search and seizure (section 8), and the right to be equal before and under the law and to equal protection and benefit of the law without discrimination (section 15). These rights can be invoked by an individual in the area of human genetics, with regard to provincial or federal legislation or policies of government entities.

Taking each of these rights and freedoms in turn, we will briefly examine the scope of their interpretation, as found in certain decisions of the Supreme Court of Canada. Each interpretation will be followed by examples of how it might apply in the area of human genetics. Finally, even where legislation violates a *Charter* right, it could survive judicial scrutiny if it is considered a reasonable limitation of a right that can be demonstrably justified in a free and democratic society under section 1 of the *Charter*.

II. Freedom of Association and of Conscience and Religion

Protection under section 2 of the *Charter* includes freedom of association, conscience and religion. Freedom of association has been held to include those "collective activities which may be said to be fundamental to our culture and traditions and which by common assent are deserving of protection."[122] The Court also suggested that a fundamental institution such as marriage "might well be protected by freedom of association in combination with other rights and freedoms."[123] Thus, any legislation linking the obtaining of a marriage licence to genetic status in order to prevent the transmission of genetic disease could run afoul of this protected sphere of activity.

Freedom of conscience and religion has received a wide interpretation by the Court. Its scope has been described as follows:

> Freedom can primarily be characterized by the absence of coercion or constraint. If a person is compelled by the state or the will of another to a course of action or inaction which he would not otherwise have chosen, he is not acting of his own volition and he cannot be said to be truly free. One of the major purposes of the *Charter* is to protect, within reason, from compulsion or restraint. Coercion includes not only such blatant forms of compulsion as direct commands to act or refrain from acting on pain of sanction, coercion includes indirect forms of control which determine or limit alternative courses of conduct available to others.[124]

This freedom has been held to extend to the expression of individual life-style[125] and to parental choices for their children in, for example, the area of education.[126]

---

122. *Reference re Public Service Employee Relations Act (Alta.),* [1987] 1 S.C.R. 313 at 401.

123. *Ibid.* at 406.

124. The words of Dickson C.J. in *R.* v. *Big M. Drug Mart Ltd.*, [1985] 1 S.C.R. 295 at 336-37.

125. *Attorney-General of British Columbia and Astaroff* (1983), 6 C.C.C. (3d) 498 (B.C.C.A.).

126. *R.* v. *Jones*, [1986] 2 S.C.R. 284.

Would this broad scope of parental freedoms be upheld in the face of legislation prescribing genetic testing prior to procreation? If it could be determined with certainty that a child would be born with severe malformations, would individuals of a certain religious faith still be free deliberately to conceive a child under the tenets of their faith? If such a choice were not based on religious precepts, could that same couple allege that any restriction of their freedom to procreate within marriage would violate the right to freedom of association?

III. Life, Liberty and Security of the Person

Triggering the operation of section 7 of the *Charter* involves a two-step process. First, it must be found that there has been a deprivation of the right to "life, liberty and security of the person"; second, this deprivation must be contrary to the principles of fundamental justice. The Supreme Court of Canada has enunciated that the three distinct elements of section 7 — life, liberty and security of the person — are independent interests that must be given independent significance.[127] However, Parliament could choose to infringe any of these rights if it did so in a manner consistent with the principles of fundamental justice.

It is difficult to imagine how the right to life could be invoked in the context of human genetics. The right of "everyone" to life has been held not to include the foetus.[128] Thus, it is difficult to see how the genome, gametes or embryos could be considered as being protected under the right-to-life provision in section 7.

A more likely avenue of contestation in the case of government intervention in the area of human genetics would be the *Charter* provisions concerning the right to liberty or to the security of the person. Madam Justice Wilson of the Supreme Court of Canada has described the scope of this right to liberty as including ". . . the right to make fundamental personal decisions without interference from the state."[129] Decisions about one's genetic health or that of one's offspring would certainly fall within the ambit of personal decisions. Mandatory screening of adults or adolescents to determine whether they are carriers of genetic disease would clearly be an interference with this right. The dignity and self-respect of those persons would be affected. Such legislation would infringe section 7 because that legislation "require[s] a person . . . to go through an identification process on pain of . . . [a sanction] for failure to comply."[130]

---

127. *Singh* v. *Minister of Employment and Immigration*, [1985] 1 S.C.R. 177.

128. *Borowski* v. *Attorney General of Canada*, [1987] 4 W.W.R. 385 (Sask. C.A.), which contains an excellent review of the similar position taken world-wide by the courts. On November 16, 1989, the Supreme Court of Canada held, in *Tremblay* v. *Daigle*, [1989] 2 S.C.R. 530, that the foetus is not a legal person under Quebec civil law.

129. *R.* v. *Morgentaler*, [1988] 1 S.C.R. 30 at 166.

130. *R.* v. *Beare*; *R.* v. *Higgins*, [1988] 2 S.C.R. 387 at 388-89, where the Court did not dispute the holding of the Saskatchewan Court of Appeal but, in the particular "criminal" context of the case, held that the fingerprinting of suspects was a justifiable interference under s. 1 of the *Charter*.

But would the mandatory screening of, say, newborns for treatable disorders also constitute an infringement of the parent's liberty interest?[131] Since there is a duty to treat a child when it is in the child's best interest to do so,[132] would this not also include a duty to know whether treatment is necessary? Would a criminal law prohibiting therapeutic genetic alteration, whether in somatic or germ cells, constitute an infringement of the liberty of the person? The answer to these questions is unclear.

In the view of Chief Justice Dickson, the right to security of the person in the *Charter* constitutionalizes the principle of the inviolability of the human person. That is, the human body ought to be protected from interference by others. This right is not limited to the concept of physical control; it also protects against "stigmatization of the accused, loss of privacy, stress and anxiety resulting from a multitude of factors, including possible disruption of family, social life and work, legal costs . . . ."[133] Thus, section 7 of the *Charter* would not only protect against the minimal physical intrusion involved in the mandatory taking of blood or tissue samples for genetic testing; it would also protect the psychological integrity of the person.[134] In the context of genetic medicine, section 7 may provide a safeguard against unwarranted interference with the autonomy and privacy of the person.

As stated earlier, Parliament could choose to infringe section 7 rights if it did so in a manner consistent with the principles of fundamental justice.[135] Determination of a possible infringement requires examination of the impugned legislation to see if, in its actual application and administrative and procedural structures, it is so manifestly unfair that it violates the principles of fundamental justice.[136] Thus, even if the rights under section 7 were found to have been violated, that infringement could be seen by the Court as being in accordance with the principles of fundamental justice.

---

131. See *Splicing Life*, *supra*, note 33 at 66ff and *Screening and Counseling*, *supra*, note 33.

132. Edward W. Keyserlingk, "Non-Treatment in the Best Interests of the Child: A Case Commentary of *Couture-Jacquet* v. *Montreal Children's Hospital*" (1987) 32 McGill L.J. 413.

133. *R.* v. *Morgentaler*, *supra*, note 129 at 55 citing Lamer J. in *Mills* v. *The Queen*, [1986] 1 S.C.R. 863. See also *Dion* v. *Attorney General of Canada*, [1986] D.L.Q. 353 (Que. Sup. Ct), where the indiscriminate taking of urine samples from prisoners for drug detection was seen as contrary to section 7 ("Le droit à l'intimité, à la discrétion et au secret des actes de la vie privée est une composante du droit à la sécurité de la personne") at 358. While urine testing may be difficult to justify in the absence of proof of reasonable grounds, blood tests may not be seen as unreasonable since they are "safe, painless and commonplace." George J. Annas, "Crack, Symbolism, and the Constitution" (1989) 19:3 Hast. Cent. Rep. 35.

134. In *R.* v. *Morgentaler*, *supra*, note 129, Dickson C.J. considered the concept of state-imposed psychological stress under the rubric of security of the person, whereas Wilson J. considered it under the rubric of liberty.

135. The principles of fundamental justice are "essential elements of a system for the administration of justice which is founded upon the belief in the dignity and worth of the human person and the rule of law." *Reference re Section 94(2) of the Motor Vehicle Act, R.S.B.C. 1979, c. 288*, [1985] 2 S.C.R. 486 at 512.

136. See *R.* v. *Jones*, *supra*, note 126.

This power of Parliament was confirmed in a case involving fingerprinting. The Supreme Court held that subjecting a person to obligatory fingerprinting with imprisonment as the sanction for failure to comply violated section 7. Nevertheless, the Court held that the infringement was in accordance with the principles of fundamental justice.[137] It reasoned that a person charged on reasonable and probable grounds with having committed a serious crime must expect a significant loss of personal privacy incidental to being taken into custody.[138]

Cases such as the foregoing that concern traditional fingerprinting are relevant to DNA "fingerprinting."[139] That is the term applied to the laboratory analysis of the DNA of an individual. Each person's DNA is unique.[140] Because of this uniqueness, DNA analysis or "fingerprinting" can identify an individual with virtual certainty, if enough gene markers are examined and the techniques are properly done.[141] These techniques have been applied to exclude or identify suspected criminals. Small samples of blood, sperm or even single strands of hair are sufficient to establish positive identity.[142]

Extrapolating from cases involving traditional fingerprinting, the use of DNA fingerprinting may not be held to infringe the principles of fundamental justice in a criminal context, but may so infringe outside of that context. Two limitations may be placed on the use of such techniques or their reception into evidence in the criminal

---

137. *R.* v. *Beare*; *R.* v. *Higgins*, *supra*, note 130, in which fingerprinting was not considered to be an unreasonable search and seizure under section 8. See also Yves de Montigny, "La protection contre les fouilles, les perquisitions et les saisies abusives: un premier bilan" (1989) 49 R. du B. 53.

138. *R.* v. *Beare*; *R.* v. *Higgins*, *supra*, note 130 at 413.

139. Even though there is no Supreme Court decision on DNA typing, there is an abundance of case law on fingerprinting: see *R.* v. *Amway of Canada Ltd.*, [1986] 2 F.C. 312 (T.D.); *R.* v. *Therrien* (1982), 67 C.C.C. (2d) 31 (Ont. Co. Ct); *R.* v. *Esposito* (1985), 24 C.C.C. (3d) 88 (Ont. C.A.); *Re Jamieson and The Queen* (1982), 70 C.C.C. (2d) 430 (Que. Sup. Ct). It has not been interpreted as a violation of the privilege against self-incrimination under s. 11(*c*). On DNA fingerprinting, see also Gilles Létourneau and André A. Morin, "Technologie nouvelle et droit pénal" (1989) 49 R. du B. 821.

140. Motulsky, *supra*, note 13 at 2855. The exception is where a person has an identical twin.

141. M.C. King, "Genetic Testing of Identity and Relationship" (1989) 44:2 Am. J. Hum. Genet. 178; Roger Lewin, "DNA Typing on the Witness Stand" (1989) 244:4908 Science 1033; Alun Anderson, "New Technique on Trial" (1989) 339:6224 Nature 408 and Alun Anderson, "Judge Backs Technique" (1989) 340:6235 Nature 582 (recognition of using DNA for forensic testing as valid). Note, however, that in *State* v. *Castro*, 545 N.Y.S. 2d 985 (1989) (Bronx Cty), the evidence was excluded since the firm involved in testing failed to meet scientific standards. This technique of DNA typing is now being used in Canada. See Cristin Schmitz, "DNA Fingerprinting" (1989) 48:8 Lawyer's Weekly 1. See also *R.* v. *Parent* (1989), 65 A.R. 307 (Q.B.).

142. Banking of such data raises questions of civil liberties, since it is theoretically possible to identify everyone in the population from samples taken for other purposes, and such samples contain information about predisposition to disease: Jean L. Marx, "DNA Fingerprinting Takes the Witness Stand" (1988) 240:4859 Science 1616. These techniques have also been used to establish parenthood in cases involving alimentary obligations or immigration. It is worth mentioning that s. 11(*c*) of the *Charter* (privilege against incrimination) has been unsuccessfully raised with regard to traditional fingerprinting. See *supra*, note 139.

context. The first is proof of their reliability;[143] the second is whether such a practice "would bring the administration of justice into disrepute" under subsection 24(2) of the *Charter*.[144]

IV. Unreasonable Search and Seizure

Section 8 of the *Charter* protects the person against unreasonable search and seizure. The Court has held that such protection must not be constrained by narrow legalistic classifications, based on notions of property and the like, that served to protect this fundamental human value in earlier times.[145] It also held that section 8 does not merely prohibit unreasonable search and seizure, and goes further to guarantee this right by providing an entitlement to be secure against unreasonable search and seizure.[146] Privacy, according to the Court, "is at the heart of liberty in a modern state" and its constitutional protection "has profound significance for the public order."[147]

Therefore, the taking of a blood sample from an unconscious patient was seen by the Court as a violation of the sanctity of a person's body and as a serious affront to human dignity.[148] Furthermore, even where there is no "search" in the physical sense of taking a blood or tissue sample, "the use of a person's body without his consent to obtain information about him, invades an area of personal privacy essential to the maintenance of his human dignity."[149] Thus, even where consent to the taking of a sample or the participation in a test is obtained, the Court was clear in its opinion that the information derived from it should be restricted to the medical purposes for which it was given. Indeed, in the context of medical care, the Court held that "[t]his is obviously necessary if one considers the vulnerability of the individual in such circumstances. He is forced to reveal information of a most intimate character and to

---

143. The *Castro* case, *supra*, note 141, failed on this point, the prosecution having relied on tests that had not met scientific standards.

144. See *R.* v. *Dyment*, [1988] 2 S.C.R. 417.

145. See *Hunter* v. *Southam Inc.*, [1984] 2 S.C.R. 145 at 160, which held that the purpose of s. 8 "is . . . to protect individuals from unjustified state intrusions upon their privacy."

146. *Minister of National Revenue* v. *Kruger Inc.*, [1984] 2 F.C. 535 (C.A.).

147. *R.* v. *Dyment*, *supra*, note 144 at 427 refering to Alan Westin's *Privacy and Freedom*.

> Grounded in man's physical and moral autonomy, privacy is essential for the well-being of the individual. For this reason alone, it is worthy of constitutional protection, but it also has profound significance for the public order.

148. *R.* v. *Pohoretsky*, [1987] 1 S.C.R. 945, involved a doctor who took a blood sample at the request of a police officer from a patient who was in an incoherent and delirious state.

149. *R.* v. *Dyment*, *supra*, note 144 at 431-32.

permit invasions of his body if he is to protect his life or health."[150] The Court went further in requiring pressing necessity or prior patient authorization for the taking of blood or other bodily substances for secondary purposes.[151] The privacy of the person, according to the Court, transcends the physical, and the seizure in question constituted a violation of human dignity.[152] This holding, although in the criminal context, is also important in the present context.

Genetic testing, and the banking and use of DNA and the genetic information it contains, could be done without the knowledge of a person, where, for example, a blood sample was obtained for other purposes. This could be a violation of section 8 of the *Charter*.

The need for prior authorization for any uses of genetic materials or information is an important step in ensuring a respect for human dignity in the medical context.[153] The difficulty is that, unlike ordinary medical treatment or diagnosis, genetic testing often involves families — sometimes extended families. Thus, testing may extend over time and over generations. If the original consent is to be respected, family members or the original participant must be contacted for authorization where use is to be made of samples, which use was not within the scope of the original consent.[154] We will see in the following chapters that the maintenance of choice and "the trust and confidence of the public in the administration of medical facilities"[155] depends on a new social construct, and on the elaboration of the concept of genetic justice.

V. Equal Treatment and Freedom from Discrimination

The remaining *Charter* right meriting discussion in relation to genetic heritage is the right to equal treatment and the prevention of discrimination. The categories under which discrimination is prohibited include race, national or ethnic origin, colour, religion, sex, age and mental or physical disability. But could one refuse to grant a right or a privilege to some individuals on the basis of their genome?

---

150. *Ibid.* at 433. The Court also noted at 439 that "the trust and confidence of the public in the administration of medical facilities would be seriously taxed if an easy and informal flow of information, and particularly of bodily substances from hospitals to the police, were allowed." This trust is crucial for public participation in preventive medicine.

151. *Ibid.* at 430, 436. See also *R.* v. *Legere* (1989), 5 W.C.B. (2d) 384 (N.B.C.A.).

152. *R.* v. *Dyment*, *supra*, note 144 at 439. The Court also referred for guidance to the report of the Law Reform Commission of Canada, *Obtaining Forensic Evidence*, Report 25 (Ottawa: The Commission, 1985) at 1.

153. See Knoppers and Laberge, *supra*, note 91 at 1024.

154. *Ibid.* at 1026.

155. *R.* v. *Dyment*, *supra*, note 144 at 439.

The right to equality before and under the law, according to the Supreme Court, also includes any discriminatory impact that a law may have.[156] Thus, distinctions founded on the personal characteristics of an individual or a group, which would have the effect of imposing obligations or disadvantages not imposed on others or which would restrict access to benefits accorded to others, would be considered discriminatory. Even if the effect of being considered and treated as genetically different would not at first glance fall into one of the prohibited categories, the Court envisaged the possibility of enlarging those categories of protected minorities under section 15 of the *Charter*.[157] Thus, theoretically, the genetically handicapped or disabled could become an additional category.

The Supreme Court saw the enumerated categories found in section 15 as characteristics inherent in the person and not acquired by his or her choice, merit or capacity. Thus, an individual would be protected from discrimination based on that individual's genome, irrespective of whether one labelled it as race, ethnic origin or handicap. Consequently, legislation mandating genetic testing could be perceived as discriminatory where it deliberately or incidentally identifies certain racial or ethnic groups carrying certain genetic traits as the basis for differential treatment. The compulsory genetic testing of pregnant women could also run afoul of section 15. If genetic testing were to be done to determine eligibility for employment[158] or other benefits in a *Charter*-regulated industry, or if it affected the right to marry or procreate, such state conduct could be seen as discrimination on the grounds of physical or mental disability.

However, the inclusion of genetic handicap in the general notion of handicap is problematic. It might mean that being genetically different is equivalent to having a disability because the distinction between a "difference" and a "handicap" is not always clear. Another view is preferable, namely, that we are all genetically equal because we all have certain genetic differences from one another. Thus, genetic difference could be seen as the foundation for a new social contract based on that genetic equality.[159]

---

156. Prior to *Andrews* v. *Law Society of British Columbia*, [1989] 1 S.C.R. 143, "a similarly situated" test was the basis of most equality cases. Others tended to accept an "invidious discrimination" test. Both these stands were rejected in *Andrews*. The first was held to be seriously deficient on account of its formalism and failure to consider the nature of the law. The second was held to confuse s. 15(1) and (2). Thus, it was sufficient for the complainant to prove a discriminatory distinction causing a "prejudice or disadvantage."

157. *Ibid.*

158. Edith F. Canter, "Employment Discrimination Implications of Genetic Screening in the Workplace under Title VII and the Rehabilitation Act" (1984-85) 10 Am. J.L. Med. 323. See also Karim Benyekhlef, "Réflexions sur la légalité des tests de dépistage de drogues dans l'emploi" (1988) 48 R. du B. 315.

159. See below, Chapter Six.

VI. Reasonable Limits

If legislation with regard to genetic testing were proposed, would it be considered reasonable and justifiable in a free and democratic society? According to section 1 of the *Charter*, legislation violating a *Charter* right will survive constitutional challenge if the reasonable limits prescribed therein "can be demonstrably justified in a free and democratic society."[160] The burden of proof falls on the legislature responsible for the impugned legislation.

The Supreme Court has ruled that not only must the limit on a protected *Charter* right be demonstrably justifiable, but also the means used in the exercise of that limit must be reasonable.[161] The objective of any legislation or a provision therein must be of "sufficient importance to warrant overriding a constitutionally protected right or freedom."[162] The "reasonableness" test ensures that the legislative means are proportional to the legislative ends.[163] The means chosen should be rational and fair, not arbitrary. They should impair as little as possible the right or freedom under consideration, and the effect of the limitation should not be disproportionate to the objective sought.[164] Finally, the Court reiterated that the values of a free and democratic society include "respect for the inherent dignity of the human person, commitment to social justice and equality, accommodation of a wide variety of beliefs, respect for cultural and group identity, and faith in social and political institutions which enhance the participation of individuals and groups in society."[165]

It is doubtful that any form of compulsory genetic screening or testing could survive this final test of section 1.

VII. Conclusion

Charter protection is limited in its scope and application. The interpretation of *Charter* rights by the Supreme Court of Canada suggests that freedom of genetic choice may be protected under the fundamental rights of: freedom of association and

---

160. Such proof may be derived from social science data, reports for Royal Commissions and Parliamentary Committees and laws in other free and democratic societies as evidenced in treatises on comparative law and in international covenants. This places a responsibility on the opposing party to rebut such evidence by showing that it is "neither cogent nor persuasive, or that the Crown has failed to demonstrate the consequences of imposing or not imposing the limit." Morris Manning, "Proof of Facts in Constitutional Cases" in Gérald-A. Beaudoin, ed., *Charter Cases 1986-87* (Cowansville, Que.: Yvon Blais, 1987) 271 at 284.

161. *R.* v. *Oakes*, [1986] 1 S.C.R. 103.

162. *R.* v. *Big M. Drug Mart Ltd.*, *supra*, note 124 at 352.

163. *R.* v. *Oakes*, *supra*, note 161 at 139-40.

164. *R.* v. *Edwards Books*, [1986] 2 S.C.R. 713.

165. *R.* v. *Oakes*, *supra*, note 161 at 136.

conscience and religion; life, liberty and security of the person; freedom from unreasonable search and seizure; and the right to equality. These rights could be a powerful tool to ensure that the inherent dignity of the person will be respected in the area of human genetics.

Geneticists have, through self-regulation, taken steps in that direction. Screening is only acceptable where the condition is serious and the testing accurate. Moreover, therapy or effective intervention must be available and the cost of screening must be commensurate with the gains to be achieved.[166] As human genetics expands to include predictive genetics for a greater number of diseases and people, do the general legal or scientific safeguards described in this chapter suffice? What serious, identifiable and treatable diseases could be screened for in a cost-effective manner so as not to infringe constitutional rights and freedoms?[167]

We have argued that, at present, the Canadian *Charter* may offer the freedom of choice necessary to safeguard the concept of human dignity on which the *Charter* is founded. However, considering current social prejudices surrounding disease, can we rely on these general *Charter* rights to safeguard the freedom of genetic choice?

The knowledge that the new genetics is providing gives rise to difficult choices. The ability to identify diseases that are not yet treatable, the expansion of carrier testing to include new diseases such as cystic fibrosis, the banking of DNA for future research (on as yet unidentified individuals for as yet unidentified diseases) and the identification of rare diseases with doubtful cost-benefit ratios will force the scientific community to re-evaluate the traditional criteria for screening and testing.[168] It may force us to go beyond relying on the *Charter* rights described. Perhaps we should ask, What do we as a society consider to be genetically "normal"? and then consider expanding or restricting legislative intervention in genetic medicine.

---

166. National Academy of Science, *Genetic Screening: Programs, Principles, and Research* (Washington, D.C.: U.S. Government Printing Office, 1975) confirmed in the President's Commission Reports, *supra*, note 33. Considering the state of knowledge in 1976, the Academy saw no relationship between compulsory public health measures for communicable diseases and those for genetic diseases. See also Robert Steinbrook, "In California, Voluntary Mass Prenatal Screening" (1986) 16:5 Hast. Cent. Rep. 5.

167. At present only screening in newborns for PKU and other treatable metabolic disorders meets these criteria. Even then, screening in Canada is presently not subject to legislative sanction. The general common law rules of informed consent apply.

168. Kathleen Nolan and Sara Swenson, "New Tools, New Dilemmas: Genetic Frontiers" (1988) 18:5 Hast. Cent. Rep. 40, argue that the four traditional criteria for good screening (serious disease; accurate test; treatment or meaningful intervention; reasonable cost) are no longer clear in the context of modern genetics. See Bartha M. Knoppers and Claude M. Laberge, "Genetic Screening: From Newborns to DNA Typing" in Bartha M. Knoppers and Claude M. Laberge, eds, *Genetic Screening: From Newborns to DNA Typing* (Amsterdam: Excerpta Medicine, 1990) 379.

CHAPTER FIVE

Genetic "Ab-normality"

I. Introduction

Differing views of human nature may lead to differing social choices; this is particularly pertinent to human genetics. Conversely, differing views of human genetics may lead to differing views of human nature and to the limitation or expansion of social choices. If we see the gene as determinant of the person, then the knowledge that someone carries a particular genetic trait acquires, in the eyes of some, a fatalistic perspective. In this situation, choices will centre around the elimination or manipulation of the gene since the person, and the person's disease, is seen as being biologically predetermined. If we view the random diversity of genetic characteristics as natural and as the essence of humanity, we may resist genetic intervention regardless of the reasons for it. If, on the other hand, we see the human being as determined by social, environmental and historical forces, a knowledge of human genetics may help to combat or to mould those forces according to the given political ideology at a given time.

In this chapter, we will survey the notions of genetic determinism, naturalism, discrimination and perfectionism. We will also point out some of the legal implications that may arise from the social choices made with respect to "normal" or "healthy" genomes.

II. Genetic Determinism

Biological or genetic determinism is the belief that "all human behavior — hence all human society — is governed by a chain of determinants that runs from the gene to the individual to the sum of the behaviors of all individuals. The determinists would have it, then, that human nature is fixed by our genes."[169] Thus, it is a reductionist view that defines the nature of humankind in terms of its biology or genes.

---

169. Richard C. Lewontin, Steven Rose and Leon J. Kamin, *Not in Our Genes* (New York: Pantheon Books, 1984) at 6.

In their book, *Not in Our Genes*, Lewontin and his colleagues trace the history of genetic determinism.[170] The dismantling of the living organism began with a demonstration that physical laws applied to the animate as well as the inanimate, and the two were assumed to be similarly constituted. However, there was a paradox. If the animate and the inanimate were similarly constituted, it ought to have been possible to create life from its inanimate components. Yet, Pasteur had shown that life could only emerge from life.

A view of how life emerged was presented in the work of Charles Darwin. He theorized that living things evolved through time by a process of natural selection acting on an over-abundance of offspring, each with varying degrees of adaptability. This dimension of time allowed Darwin to speculate that the first step in this progression was the formation of life from non-living substances. Thus, materialist biology replaced God with science as the determinant of the social order.[171]

What was left unexplained by Darwin's theory was how the inherited variation within a population, upon which selective forces acted, was maintained. Mendel's theory of the gene as the unit of inheritance provided the answer. A description of how information transfer occurred between the gene and the cell products awaited the work of Watson and Crick who, in the 1950s, elucidated the genetic code. Thus, the working of the cell in producing proteins from mRNA, and from DNA, came to be seen as an assembly line and the organism came to be seen as "merely DNA's way of making another DNA molecule."[172]

Shortly after Darwin developed his theory of evolution, Galton attempted to reduce behaviour to quantifiable norms and to attribute its origin to ancestral inheritance.[173] His erroneous view that mental illness and criminality were largely biologically determined fuelled the eugenics movement that he founded. That movement gave rise to restrictive immigration policies, sterilization programs and, eventually, the extermination of those considered by the Nazis to be undesirable.

Unfortunately, the horrors of the Holocaust did not make genetic determinism go away. It re-emerged as an explanation for social phenomena with the publication of Arthur Jensen's treatise on IQ in which he argued, in a way that has since been shown to be flawed,[174] that IQ differences between the races could be largely explained by genetic differences. This was followed by the work of E.O. Wilson, who captured the attention of the popular press with his socio-biological theory of human nature. His

---

170. *Ibid.*, Chapter 3 at 37.

171. *Ibid.* at 51

172. *Ibid.* at 58.

173. *Ibid.* at 56.

174. *Ibid.* at 118.

proposal, which has been systematically and thoroughly criticized,[175] was that many human characteristics, such as tribalism, xenophobia and altruism, are also found in animals. He proposed that, like physical characteristics, these behavioural characteristics have been moulded by evolutionary forces. Thus, in this view, the characteristics of society as we know it are predictable, if not inevitable.

Lewontin and his colleagues, on the other hand, argued for a broad vision of the complexity of the forces that shape us as individuals and as a society — one that would give meaning to freedom:

> What characterizes human development and actions is that they are the consequence of an immense array of interacting and intersecting causes. Our actions are not at random or independent with respect to the totality of those causes as an intersecting system, for we are material beings in a causal world. But to the extent that they are free, our actions are independent of any one or even a small subset of those multiple paths of causation: that is the precise meaning of freedom in a causal world.
>
> . . .
>
> For biological determinists we are unfree because our lives are strongly constrained by a relatively small number of internal causes, the genes for specific behaviors or for predisposition to these behaviors. But this misses the essence of the difference between human biology and that of other organisms. Our brains, hands, and tongues have made us independent of many single major features of the external world. Our biology has made us into creatures who are constantly re-creating our own psychic and material environments, and whose individual lives are the outcomes of an extraordinary multiplicity of intersecting causal pathways. Thus, it is our biology that makes us free.[176]

Another opponent of the reductionist view of man is Albert Jacquard, who attempted to establish the specificity of the human person. While recognizing the interaction and mutual influence of the gene with the environment in general, he introduced a particular environmental influence, that of a specific culture in a given society. This cultural influence could be random or even unknown in its effect. According to Jacquard, the dialectic of all these factors demonstrated individual genetic complexity. In that complexity lay the possibility to move from *animalité* based on biological determinism to *humanitude*. *Humanitude* was based on the belief of an active contribution by each person to the further construction and complexity of the human person, individually and collectively.[177] Thus, each person is an active agent in the definition of what is and what will be the human person and society. How the individual acts on genetic knowledge will, in turn, be influenced by the collective concept of normality.

Despite the strong criticism that has been levelled at biological determinism, it seems to underlie certain proposals to justify budget cuts for welfare and education, to

---

175. *Ibid.*, Chapter 9 at 233, refutes Wilson's theory as to its description of human nature, as to the characters he chose to describe human nature being a consequence of gene action, and as to his attempt to show that these characters were established by the evolutionary forces of natural selection.

176. *Ibid.* at 289-90. See also François Jacob, *La logique du vivant: une histoire de l'hérédité* (Paris: Gallimard, 1970) and François Jacob, *The Statue Within* (New York: Basic Books, 1988).

177. Albert Jacquard, *L'héritage de la liberté: de l'animalité à l'humanitude* (Paris: Seuil, 1986) at 178-79.

support restrictive immigration policies and to prevent equality in the workplace.[178] According to this position, the existing hierarchy is natural and inevitable, since it is based on intrinsic hereditary factors. All the more reason to appeal to a system of justice and political order to redress inequalities.[179]

This cursory overview of genetic determinism, while in no way philosophically complete, illustrates the relationship between scientific knowledge and our understanding of human origins and of human nature. It also highlights the possible use of deterministic biology in the political process. We must be aware of this in finding solutions to the problems raised by advances in human genetics.

One author points out, for example, that while geneticists may appreciate that the environment as well as genes play a role in expression, ''in the popular mind genes are widely perceived as emissaries of biological destiny.''[180] As a result, ''probes may acquire a misleading status in our medical armamentarium as indicators of a new kind of biological determinism.''[181] The foregoing emphasizes the great need for education in this area. The human person is neither programmed nor programmable. Indeed, the genetic composition of any person is changeable.[182]

III. Genetic Naturalism

Genetic determinists would have it that we cannot change our social condition because it is fixed by our genes. Genetic naturalists argue that our genetic constitution is natural, that this naturalness determines our humanity and that, therefore, we should not tamper with it.

The naturalist view was expressed in the Enquete Commission.[183] It said: ''the humanity of human beings rests at its core on natural development . . . . The dignity of human beings is based essentially on their being born and on the naturalness of their origins.''[184] In its view, an essential element of this naturalness was that we are a ''product of chance,'' and that this ''secures the independence of human beings from each other.'' Thus, in its view, any manipulation that detracts from this chance event would be ''incompatible with the essence of a free person.''[185] This view led the

---

178. Lewontin, Rose and Kamin, *supra*, note 169.

179. *Ibid.*

180. Lappé, *supra*, note 7 at 8.

181. *Ibid.* at 10.

182. David Suzuki and Peter Knudtson, *Genethics: The Ethics of Engineering Life* (Toronto: Stoddart, 1988).

183. Enquete Commission, *supra*, note 39. See also Conseil d'État, *supra*, note 37; Edelman and Hermitte, *supra*, note 52; Commission d'experts, *supra*, note 38.

184. Enquete Commission, *supra*, note 39 at 257.

185. *Ibid.*

Enquete Commission to recommend a ban on any gene technology that would interfere with the human germ line.

This and other aspects of the Enquete Commission were severely criticized by Hans-Martin Sass.[186] He points out that we are not "products of chance." Rather, there are many ways in which we manipulate our lives socially and culturally. Others have agreed that such an approach would view "randomness" as being the sole source of our uniqueness and thus deserving protection as immutable and untouchable. This fear of the elimination of chance, of the stifling of the authenticity of the human person, is based on the erroneous view that we are fundamentally no more than our genetic material.[187] That is, genetic naturalism, like genetic determinism, is a reductionist view of humankind.

Boone suggests that what is natural "should be based on some human conception of what is natural, not on a naturalistic definition of what is human."[188] Furthermore, Sass argues that even if we were to accept a naturalistic view of human nature we may ask: "Are humans naturally biological beings or manipulating beings; . . . ?"[189] — that is, What is the nature of humans: to protect or to manipulate their nature? "The issue is not whether or not human dignity allows germ-line manipulation, but which forms of germ-line manipulations or any other manipulations are morally acceptable and which are not."[190]

Thus, there are two issues. The first is the nature of humanity and human dignity. The second is the changes that might be morally permissible if we reject that humans must remain unalterable, natural biological beings.

We have seen that the concept of human dignity underlies international law and the *Canadian Charter of Rights and Freedoms*.[191] It is a term that is interpreted rather than defined. However, "[w]ithout a reasonably clear general idea of its meaning, we cannot easily reject a specious use of the concept."[192] Sass suggests that what human dignity "means in concrete situations has to be analyzed and assessed in moral argumentation, in public debate, by the educated citizen as the prime moral agent, by professional organizations, also by regulators and legislators, but it cannot be pre-determined by . . . referring to obscure natural law concepts."[193]

---

186. *Supra*, note 39.

187. Wolfgang Schirmacher, "*Homo Generator*: The Challenge of Gene Technology" in Paul T. Durbin, ed., *Technology and Responsibility* (Dordrecht: D. Reidel, 1987) 203.

188. Boone, *supra*, note 2 at 11.

189. *Supra*, note 39 at 270.

190. *Ibid.* at 269.

191. Above, Chapters Three and Four.

192. Schachter, *supra*, note 116 at 849.

193. Sass, *supra*, note 39 at 272.

Respect for the dignity of man has always been seen as one of the few absolute rights[194] and the assertion and proclamation of human rights themselves as a refusal to submit to humankind's interpretations of the laws of nature.[195] It would be paradoxical, therefore, to limit respect for human dignity to a biological, naturalistic conception of the human person.[196]

The second issue concerns the decision as to when manipulation might be morally permissible, were we to reject genetic naturalism. The natural law position closes the door on frightening scenarios of unethical manipulations by prohibiting outright all interventions affecting the gene. But, the question is "not whether we should alter the human genetic code, but with which consciousness we do it."[197] In response to the challenge of the new genetics, one author suggests that in deciding what is permissible in science we must adopt the principle of "moral imagination" to determine what the consequences of our actions might be.[198]

IV. Genetic Discrimination

Discrimination as to genotype can be seen as either a means of informing one's personal decisions, or as a means of imposing the decisions of others.[199] We will look at three areas in which genetic disposition may be used to discriminate against the individual: testing in the workplace, testing for access to insurance and testing for reproduction.

A. Workplace Testing

The purposes of genetic screening in the workplace include the determination of the cause of an illness (for example, to what degree it is genetic or environmental in origin), and the prevention of illness by the detection of genetic susceptibility. This could be of benefit to both the employee and the employer. Since genetic information demonstrates individuality, it can provide the employee or the potential employee with information to make occupational, environmental or life-style choices that are in his or

---

194. Mireille Delmas-Marty, "Droits de l'homme et conditions de validité d'un droit de l'expérimentation humaine" at 155 and Patrick Verspieren, "Le respect de la dignité humaine" at 147 in Fondation Marangopoulos pour les Droits de l'Homme, *Expérimentation biomédicale et Droits de l'Homme* (Paris: P.U.F., 1988).

195. Delmas-Marty, *supra*, note 194 at 155.

196. Laberge, *supra*, note 9 at 231.

197. Schirmacher, *supra*, note 187 at 214.

198. Daniel Callahan, "Ethical Responsibility in Science in the Face of Uncertain Consequences" (1976) 265 Annals N.Y. Acad. Sci. 1.

199. Suzuki and Knudtson, *supra*, note 182, Chapter 7 at 160.

her own interests. Such information also provides the employer who has access to it with the power to control or exclude the person tested. At the same time, it gives the employer a greater responsibility for employee health and safety, based on that information.[200]

Genetic screening may be lawful if directly related to qualifications for doing a task or if necessary for employee safety. It could be argued, however, that refusal or termination of employment should only be permitted on the basis of the employee's current capabilities and not on predicted future incapacities.[201]

Furthermore, while the employee should have a right to any information obtained about himself or herself, workplace testing poses a special problem with regard to medical confidentiality. The employer is privy to information that is usually confined to the physician-patient relationship. The potential for breaches of confidentiality may be of special concern where personnel data are computerized.[202]

In 1982, the United States Office of Technology Assessment conducted a nationwide survey on genetic testing in the workplace. Its report[203] revealed that such testing, used by many employers, may be scientifically unfounded. This was the case, for example, with sickle cell testing.[204] Sickle cell anaemia is a life-threatening autosomal recessive disorder with a high frequency among blacks. Those who carry only one of the two mutant alleles are said to have the sickle cell trait. Even though there was, and is, no evidence that having the trait affects work performance, blacks were often screened for it and were excluded from some occupations on that basis.

It could be asked whether protection against discrimination on the basis of mental or physical disability as provided by the *Charter*,[205] or by provincial human rights codes,[206] would be broad enough to include genetic discrimination.

While awaiting the diffusion of genetic education at all levels of society, the balance to be struck between workplace safety, individual rights and employer or public

---

200. See Bartha M. Knoppers "Genetic Screening and Genetic Information in the Workplace" (Address to the American Society of Human Genetics, October 1986) [unpublished].

201. *Ibid.* The author argues that employers should only be able to require genetic screening when the probability of risk of disease can be measured effectively to determine actual job fitness.

202. *Ibid.* See especially Thomas H. Murray, "Warning: Screening Workers for Genetic Risk" (1983) 13:1 Hast. Cent. Rep. 5.

203. OTA, *The Role of Genetic Testing in the Prevention of Occupational Disease* (Washington, D.C.: OTA, 1983). The OTA is currently updating its assessment.

204. See also Daniel J. Kevles, *In the Name of Eugenics: Genetics and the Uses of Human Heredity* (New York: Alfred A. Knopf, 1985) at 257, 278, who demonstrates that voluntary and congressional-supported testing for Tay-Sachs disease for Ashkenazic Jews was much more successful and less stigmatizing than testing mandated for sickle cell disease.

205. *Canadian Charter of Rights and Freedoms, supra*, note 6, s. 15. See above, Chapter Four.

206. *E.g.*, *Charter of Human Rights and Freedoms, supra*, note 76, s. 10.

health care costs is a delicate one. In the absence of widespread genetic education, we may need a specific legal prohibition on genetic discrimination.[207]

B. Insurance Testing

The issue of genetic testing as a prerequisite for insurance raises similar concerns. The Canadian health care system, with its universal coverage of the costs of illness, gives greater protection to Canadians than does the American system to their counterparts.[208] Nonetheless, private disability insurance, life insurance policies and employer-sponsored programs share similar problems with the United States of rating persons "at risk." Parallels could be made with current insurance practices on HIV seropositivity where high-risk individuals pay a higher rate or may be denied coverage altogether. Unlike the situation in employment testing, testing for insurance usually does not directly benefit insurance applicants; moreover, knowledge derived from such testing could be just as easily acquired through one's personal physician without the above consequences.[209]

For personal policies, the insurance company must be privy to sensitive health information concerning an individual. But test reliability and validity, as well as the unjustifiable discriminatory exclusion of those persons with a high risk of disease, are factors to be considered in the development of future legislative policies.[210] The very nature of private insurance legitimates discrimination. However, a basic disability or life insurance for all applicants with "no questions asked" could provide minimum coverage to everyone and avoid problems of discrimination. Additional coverage could be dependent on an agreement by the applicant to be tested for genetic disorders.

C. Reproductive Testing

Certain legal and canonic rules have always imposed restrictions on consanguineous marriages (that is, between genetically related individuals). Nevertheless, genetic screening is not a legal requirement for marriage.[211] Unlike blood testing for rhesus

---

207. See Science Council of Canada, *supra*, note 34.

208. A recent OTA Report, *Medical Testing and Health Insurance*, (Washington, D.C.: OTA, 1988) at 7, revealed that in the U.S., 20 per cent of individuals and 15 per cent of group members were rated as "substandard" and issued health insurance policies at higher rates while 8 per cent of individuals and 10 per cent of small group applications were judged uninsurable and denied coverage.

209. L.D. Jones, "The Use of Genetic Information in Evaluating Insurability" (Address to the American Society of Human Genetics, October 1986) [unpublished].

210. Knoppers, *supra*, note 200.

211. Four American states mandate pre-marital genetic screening. See Andrews, *supra*, note 8 at 233. This is not to be confused with the situation in those countries or states that do ordinary blood testing (rhesus, toxoplasmosis or rubella titre, infectious diseases, etc.) before the issuance of a licence.

compatibility, which is generally mentioned to prospective couples by their physician, other genetic testing is not.[212] However, as family linkage studies develop and expand, and as individuals become genetically informed and sensitized, voluntary recourse to genetic testing before marriage or reproduction will be more frequent. Yet, even for certain populations at identifiably high risk,[213] the state should have to justify mandatory screening that interferes with such a personal decision as marriage or procreation.

In Chapter Three, we discussed a proposal by the Parliamentary Assembly of the Council of Europe to legislate a right to an unaltered genetic heritage. A genome could be considered "altered" if it would result in one of a list of serious illnesses. It was suggested that the right of an individual with such an "altered" genome to have children might be tied to the individual's agreeing to undergo genetic engineering.[214] Available and accessible genetic testing would be more effective and less intrusive routes of health policy, by allowing carriers to make their own choices with respect to such risks, that is, whether to marry, have children and use prenatal testing where available.

In the field of reproductive technologies, physicians are advised to offer donor gametes or embryos to couples at genetic risk or to follow up those persons (or their progeny) found to be at genetic risk.[215] Furthermore, the risk of transmitting serious genetic disease is generally accepted as one of the criteria for the use of reproductive technology.[216] Will the availability of the technology and the choices for the selection of "healthy" gametes or embryos bring us one step closer to striving for genetic perfectionism?

---

212. See, however, the recent Illinois legislation, *An Act (Public Act 86-884, Laws 1989) in relation to sexually transmitted diseases and inherited metabolic diseases, amending named Acts*, approved 11 September 1989 as cited in (1990) 41:1 Int. Dig. Hlth Leg. 57. S. 204 reads as follows: "The country clerk shall distribute . . . to all persons applying for a marriage license, a brochure . . . concerning sexually transmitted diseases and inherited metabolic diseases."

213. During to the high incidence of thalassaemia in Cyprus, the Greek Orthodox Church requires all couples intending to marry to be tested for carrier status. (Personal Communication, Council of Europe, Mrs. Nafsika Kronidou, Cyprus, 1989).

214. *Supra*, note 89ff and accompanying text; see also Kevles, *supra*, note 204 at 277 citing Paul Ramsey: "The freedom of parenthood is a freedom to good parentage, not a license to produce seriously defective individuals to bear their own burdens." Kevles also notes that the Chicago Bar Association is in favour of obligatory pre-marital genetic screening and therapy, where available.

215. Bartha M. Knoppers, "L'arbitrage du médecin face aux normes régissant la fécondation 'in vitro'" in Christian Byk, ed., *Artificial Procreation: The Present State of Ethics and Law* (Lyon: Lacassagne, 1989) 49.

216. *Ibid.*

V. Genetic Perfectionism

The most common fear is that of striving for genetic perfectionism.[217] The policy of genocide for the purpose of attaining "racial purity" has already been mentioned.[218] This erroneous equation between race or nations and genetic bases reached its nadir with the Nazi policies of World War II. Considering the associations between the Holocaust and eugenics, it was hoped that the eugenic ideal would be put to rest after that war.

In the United States during the 1970s, seven states passed laws mandating the screening of the black population for the sickle cell trait. In at least five of those states, marriage licences were denied to those who refused to participate.[219] A decade later, a sperm bank offering gametes of "superior" quality was set up in California.[220] And in Canada, as in the United States, some laws making sterilization of the mentally disordered compulsory were not repealed until the 1970s.[221]

State eugenic policies are often disguised under the language of common good, cost-benefit or public health. The availability of amniocentesis for the prenatal diagnosis of disorders such as Down syndrome, and the inclusion of eugenic clauses in the abortion statutes of some countries,[222] now make these choices as to what is "normal" more a part of personal decision making. As more and more genetic conditions of less and less severity are detectable prenatally, there may be greater social pressure in reproductive decision making. This may detract from research seeking appropriate therapy[223] or from the improvement in the social conditions of the "less than genetically perfect." Should control be exercised over such choices? If so, by whom?

There are two types of eugenics, negative and positive. Negative eugenics aims to decrease the frequency of disadvantageous genes, and positive eugenics aims to increase the frequency of advantageous genes.

---

217. Boone, *supra*, note 2; see also Lappé, *supra*, note 7; J. Frézal, "Les problèmes éthiques en génétique humaine" (1985) 104 Louvain Medical 38.

218. See also Raphaël Lemkin, *Axis Rule in Occupied Europe* (Washington, D.C.: Carnegie Endowment for International Peace, 1944), Chapter 9, "Genocide," at 79. Lemkin coined the term in this germinal work and tirelessly fought to have the concept both recognized by the United Nations and ratified by more than 100 nations (*Convention on the Prevention and Punishment of the Crime of Genocide* (1948) 78 U.N.T.S. 277).

219. See Holtzman, *supra*, note 8 at 219.

220. See Kevles, *supra*, note 204 at 262-63. See also Gwen Terrenoire, "Conseil génétique et eugénisme: le passé du conseil génétique aux États-Unis" (1986) 11 Cahiers Science, technologie et société (Éthique et Biologie) Paris, Éd. du C.N.R.S. 171.

221. See, *e.g.*, *The Sexual Sterilization Act*, S.A. 1928, c. 37, and *Sexual Sterilization Act*, S.B.C. 1933, c. 59, repealed in the early 1970s.

222. See *Crimes against the Foetus*, *supra*, note 113 at 69.

223. Lappé, *supra*, note 7 at 9; see also Holtzman, *supra*, note 40 at 628.

When a genetic disorder is not completely treatable,[224] the approach has been to counsel those individuals who are at risk. They could then exercise informed procreative choice. This is negative eugenics.[225] At the same time, advanced technology may also allow embryo selection (or, less likely, germ-line selection) aimed at increasing the transmission of genes considered advantageous. This is positive eugenics.

There are, however, limits as to the effectiveness of either positive or negative eugenics in altering the gene pool, which is the ultimate aim of eugenics. The most forceful restraint on the revival of eugenics is nature itself,[226] because only a fraction of human traits and disorders is traceable to single genes, for or against which selection might be made. The common familial disorders have a polygenic basis. This limitation constitutes a balm to the exaggerated fears often accompanying debates on human genetics.[227] Nevertheless, in addition to being confronted with choices of normality in everyday life, we now face choices as to what we will consider genetically "normal" for future generations.

One area where policies concerning genetic selection or perfectionism have to be formulated immediately is that of reproductive technologies. These technologies provide usable and accessible human genetic material in the form of gametes (egg or sperm) and human embryos. In conformity with all of the international reports published to date,[228] a recent Working Paper of the Law Reform Commission of Canada suggests prohibiting the more extreme forms of genetic experimentation on the human embryo.[229] Similarly, the Parliamentary Assembly of the Council of Europe recently recommended limiting genetic experimentation to therapeutic purposes. Thus, the assembly would prohibit the more extreme possibilities of genetic engineering such as the cloning of individuals and non-therapeutic genetic manipulation for the purpose of sex or race

224. *E.g.*, PKU, which can be detected by newborn screening and treated with a low protein diet. Nevertheless, the burden so incurred still influences some parents to seek prenatal diagnosis.

225. The term "eugenics" is generally avoided in referring to prenatal diagnosis and the emphasis is placed on its permitting couples at risk to have normal children.

226. Kevles, *supra*, note 204 at 289.

227. *Ibid.*; Boone, *supra*, note 2.

228. See generally Knoppers, *Reproductive Technology*, *supra*, note 89 at 336-58 and the follow-up report. We have argued that the existing international human rights texts are insufficient and lack the specificity necessary to protect the human person in the light of scientific advances. However, while awaiting legislative intervention, the interpretation of these legal texts on human experimentation could be expanded. See especially Fondation Marangopoulos pour les Droits de l'Homme, *supra*, note 194 and Law Reform Commission of Canada, *Biomedical Experimentation Involving Human Subjects*, Working Paper 61 (Ottawa: The Commission, 1989).

229. See *Biomedical Experimentation Involving Human Subjects*, *supra*, note 228 (which did not cover somatic or germ-cell therapy or alteration); *Crimes against the Foetus*, *supra*, note 113 at 60.

selection: "human embryos and foetuses must be treated in all circumstances with the respect due to human dignity."[230]

Genetic studies outside the field of reproductive technologies have just begun. In a recent paper of the Medical Research Council of Canada committee on gene therapy, the use of genetic manipulation for enhancement purposes was considered as unlikely.[231] Furthermore, any techniques that would seek to improve such traits as intelligence are not scientifically feasible.[232]

The issue of genetic perfectionism involves weighing social obligations against individual rights and reproductive freedoms against notions of public order, public health and public welfare. Is there a right to a "healthy" genome? A brief review of wrongful birth and wrongful life suits and other related legal developments might provide some insights.

VI. Genetic Wrongs

In the last half-century, there has been an increase in knowledge of environmental teratogenic risks to the foetus and an increased ability to diagnose genetic conditions preconceptually and prenatally. This laid the groundwork for suits following the birth of a child whose injuries were claimed to be caused by the fault of another. The fault could be direct harm to the foetus *in utero* causing it to be born injured. It could also be an incorrect diagnosis before or after conception followed by the birth of a child with malformations.[233]

In the first situation, the basis for recourse was the legal fiction that an unborn child can be considered born under law, provided this is in the child's interest. Thus, following the birth of a child who was alive and viable, parents could recover damages in the name of the injured child under the general principles of liability for negligence, even though the negligence occurred prior to birth.

---

230. *Recommendation 1046, supra*, note 97, s. 10; also see *supra*, notes 98-99. This was also the position taken in a Quebec governmental report on reproductive technologies entitled *Rapport du comité de travail sur les nouvelles technologies de reproduction humaine* (Québec: Ministère de la Santé et des Services sociaux, 1988) at 90 and that of the Barreau du Québec, "Rapport du comité sur les nouvelles technologies de reproduction" (1988) 48:2 suppl. R. du B. at 37-40.

231. See Medical Research Council of Canada, *supra*, note 30 at 12, which recommends restricting research to somatic cells as did other commissions around the world. See generally the Benda report, *supra*, note 39; Enquete Commission, *supra*, note 39; Commission d'experts, *supra*, note 38.

232. Friedrich Vogel and Arno G. Motulsky, eds, *Human Genetics: Problems and Approaches*, 2d ed. (Berlin: Springer-Verlag, 1986) (see especially Chapter 8, "Genetics and Human Behavior," at 584); Eve K. Nichols, *Human Gene Therapy* (Cambridge, Mass.: Harvard University Press, 1988) at 166.

233. Knoppers, *supra*, note 111.

In the second situation, that of faulty diagnosis or counselling, the suit of the parents for "wrongful birth" was based on the assumption that they would not have conceived or would have aborted the foetus legally in the absence of such fault. Subsequently, it was not long before claims for "wrongful life" were brought by a child on the child's own behalf. It was argued on behalf of the child that, had the parents been properly diagnosed or counselled, the child would not have been wrongfully conceived.

Parents' claims for wrongful birth have been granted in numerous cases under traditional legal principles of negligence. However, wrongful life claims by the child have met with resistance. Except in a few cases,[234] the courts in all jurisdictions have denied what was perceived to be a request to measure life with a defect against no life at all. This, together with the problem of calculating damages for such a "wronged" existence, constituted insurmountable existential difficulties and an affront to the dignity and respect owed to all human life. In the exceptional cases where the claims were successful, the courts dismissed those arguments and side-stepped the legal problem of proving causation. Instead, they concentrated on the very real injury of the child, and on the fact that damages awarded to the parents only gave the child financial protection until the age of majority. Calculation of damages for the child was considered to be no more difficult than in other personal injury cases.[235]

Parallel to these developments in legal liability in respect of those not yet born has been the emergence of foetal protection policies. These have taken the form of restrictions or limitations to abortion, foeticide statutes to protect viable foetuses from criminal acts and the obtainment of court orders mandating certain behaviours by women during pregnancy or birth.[236] In the next decade, we can expect embryonic life *in vitro* or in "storage" to be protected through the legislative regulation of reproductive technologies.[237]

Considering these legal developments, will the general obligation of individuals not to harm "others," together with the specific obligation of parents to act in the best interests of their child, form the basis of claims for birth defects that could have been

---

234. *Curlender* v. *Bio-Science Laboratories*, 165 Cal. Rptr. 477, 106 Cal. App. 3d 811 (1980); *Turpin* v. *Sortini*, 119 Cal. App. 3d 690, 174 Cal. Rptr. 128 (1981), rev'd., 182 Cal. Rptr. 337, 643 P. 2d 954, 31 Cal. 3d 220 (Sup. Ct 1982); *Harbeson* v. *Parke-Davis, Inc.*, 656 P. 2d 483, 98 Wash. 2d 460 (Sup. Ct 1983); *Procanik* v. *Cillo*, 478 A. 2d 755, 97 N.J. 339 (1984); *Siemieniec* v. *Lutheran General Hospital*, 480 N.E. 2d 1227 (Ill. App. 1 Dist. 1985). In the latter case, the wrongful claim was said to be derivative of the parents' wrongful birth claim.

235. For a recent Quebec case denying damages on the basis of the majority of American jurisprudence, see *Engstrom* v. *Courteau*, [1986] R.J.Q. 3048 (C.S.). See also Knoppers, *supra*, note 111, for the possible applicability of liability for injury to life *in utero*, *in vitro* or "in contemplation."

236. Rodgers, *supra*, note 112. See also Bonnie Steinbock, "The Logical Case for 'Wrongful Life'" (1986) 16:2 Hast. Cent. Rep. 15; Shaw, *supra*, note 110; Margery W. Shaw, "Should Child Abuse Laws Be Extended to Include Fetal Abuse?" in Aubrey Milunsky and George J. Annas, eds, *Genetics and the Law III* (New York: Plenum Press, 1985) 309; Bartha M. Knoppers, "Comparative Abortion Law: The Living Abortus" in K. Mason, ed., *Paediatric Medicine* (London: Chapman & Hall, 1989) 387-97; Knoppers, *supra*, note 89; *Crimes against the Foetus*, *supra*, note 113.

237. Knoppers, *supra*, notes 89 and 111.

avoided? If gene alteration were possible, this obligation could be seen as reasonable, in the same way that prenatal or post-natal therapy now is. Thus, according to one author, were parents to refuse gene alteration, the right to be born with a particular genome would be violated because that genome was available through gene therapy and would have prevented the severe handicap.[238]

The same author argues that procreative freedom:

> must, at a minimum, include the freedom to prevent, either by abortion or by treatment before birth, the birth of a child with harmful genes. If it is permissible — indeed, even obligatory — to treat the child's condition after birth or prenatally, it should be permissible to treat the condition at the embryo or preconception stage as well, for it will save the offspring and their descendants the burden of doing it later. Indeed, the child might not otherwise be born, if the parents are limited to postnatal remedies. [Thus] the right to procreate includes a right to practice negative eugenics — to deselect harmful characteristics from future generations.[239]

One might agree that germ-line alteration is beneficial to future generations and avoids needless suffering. Or, one might accept that a person has the "right to prevent harm in one's offspring and their descendants."[240] But it is quite another argument to maintain that "offspring may have a right to gametic therapy from the parents when essential for a healthy genome."[241]

Considering the fact that gametic and germ-line alteration are still experimental, should potential parents be offered the choice of genetically "healthy" gametes or embryos from donors? Is there a duty to do so?

Unless reproductive choice includes the freedom to transmit "unhealthy," "abnormal" or unaltered genes, the legal recognition of an obligation not to harm and to act in the best interests of descendants could mean that there is a duty to eliminate such genes and not just to treat the resulting disorder.[242] The right to an altered genome could mean that benefit would accrue to the individual (somatic alteration), or to future generations as well (germ-line therapy or recourse to donated gametes or embryos).

The outcome of this approach might be that potential parents would have a higher standard of duty to not-yet-conceived or not-yet-born children than they would have to their born and living children.

According to one author, "[p]rocreative freedom includes the freedom to avoid procreation and the freedom to procreate. The latter must include some measure of freedom to select or control the characteristics of offspring, such as to prevent harm to

---

238. John A. Robertson, "Genetic Alteration of Embryos: The Ethical Issues" in Milunsky and Annas, *supra*, note 236 at 115.

239. *Ibid.* at 125.

240. *Ibid.*

241. *Ibid.*

242. *Ibid.*

them.''[243] This is not the equivalent of approved or enforced genetic choice as a condition for the right to reproduce. The notion of parental ''rights'' to healthy children would encourage physicians to suggest abortions or to select or eliminate unhealthy embryos for fear of legal actions. The advocacy of genetic ''rights'' of foetuses or born children would have similar consequences. While ''[a] sizable number of people may argue that the right to have genetically diseased children, or even to transmit deleterious genes to future generations, must be limited or denied,''[244] the resolution of such public problems must turn on ''the willingness of society to bear the social costs of individual freedom.''[245] It may seem anomalous (and even repugnant) that, in the name of religious or reproductive freedom, one deliberately and knowingly creates a child doomed to a life of suffering.[246] Yet, in the rare cases where this option would be selected, is it not a necessary societal risk for the greater freedom of procreative choice? It would be equally repugnant to mandate procreative choices in the name of societal ''normality.''

Respect for the inherent dignity of the human person is manifested in a respect for decisions that are as private and personal as the decision to bear a child, under what conditions and with whom. The legitimate rights of the injured child in cases of negligence by third parties cannot be extended to require parents to avoid giving birth to a genetically disabled child. The possibility of legal action by disabled children against their parents constitutes a grave threat to familial relationships. ''In a society where individual values and mores are revered and closely guarded, legal actions by defective children against their mothers would seem to fly in the face of this reverence, and confound traditional freedom of choice.''[247]

We have seen that there are those who would compel parents to take certain reproductive decisions in order to avoid having children with serious medical disorders.[248] However, parental choice could also be limited by limiting the availability of the technology and health care resources necessary to prevent such births. We saw that the Enquete Commission would ban, outright, manipulation of the genome (were such techniques feasible) because it considered such manipulation an affront to human dignity.[249] A more important way that parental choice could be circumscribed is by

---

243. *Ibid.*

244. Kevles, *supra*, note 204 at 300.

245. *Ibid.*, Daniel Callahan as cited in Kevles.

246. Joseph Fletcher, *The Ethics of Genetic Control: Ending Reproductive Roulette* (New York: Anchor, 1974) at 187: ''People who know a child will be defective, or could have known if they had cared but nonetheless allowed it to be born, are as guilty of wrongdoing as those who culpably contribute to a wrongful death.''

247. Catherine J. Damme, ''Controlling Genetic Disease through Law'' (1982) 15 U.C. Davis L. Rev. 801 at 837. See especially the convincing arguments in The Law Commission, *Report on Injuries to Unborn Children* (London: HMSO, 1974) at 23-26; Alexander M. Capron, ''Tort Liability in Genetic Counseling'' (1979) 79 Colum. L. Rev. 618.

248. See discussion of the hearings of the Council of Europe, *supra*, note 99ff. See also Kevles, *supra*, note 204, citing Paul Ramsey at 277; Shaw, *supra*, note 110; Fletcher, *supra*, note 246.

249. *Supra*, note 39 and following text.

limiting the availability of prenatal diagnosis. If our goal is to maximize reproductive decision making, we must find a way to have meaningful public discussion of policies that affect that freedom.

VII. Conclusion

The use of the language of rights in the genetic context favours conflicts and presumes that the present state of genetic ideologies (determinism, naturalism, discrimination and perfectionism) will continue. However, the future of human genetics does not lie in the obvious controversies surrounding manipulation or elimination. Rather it is in the elucidation and communication of genetic information, in genetic education and in informed genetic choices.

At present, the three areas of genetic testing (workplace, insurance and reproductive testing) pose risks of adverse genetic discrimination while at the same time providing information on cause and prevention. It is not too early to begin a societal debate on these issues with the aim of developing a coherent policy respectful of human rights and dignity. The development of such policy for social change should come from a process of public education so that it emerges from the participation of informed individuals. In other words, we should not wait to act until the effects of genetic discrimination and the promotion of genetic "naturalness" or "rights" are evident.

If we were to abandon the language of "rights to a particular genome," healthy or not, altered or not, what reasonable limitations, if any, could be envisioned in a free and democratic society, in accordance with section 1 of the *Canadian Charter of Rights and Freedoms*? What would be the ethical and legal framework that might maximize genetic information and freedom of choice, and yet limit potential abuses? What would constitute "genetic justice"?

CHAPTER SIX

Towards Genetic Justice

I. Introduction

The previous chapters have described the technical possibilities of the new human genetics and the complexity and variability of the individual and collective genetic heritage, and in them we maintain that the protection of our genetic heritage is essential for the preservation of human rights. In this chapter we will explore the normative and moral precepts underlying human rights legislation in the medical context. Do these principles require further elaboration or expansion because of the problems specific to human genetics? Is there a need for a new ethic for this scientific era? Now that we are moving from chance to control, that is, to the end of "reproductive roulette,"[250] are we starting from a *tabula rasa*? Has the old alliance between humankind and creation been reduced "to a tenuous and fragile thread"?[251] If so, upon what values can we construct the foundations of our new responsibilities as we decipher the genetic language of "The Book of Man"?

This background of principles could serve as a standard of judgment or criticism, a "moral" well-spring,[252] against which to measure the applicability of current theories of justice derived from these principles, or we could search for new legal rules and systems — a new "genetic justice."[253]

While an ethical framework must form the basis for the construction of a theory of genetic justice, the formulation of a viable theory cannot be isolated from more pragmatic considerations. The social and economic costs of respecting or curtailing certain freedoms must be part of the discussion of public health policy. We must also take into account the clinical or research context, where ultimately the policies will be expressed. And most important, a theory of justice must consider the individual who will be affected by it, and who will thus influence its formation.

---

250. Fletcher, *supra*, note 246.

251. See Kurt Bayertz, quoting Jacques Monod in "Increasing Responsibility as Technological Destiny? Human Reproductive Technology and the Problem of Meta-Responsibility" in Durbin, *supra*, note 187, 135 at 146.

252. Alexander M. Capron, "Legal Rights and Moral Rights" in Hilton et al., *supra*, note 68 at 221-27.

253. This term was used by George J. Agich, in "Genetic Justice" (1986) 24 U.W.O. L. Rev. 39, who discussed the application of theories of justice to genetic engineering.

II. Ethical Considerations

The most comprehensive reviews of the ethical issues specific to genetic screening, counselling and therapy are found in the 1982[254] and 1983[255] reports of the American President's Commission for the Study of Ethical Problems in Medicine and Biomedical and Behavioral Research. More recently, other commissions dealing with reproductive technologies have begun to discuss the ethical and legal issues of those technologies in relation to human genetics. Notable among them are the Benda report from West Germany,[256] the report of a group of experts of the Ministry of Justice in Switzerland[257] and the Canadian report emanating from the Medical Research Council of Canada[258] and the Science Council of Canada.[259] Moreover, having been a forerunner in its recommendations to prohibit and control the more extreme applications of genetic engineering, the Council of Europe, through the work of its Ad Hoc Committee of Experts, is now studying genetic screening, counselling and therapy.[260]

Genetic testing, screening and counselling include: research, diagnosis, susceptibility testing, risk prediction, carrier testing, DNA banking, gene therapy, preconception counselling, prenatal diagnosis and the offering of reproductive choices including donor gametes or embryos. All of these raise ethical issues, some of which are new. Thus, we will examine some ethical principles common to medicine and human genetics: autonomy, beneficence and its companion, non-maleficence.

A. Autonomy

Autonomy, meaning self-rule, generally refers to a view that we have of ourselves and of others as being self-governing. Autonomy implies both physical and psychological control. The physical control has recently been held, in a California

---

254. *Splicing Life*, *supra*, note 33.

255. *Screening and Counseling*, *supra*, note 33. See also the excellent OTA reports on counselling and screening in human genetics, *Human Gene Therapy*, *supra*, note 26; *New Developments in Biotechnology*, *supra*, note 52.

256. *Supra*, note 39. See also Enquete Commission, *supra*, note 39.

257. Commission d'experts, *supra*, note 38.

258. *Supra*, note 30.

259. *Supra*, note 34.

260. Council of Europe, Ad Hoc Committee of Experts on Progress in the Biomedical Sciences (CAHBI), *Prenatal Genetic Screening, Prenatal Genetic Diagnosis and Associated Genetic Counselling* (Strasbourg: The Council, 1989).

case,[261] to include control over body cells and tissues. The cells of the plaintiff, John Moore, had been used in scientific research and for profitable commercial exploitation, because of the unique and valuable genetic information and properties they contained. The issue in the case was whether the plaintiff's physician could use the plaintiff's cells without his consent. The California Court of Appeal stated: "For better or worse, we have irretrievably entered an age that requires examination of our understanding of the legal rights and relationships in the human body and the human cell."[262] The Court held that "[a] patient must have the ultimate power to control what becomes of his or her tissues. To hold otherwise would open the door to a massive invasion of human privacy and dignity in the name of medical progress."[263] Thus, respect for the person is often linked to autonomy. In the context of human genetics, the storage of DNA and the exchange of genetic information put in jeopardy this respect for the autonomous, independent actions of individuals.

Autonomy also includes the person's control over his or her choices and actions.[264] In the previous chapter we saw how certain ideologies or beliefs can affect choice. For example, a person whose characteristics are considered predetermined by his or her genetic make-up is not considered as someone who has much choice. Persons with particular genotypes may then be barred from certain work environments because of their genetic make-up. There has been a gradual emergence of a quality-of-life ethic. This ethic is especially evident at the boundaries of conception and death. It is emerging in the questions surrounding the reproductive technologies, in the artificial measures used to sustain the dying and in the allocation of health care resources, to give but a few examples. If we view the quality of life of those destined to have inherited disorders as being so dismal that avoiding their birth is seen as the only option, parents lose their autonomy of reproductive choice.[265]

If, on the other hand, we view the availability of prenatal diagnosis as a move towards perfectionism, we may react by restricting the reproductive options parents have. Thus, there are many ways in which our ideologies or moral views may affect social and reproductive autonomy.

As early as 1972, it was recognized that genetic screening must be voluntary to preserve autonomy. The means to do so is through informed consent. The duty to inform is based on the moral principle of autonomy. Its goal is to protect against not

---

261. *Moore* v. *Regents of the University of California*, 249 Cal. Rptr. 494 (App. 2 Dist. 1988), reh'g granted 252 Cal. Rptr. 816 (1988). For a discussion of the plaintiff's claims under private law see Andrews, *supra*, note 8 and Marie-Angèle Hermitte, "L'affaire Moore" (December 1988) 417 Le Monde Diplomatique 20, 21.

262. *Moore* v. *Regents of the University of California*, *supra*, note 261 at 504.

263. *Ibid.* at 508.

264. John C. Fletcher, "Ethical and Social Aspects of Risk Predictions" (1984) 25 Clin. Genet. 25 at 25-26.

265. *Screening and Counseling*, *supra*, note 33 at 44; see also Robert M. Veatch, *The Foundation of Justice: Why the Retarded and the Rest of Us Have Claims to Equality* (New York: Oxford University Press, 1986).

only physical risk, which is minimal, but also "psychologic or social injury."[266] One statement reads:

> [W]e strongly urge that no screening program have policies that would in any way impose constraints on childbearing by individuals of any specific genetic constitution, or would stigmatize couples who, with full knowledge of the genetic risks, still desire children of their own. It is unjustifiable to promulgate standards for normalcy based on genetic constitution.[267]

Likewise, the President's Commission found no justification for compulsory screening, except to prevent serious harm to the defenceless (such as children). Even then, parental choices and freedoms were considered to be paramount.

The preceding pronouncements on the principle of autonomy were made before the widespread use of genetic testing *in utero*, before wrongful life suits by disabled children, before recourse to gamete or embryo donors for genetic reasons was possible and, certainly, before the possibility of experimental pre-implantation genetic testing or gene therapy.[268] Those developments bring into focus that some harm is preventable, and thus, the principle of autonomy may come into conflict with the principle of beneficence.

Another area in medicine where autonomy has an important role is that of the maintenance of confidentiality, the guarding of shared secrets. In the context of genetic screening, it is a "principle [which] serves to protect the welfare of those screened and to guard against improper uses of information acquired through screening."[269]

The confidentiality issue will affect most people as population testing for susceptibility to common disorders becomes feasible.[270] That is, genetic disease comprises not only rare single-gene disorders but also multifactorial disorders such as cancers, heart disease, diabetes, schizophrenia and so on, many of which are relatively

---

266. Special article, "Ethical and Social Issues in Screening for Genetic Disease" (1972) 286:21 N. Engl. J. Med. 1129 at 1131; see also National Academy of Science, *supra*, note 166.

267. Special article, *supra*, note 266 at 1130-31.

268. See, however, the warnings of the President's Commission, *Splicing Life*, *supra*, note 33 at 66:

> If genetic engineering and related reproductive technologies enable a marked reduction of genetic defects and the burden they impose on their victims and on societal resources, however, mandatory genetic treatments may be advocated . . . . Future developments in gene surgery or gene therapy may lead to further departures from the principle that a competent adult may always refuse medical procedures in nonemergency situations and form the assumption that parenting and reproduction are largely private and autonomous activities.

And from *Screening and Counseling*, *supra*, note 33 at 55-56:

> Such a response would be indefensible; the claims of a handicapped child on societal resources should not be dependent on the decision of the child's parents to undergo screening. Such a response would also be out of keeping with current efforts to assure rights and opportunities for the handicapped.

269. Fletcher, *supra*, note 264 at 27. See also *Screening and Counseling*, *supra*, note 33.

270. Dorothy C. Wertz and John C. Fletcher, eds, *Ethics and Human Genetics: A Cross-Cultural Perspective* (Berlin: Springer-Verlag, 1989).

common. This means that, soon, a large segment of the population could be subject to genetic surveillance, making problems of confidentiality more widespread.

The President's Commission said that genetic information should never be given to third parties such as employers or insurers without the explicit consent of the patient.[271] However, forbidding all third-party access may not be feasible. For example, the very nature of insurance requires that the insurer know of health risks, and employers may need such information to protect their workers. Thus, guidelines on confidentiality are needed to ensure respect for the dignity and autonomy of the human person and the person's right to employment or insurance.[272]

B. Beneficence

The second principle is that of beneficence, that is, serving the well-being of others either individually or collectively, by promoting their good. It implies balancing the benefits and harms of actions affecting others. For example, we saw that, in general, autonomy is achieved partially by maintaining confidentiality. However, this duty of confidentiality is not absolute and may be tempered when maintaining that confidentiality presents a potential for serious harm to others. The President's Commission held that confidentiality could be overridden in certain cases where blood relatives were at risk of serious harm.[273] With the proliferation of genetic testing and the need to involve relatives in DNA linkage studies, we will need to re-examine the situations in which the revealing of genetic information to relatives at risk for serious harm will be justified.

C. Non-maleficence

Non-maleficence is the counterpart of the principle of beneficence.[274] Its meaning, to do no harm, differs from beneficence in that in certain situations it may require a positive duty to achieve the goal of doing no harm. For example, we have seen that the principle of beneficence may, in some circumstances, require the autonomy of an individual to be reduced in order to prevent harm to others. However, the principle of non-maleficence might require more, namely, that the person with the confidential

---

271. *Screening and Counseling*, *supra*, note 33.

272. Employers should have to prove that exclusion of potential employees is related to and justified by an existing medical condition. Discrimination on the sole basis of susceptibility to common multifactorial disorders or to late-onset disorders should be prohibited. See above, Chapter Five.

273. *Screening and Counseling*, *supra*, note 33.

274. See generally H. Tristram Engelhardt, *The Foundations of Bioethics* (New York: Oxford University Press, 1986); Robert M. Veatch, *A Theory of Medical Ethics* (New York: Basic Books, 1981); Norman Fost, "Regulating Genetic Technology: Values in Conflict" in Milunsky and Annas, *supra*, note 236 at 15.

information have a positive duty to tell others. This can be likened to a duty to "rescue" so long as doing so does not involve danger or risk to oneself.[275] Thus we may ask whether there is a positive duty to know one's genetic make-up and to reveal genetic information that is vital to a blood relative, in the making of the relative's life-style or procreative decisions; likewise it may be asked whether there is a positive duty to avoid conceiving a child who may be burdened with a known genetic disorder.

III. Theories of Justice

Principles of justice are founded not only on ethical principles but also on social concepts of fairness. Where resources are limited and there is competition, we must find a basis for allocating goods to individuals. Thus, there is the principle of distributive justice.[276] Distributive justice requires that like cases be treated alike and different cases differently, in proportion to the relevant differences between them. Therefore, health care resources should be distributed on the basis of relevant differences between individuals.[277] How do these ethical principles fit within the traditional theories of justice when we realize that everyone is genetically different, and that we share "genetic vulnerabilities"?[278]

A recent world-wide study of cross-cultural perspectives in ethics and human genetics identified the issue of fair distribution as being acute, especially at a time of increasing demand.[279] What priority should genetic services have in a country's overall health care expenditures, particularly in those countries where prevention has become a major goal of medical care but resources are limited?

In the recommendations of a world-wide survey on the American health care system, the authors suggest that to attain fairness:

> genetic services should be available to all persons equally, regardless of ability to pay, their geographical location, views about abortion, education or ethnic origins. Persons who pay for special services should not be given priority. Commercial labs should be reimbursed by the government and should be regulated so that they serve all persons

---

275. An affirmative obligation to rescue is unique to the civil law. See, *e.g.*, *The French Penal Code*, G.O.W. Mueller, ed. (South Hackensack: Fred B. Rothman & Co., 1960) art. 63, and the Quebec Charter, *supra*, note 76, s. 2. For a study of the common law approaches, see Law Reform Commission of Canada, *Omissions, Negligence and Endangering*, Working Paper 46 (Ottawa: The Commission, 1985) at 17.

276. The common definition of distributive justice is entitlement based on needs. See *infra*, note 287.

277. Rebecca Dresser, "Social Justice in New Reproductive Techniques" in Milunsky and Annas, *supra*, note 236 at 159-60.

278. Nolan and Swenson, *supra*, note 168 at 42. See also Schirmacher in Durbin, *supra*, note 187 at 211: "[W]e must still learn to use the variability of our existence."

279. Wertz and Fletcher, *supra*, note 270.

> equally and so that they perform only medically indicated procedures under the guidelines set for government or university settings.[280]

Application of this principle would require governmental regulation and surveillance of genetic services beyond the public health sector to the private and commercial.

Traditional theories of justice that attempt to find a basis for distribution of resources can be classified as utilitarian, libertarian or egalitarian.[281] In the context of health care, and all the more so in a system of socialized medicine, a fourth classification can be added: that of John Rawls' social contract.[282]

A. Utilitarianism

Utilitarians measure justice in terms of the greatest overall good. "In this framework, unequal treatment of individuals is morally permissible if the aggregate harm that such [unequal] treatment produces is less than the aggregate benefit that it produces."[283] However, there are problems in the application of this theory. First, leaving aside the problem of measuring benefit and harm in the health care context (beneficence), utilitarianism reduces all human goods or choices to a single scale rather than recognizing the diversity of human behaviours and choices. We know, however, that life and health are not "commodity values."[284] Second, this cost-benefit approach embodies a high standard of rationality. We know, however, that workplace or career choices are often seen by others as "irrational,"[285] as may be the choices of individuals

---

280. Personal communication of John C. Fletcher and Dorothy C. Wertz, to the Science Council of Canada, Committee for the Study of Genetic Predisposition to Disease, 1988.

281. See Joel Feinberg and Hyman Gross, eds, *Philosophy of Law*, 3d ed. (Belmont, Calif.: Wadsworth Pub., 1986).

282. John Rawls, *A Theory of Justice* (Cambridge, Mass.: Belknap Press of Harvard University Press, 1971).

283. Dresser, *supra*, note 277 at 161.

284. Elizabeth Anderson, "Values, Risks, and Market Norms" (1988) 17 Phil. Pub. Aff. 54. See also Angus Clarke, "Genetics, Ethics, and Audit" (1990) 335:8698 Lancet 1145 at 1147, 1146, who warns against "the simplistic application of cost-benefit analysis to the population provision of genetics services. In particular, such analysis should not be used as an audit of the effectiveness of genetics units." To do so puts "pressure upon clinicians to maximise the role of terminations of pregnancy for 'costly' disorders."

285. Anderson, *supra*, note 284 at 59.

> What is needed is an interpretive method which attempts to understand human action in the terms the agents use to understand themselves. In order to evaluate the relevance of the data used by cost-benefit analysis, we thus need to find out how people understand their market choices about risks to life and health.

or couples following genetic counselling.[286] Thus, the utilitarian approach in human genetics would undermine freedom of choice (autonomy) and consequently, respect for human dignity.

B. Libertarianism

The principle of autonomy is of major importance to libertarians. Libertarian theories of justice are grounded in the philosophy of John Locke. They hold paramount the free disposition of one's property and of one's body. A libertarian approach to policy making presumes both a minimum of government interference and informed and free decision making on the part of individuals.[287] "This freedom overrides any conflicting societal interest in providing equal access to health care. For libertarians, the free market and its attendant inequities reign in a just health-care system."[288]

In the context of human genetics, the libertarian view prizes the inequality of the genetic distribution. Thus one's genes, considered under this view to be private property, would be subject to free market forces "in which one's genetically-determined strengths and weaknesses can develop."[289] This form of social Darwinism is incompatible with the universality of the Canadian health care system which is based on an egalitarian principle.

C. Egalitarianism

Egalitarian justice emphasizes respect for persons as being equal by the very fact of their being human. Drawing from the Rousseaunian tradition, all human beings are considered to be of equal moral worth with an equal right to well-being and freedom.

---

286. According to Emery et al., as cited in Sherman Elias and George J. Annas, *Reproductive Genetics and the Law* (New York: Yearbook Medical Publications, 1987) at 51, "a third of those who were told they were at high risk of having a child with a serious genetic disease were undeterred and actually planned further pregnancies." For an analysis of how parents do make reproductive decisions, see A. Lippman-Hand and F. Clarke Fraser, "Genetic Counseling — The Postcounseling Period: II. Making Reproductive Choices" (1979) 4 Am. J. Med. Genet. 73.

287. For a libertarian view of justice in health care see Engelhardt, *supra*, note 274 at 85. For a criticism of Engelhardt's approach, see Robert M. Veatch, Book Review of *The Foundations of Bioethics* (1986) 105:6 Ann. Intern. Med. 987 at 988:

> Engelhardt's concept of justice in health care is one based merely on freely made deals in which people with power get whatever they can get. Those who have lost in the natural or social lotteries, who are medically needy because of genetic or social deprivation, are just out of luck unless aided by charity.

See also Engelhardt's and Rie's refutation of the ethic of distributive justice in H. Tristram Engelhardt and Michael A. Rie, "Morality for the Medical — Industrial Complex" (1988) 319:16 N. Engl. J. Med. 1086. For a further criticism of Engelhardt, see Veatch, *supra*, note 265.

288. Dresser, *supra*, note 277 at 161; *New Developments in Biotechnology*, *supra*, note 52.

289. Agich, *supra*, note 253 at 43.

The egalitarian view regards "the inequality of the natural distribution as a moral predicament requiring remedial social action [and] presupposes that each individual has an equal claim on the totality of assets and liabilities which comprise the gene pool."[290] The goal of egalitarianism is to modify social institutions so as to minimize or compensate for unequal opportunity.

The problem with the egalitarian approach is that it may conflict with liberty. As we have seen,[291] liberty or free choice is an important element in protecting the inherent dignity of the person, which is the underlying basis of international and Canadian constitutional law. Most would agree that at least minimal distributive justice is required to compensate for the disparities within a society.[292] However, "[s]ome would probably go beyond this and contend that substantial equality is a necessary condition of respect for the intrinsic worth of the human person."[293] Therein lies the conflict because "such egalitarian objectives cannot be realized without excessive curtailment of individual liberty and the use of coercion."[294] Thus, a new theory of justice is required.

D. Social Contract

John Rawls, in his *A Theory of Justice*,[295] describes the distribution of natural endowments as neither just nor unjust, but simply a fact. Rather, it is the way that institutions deal with this fact that gives rise to justice or injustice. His social contract theory of justice is based on what a society of rational individuals would decide to be just if they did not know what their actual lot in life would be with regard to natural talent or social status. Thus, Rawls assumes that the future is hidden by a "veil of ignorance" and from this "original position" participants in the social contract will devise a self-interested system of justice. The result would be, firstly and necessarily, that each person would have the most extensive liberty compatible with a similar liberty for others. Secondly, there would be equality of opportunity. Thirdly, any inequality resulting from differences in natural ability or merit would be adjusted in a way that would give the greatest benefit to the least advantaged. This is called the "difference principle." How, then, can this social contract approach be applied to human genetics?

The President's Commission[296] considered Rawls' theory of justice in the context of health care. It foresaw that one could substitute the notion of one's initial genetic

---

290. *Ibid.*

291. Above, Chapters Two and Four.

292. Schachter, *supra*, note 116 at 851.

293. *Ibid.*

294. *Ibid.*

295. Rawls, *supra*, note 282.

296. *Splicing Life*, *supra*, note 33 at 68. See also *New Developments in Biotechnology*, *supra*, note 52.

assets for the lottery of social or natural assets described in Rawls' social contract theory. Thus, inequalities of opportunity arising from one's genetic constitution could be minimized through intervention in this natural biological lottery. The values of liberty and equality could be realized through the participation of "reasonable" citizens[297] who would devise a system of co-operation to their mutual advantage.[298]

Rawls' theory of justice has been applied by George Agich to develop a theory of genetic justice.[299] In Rawls theory, genetic inequalities would be dealt with by a readjustment of inequalities in a way that would work for the good of the genetically less fortunate. Agich argues that genetic attributes should be included in the original position, because knowledge of the possibilities for genetic intervention is necessary to decide what is just.[300] He also argues that decisions as to whether to prevent or to treat genetic disease would require some alterations of Rawls' theory, to allow those in the "original position" to deal with future generations. Furthermore, as he points out, no disease is purely genetic and therefore what is required is knowledge not only of genetics but also of environment and of the possibilities for social remedial action. Thus, "[t]he predictive uncertainty and potential long-range consequences of human genetic intervention when coupled with the possibly reductive character of genetic explanation have important implications for the task of justifying the practice of genetic screening and treatment especially in terms of the principle of justice."[301]

We agree with Agich that Rawls' theory needs to be altered so that those in the original position (veil of ignorance) are given genetic information. However, this should be done in a way that not only promotes the individual, but also ensures informed participation in the new social contract. Such participation would come from the enlightened notion that "the collective human gene pool knows no national boundaries but is the biological heritage of the entire human species."[302] Thus, the social contract could be reconsidered on the principle of informed genetic equality.

---

297. John Rawls, "Justice as Fairness: Political Not Metaphysical" (1985) 14 Phil. Pub. Aff. 219. In this article at 237, note 20, Rawls explains that it was an error in his seminal work, *supra*, note 282, "to describe a theory of justice as part of the theory of rational choice."

298. *Ibid.* For an excellent critique of Rawls, see Catherine Audard et al., eds, *Individu et justice sociale: autour de John Rawls* (Paris: Seuil, 1988). See also Marie-Angèle Hermitte, "Le droit civil du contrat d'expérimentation" in Fondation Marangopoulos pour les Droits de l'Homme, *supra*, note 194, 38 at 39:

> Les tendances actuelles de l'expérimentation sur l'homme répondent donc assez exactement à la philosophie de John Rawls, mélange d'utilitarisme et de respect des droits de l'homme; l'utilitarisme fournit la base de raisonnements que la philosophie des droits de l'homme et du contrat social vient réorganiser plus ou moins profondément.

299. *Supra*, note 253.

300. *Ibid.* at 47.

301. *Ibid.* at 42.

302. Clifford Grobstein and Michael Flower, "Gene Therapy: Proceed with Caution" (1984) 14:2 Hast. Cent. Rep. 13 at 16.

Furthermore, we need not consider that our genetic lottery is something that makes us unequal. We now know that every individual is genetically unique.[303] Individual difference could be interpreted as the underlying basis of the principle of equality.[304]

IV. New Ethical Principles

If knowledge of genetic differentiation will permit the development of the social contract from a position of informed "genetic equality" as we have suggested, what additional ethical principles should contribute to a formulation of the social contract? Two founding principles are suggested, the first being that of reciprocity[305] — of exchange, and the second being that of mutuality — of civic responsibility. The two could constitute the ethical principles of checks and balances emanating from an informed citizenry, rather than from ignorance or state prerogative.

A. Reciprocity

The first founding principle of the new social contract is reciprocity, or exchange. It recognizes a "difference," that is, an inequality between the knowledge held by ordinary individuals and that held by practitioners of medical genetics. Justice requires that such knowledge be redistributed in a way that is beneficial to the less well-informed, that is, the ordinary citizen. A redistribution is essential to ensure that knowledge of medical genetics is not used by the state to impose decisions on individuals and to monitor their compliance. To ensure that it is the least advantaged who benefit from this exchange of knowledge, the exchange is best conducted within the physician-patient relationship, which has traditionally provided protection for the patient.[306] This protection comes in the form of the doctrine of informed consent, based on the principle of autonomy. Traditionally, informed consent implied the communication of risks of physical harm. Today, it includes the avoidance of psychological and social prejudice, not only to the participant, but also to the participant's family and to society at large. Through informed consent, individuals are given the power to act on risk information in a way that is best for them, and even to decide whether they want to know of certain risks.

---

303. See above, Chapter Four, note 140.

304. Bartha M. Knoppers, "Human Genetics, Predisposition and the New Social Contract" in International Conference on Bioethics, *supra*, note 29 at 168.

305. Rawls, *supra*, note 282, uses this term to mean co-operation which is not the same as our interpretation of reciprocity as meaning exchange or transfer. Co-operation, however, is the traditional meaning of the term reciprocity: see Feinberg and Gross, *supra*, note 281 at 416.

306. Knoppers and Laberge, *supra*, note 91 at 1024.

Such individual control and

> [t]he protection of free choice depends on an educated citizenry aware of the purposes of genetic tests as well as of their benefits, costs, and risks. This can be approached in a general way by improving public education but, more specifically, by assuring that genetic tests are only performed when the person offered the test has substantial understanding and will not be penalized as a result of either choice being made. That is informed consent.[307]

A truly informed consent also implies an educated and informed medical body; this is an urgent priority.[308] It requires a transfer of knowledge from the molecular biologist or geneticist to the general practitioner. If the aim is true reciprocity in the patient-physician relationship, the greater goal of mutuality, of community, of civic responsibility can be achieved.

B. Mutuality

The second founding principle of the new social contract is mutuality or civic responsibility. It recognizes that genetic diseases affect not only individuals but also families and communities. Recognition of that fact gives rise to a need for a responsible sharing of genetic information. Thus, mutuality is based on the principle of beneficence and is compatible with the principle of liberty or free choice which ''implies proper regard for the responsibility of individuals.''[309]

Under the principle of mutuality, the individual is supplied with genetic knowledge and is at liberty to act upon it. However, individuals who do not act remain bound by the classical social contract. Under that contract, the individual continues to submit to state-imposed exceptions to individual freedom based on the notion of the ''common good.'' The ''common good'' might be perceived by the state as including imposed eugenic programs. Thus, the maintenance and survival of individual liberty actually reside in civic participation.

At the family level, the individual would have a social obligation not to withhold information useful to other members of the family, where to do so could cause harm. Thus, mutuality is based on the principle of non-maleficence. In the exception, where after counselling a patient still refuses to inform relatives who are consequently subject

---

307. Holtzman, *supra*, note 40 at 629. See also David Roy and Maurice de Wachter, *The Life Technologies and Public Policy* (Montreal: Institute for Research on Public Policy, 1986) at 148-49.

308. Holtzman, *supra*, note 40 at 626-28. Without this reciprocity and open, truthful exchange as to what DNA sampling and the search for markers and the gene entail, we risk the development of legal protectionist policies based on notions of property, ownership, copyright and patent law instead of viewing the genetic information as an attribute of the person.

309. Schachter, *supra*, note 116 at 850.

to serious genetic risk, information relevant to family planning or to one's life-style could be communicated by the physician in spite of such a refusal.[310]

At the community level, the individual could freely participate in DNA sampling, banking and the use of markers aimed at establishing linkage maps.[311] This participation is the first step in the planning of preventive health care programs. Such programs should respect individual genetic differences and freedom of choice in decision making.

In return for patient participation and communication, the state would have the mandate to provide the resources not only for diagnosis but also for education in research, treatment and care. Education must be broad in scope. The goal of mutuality is to come to an understanding that will allow us to protect what is human in our genetic nature and yet allow us the freedom to relieve suffering and to progress as a species.

Thus, we must explore what human dignity means in the context of human genetics. We must beware of the tendency "to consider against human dignity whatever one intensely, if irrationally, dislikes. This way, through the breach of human dignity, one can smuggle into positive law personal ideologies in the form of norms binding the legislature."[312]

It would be ironic if respect for the inherent dignity of the human person became the source of self-directed genetic imperialism. This imperialism could take the form of a program seeking to wipe out "bad" genes in the name of the genetic rights of future generations, or a prohibition against all genetic therapies affecting the heritage.

The debate must not remain polarized. A polarized debate makes use of "bad axioms" that have the "power to convince the hearer that a partial insight comprises the whole truth."[313] One such axiom is that of the slippery slope. The fear of "slipping" as a reason to halt genetic engineering is equivalent to denying afflicted individuals therapies "on the ground that we cannot make distinctions between remedial germline alterations and eugenic enhancements [and] indicates a lack of trust in the human ability to act discriminately on the basis of distinctive ethical classifications."[314]

---

310. This position is consistent with that of the President's Commission, *Screening and Counseling*, *supra*, note 33 at 44. The author takes "family" to mean one's social and personal relationships, not only those legally recognized.

311. See above, Chapter One, under the heading, "V. The Changing Practice of Medical Genetics."

312. Jan Stepan, "State Intervention in Family Procreation Decisions" (1988) Reports II (VIIIth World Congress on Medical Law) [unpublished] 233 at 237.

313. Boone, *supra*, note 2 at 10.

314. *Ibid.* at 11. See also Fletcher, *supra*, note 246 at 5ff, on the errors of the capacity fallacy (we can do something, so we ought to) and the necessity fallacy (we can do something, so we will).

V. Conclusion

The utilitarian moral principle underlying the public health model, with its cost-benefit calculation, is an inappropriate model considering the problems of privacy and free choice posed by new genetics.[315] The social contract theory of justice offers more promise in giving meaning to the inherent dignity of the human person in the field of human genetics.[316] We propose that a new social contract be developed from a position of informed genetic equality. Such a contract would be based on the principles of reciprocity and mutuality.

Reciprocity, or exchange of knowledge, would occur within the traditional protected relationship of the physician and patient. In this way, individuality, confidentiality and freedom of choice could be preserved.

Genetic disease implicates not only the individual but also the family, the community and future generations. This fact imposes a duty on the individual to contribute to the detection and understanding of genetic disease and illustrates a need for the principle of mutuality or civic responsibility. This responsibility could be met by voluntary participation in such programs as the banking of DNA. In exchange, the state would provide resources in the areas of research, education, diagnosis, treatment and care.

The two principles, namely, of reciprocity and mutuality, would constitute a solid basis for shared responsibility and for patient participation in the practice of genetic medicine, with a view to establishing genetic justice based on individual genetic responsibility.

---

315. Ruth Macklin, "Mapping the Human Genome" in Milunsky and Annas, *supra*, note 236 at 107-11.

316. Hermitte, *supra*, note 298 at 43:

> Il faut suivre pas à pas la théorie générale des obligations; elle est probablement plus liée qu'on ne l'imagine généralement à la protection des droits de l'homme, ou du moins à un type de protection, empirique certes, mais relativement proche, finalement, du message des droits de l'homme.

Conclusion

We have seen that human genetics offers the promise of the capacity to predict many diseases, both rare and common. Soon, most of the world's population may be touched by this capacity, either directly or indirectly. In the past, many couples did not know that they were carriers for a disease-causing recessive gene until they had a child with the disorder. In the future, many individuals will discover that they are carrying alleles for disorders of which they have no personal understanding. Previously, for late-onset diseases, a person known to be at, say, a 50 per cent risk from his or her family history would live with uncertainty as to whether he or she had the gene and would develop the disease. Now, such an individual may have more information on which to base choices. For common multifactorial diseases, particular gene markers can now warn persons that they have a higher probability than the rest of the population of developing a particular disease.

Eventually, we will have the technical ability to "treat" the gene itself. This will be possible in somatic cells for some single-gene disorders, but is likely to remain impractical in germ cells, even if technically feasible. For now, a wide gap exists between our ability to identify particular genes and our ability to treat them. Thus, a couple in which both partners carry a gene for a recessive disorder may have to decide whether to risk having children, or whether to avoid the risk by using prenatal diagnosis and selective abortion or by using reproductive technologies. These decisions will be influenced by, and will be likely to influence, our views of the disabled. Individuals at risk to inherit disease-causing genes may be under social and medical pressure to know whether they have the gene, and if so, to tell family members whose lives may be affected by that knowledge. Likewise, employers and insurers may have a stake in having such information. Individuals at risk for multifactorial disorders may be under close scrutiny to do what they can to avoid developing a disease by manipulating their environment or life-style. All of these changes will affect our daily lives as individuals and our future as a society.

The Council of Europe recommended in 1982 that there be a right to an unaltered genetic heritage based on the notion of human dignity. Thus, we examined the notions of genetic heritage and human dignity.

We saw that, through the biological processes of mutation and meiosis, each of us is unique and yet genetically tied to one another in both time and space through the collective gene pool. We saw that gene therapy of the somatic cells would have a small, indirect effect on the gene pool, as does conventional medical treatment, and that germ-line therapy, if it were possible and practical, would have a small direct effect. However, there is a moral difference between the two, because somatic therapy affects a single genome and may be seen as a private matter whereas gene therapy, by directly affecting our gene pool, may be seen as a public matter. This conjures up the murky political history of the eugenics movement. This history is relevant not only to germ-line manipulation, which seems unlikely to occur, but also to the manipulation of individuals by more conventional social means such as discrimination.

Although the human person is more complex than a set of genes, our genetic make-up is perceived as an important part of the human person and thus an important constituent of human dignity. The meaning of human dignity has not been fully interpreted in international law, but that human dignity is its underlying theme, and all human rights are seen as deriving from it. The same can be said of the *Canadian Charter of Rights and Freedoms*, although it does not explicitly use the term, human dignity. Important components of dignity, autonomy and equality can be seen in the various sections of the *Charter*. We mentioned that these guarantees may have direct applicability to genetics in a number of ways relating to genetic testing and the use of DNA samples.

How our genetic heritage is to be protected is not clear. There is international consensus on the need to prohibit the more extreme possibilities of human genetics. However, we must learn to exercise caution without placing an *a priori* prohibition on all research affecting the gene. As with any technology, we must ensure that it does indeed lead to more choice, not less. Not only do we need to regulate with respect to abuse, we should also question the direction of the inquiry into genetic knowledge. We must decide on the limits of free choice to maintain that direction, and we will have to find a formula that respects the complexity, variability and uniqueness of the human person.

We reviewed the danger of creating a right to an unaltered genetic heritage, as proposed in 1982 by the Council of Europe. Under the guise of protection, such an interpretation could lead to genetic pre-selection, to genetic screening for suitability and, ultimately, to lawsuits within the family and between generations. Human beings are complex; our genetic uniqueness is only one factor making up our humanness. We have the ability to interact with, and to re-create, our environment. The laws and social policies we devise may be influenced by a view of the human person that is less than this view. Genetic determinism holds that we are fixed by our genes and thus we cannot create a social environment that accommodates biological differences. This position could have important consequences. It may lead to policies that manipulate the person out of certain environments (for example, the workplace) rather than manipulating the environment and social structure to fit the person. This view might also be evident in prenatal diagnosis. To eliminate foetuses with biological imperfections may seem simpler and less costly than to devise a social and educational system that accommodates them as children. In its extreme form, genetic determinism has led to suggestions that children who would inherit certain genetic disorders have a right not to be born, and consequently, potential parents have the duty to see that they are not.

An equally reductionist view of human nature is that of the ''naturalists.'' According to genetic naturalism, the random diversity of our genetic constitution is seen as the essence of our humanity. Thus, any attempts to change it would be an affront to human dignity. Such a stance precludes a discussion of when genetic alteration might be morally acceptable and reduces our scope for progress as a species. Under this view, any prevention of human suffering through genetic therapy could be considered an affront to our humanness, because chance biological diversity is an important part of it. Therefore, those who hold the naturalist position might restrict funding for genetic technology and medical services.

How can we reconcile these polarized views so that our uniqueness can serve as a source of respect for the individual and for collective humanity? What kind of legal and ethical framework can we devise to maintain free choice while limiting abuse and undesirable social side-effects?

Such questions led us to explore a theory of genetic justice to achieve those ends. We saw that the ethical principle of autonomy may conflict with the principles of beneficence and non-maleficence, which thus do not provide us with an answer. Principles of justice or fairness are broader and consider how resources can be fairly allocated. Utilitarian theories of justice present serious problems because the individual becomes the means to achieve a goal of efficiency, usually economic efficiency. The disabled may come to be seen as an "avoidable cost."

A libertarian theory of justice for health care takes the form of social Darwinism, and egalitarianism may conflict with our view of liberty or free choice which, like equality, is an important element in the protection of our inherent human dignity.

A theory of justice based on social contract could allow for both the protection of individual rights and the promotion of community responsibility in genetics. It depends on a societal commitment to the dissemination of knowledge of human genetics with its language of probabilities, probes and prediction. To so inform the population requires public education at all levels, the medical contract remaining as the privileged and confidential focus of the individualization of that knowledge. The principle of respect for autonomy resides in the informed consent of the individual and in voluntarism within a society that provides the foundation of public knowledge and understanding of genetic difference and genetic vulnerability.

The necessary international debate must recognize that the genetic pool has no political, social or racial boundaries. The meaning and the protection of the inherent dignity of the human person also includes the dignity of mankind and must necessarily be international in scope.

The new human genetics requires that a more thorough examination be made of the human rights questions it raises. We have only alluded to the issues of discrimination, insurance, employment, the rules of evidence, data-sharing or theft and especially the possible impact of the new human genetics on health policy and legislation. More study is needed into the particular ways that it will affect the social fabric of Canadian society, in particular with regard to the adequacy of current public and private law concepts. The impact of the new human genetics on the common law and on the Quebec civil law of contracts, property, intellectual property, family law, the law of persons and liability needs to be examined.

The protection of human rights within a genetic context will have a high economic cost, not only for the technology but, more importantly, for education and the provision of genetic services. We will have to decide how much of our social resources we are willing to spend on this and how genetics will rate in relation to other equally expensive procedures.

Individuals as moral agents are responsible for genetic choices, for controlling their genetic ''capital'' or investment. Such choices must be informed and must consider societal implications and context. The multiplication of technological possibilities is not equivalent to a technological imperative. Rather, it demands responsibility on a societal level. We return in this way to the notion of genetic heritage as being individual and also the common heritage of humankind, a heritage held in common trust.

Glossary

ALLELE. One of two or more alternative forms of a gene at a specific site on a chromosome.

AMNIOCENTESIS. A medical test in which a needle is used to withdraw a small amount of amniotic fluid surrounding the foetus in the uterus. This fluid contains foetal cells. These are grown in cell culture and analyzed for a variety of chromosomal or biochemical disorders.

AUTONOMY. In ethics, the principle that independent actions and choices of an individual should not be constrained by others.

AUTOSOME. Any chromosome other than the sex chromosomes.

BENEFICENCE. Mercy, kindness or charity. In ethics, it is the principle that one has a duty to confer benefits or to help others further their legitimate interests.

CARRIER. An individual who has one disease-causing allele rather than the two necessary for the expression of a recessive disorder, or someone who has a dominant disease-causing gene that has not yet resulted in overt disease.

CELL. The fundamental unit of the structure of living organisms. The smallest membrane-bound protoplasmic body, consisting of a nucleus and its surrounding cytoplasm, capable of independent replication.

CHROMOSOME. The thread-like structure within the nucleus of a cell, containing DNA, the hereditary material (*i.e.*, genes). The normal number of chromosomes in humans is 46 — 22 pairs of autosomes and two sex chromosomes (XX or XY).

CHROMOSOMAL DISORDERS. Disorders resulting from additions or deletions of entire chromosomes or parts of them.

CLONING. The process of producing a group of cells (clones), all genetically identical to the original ancestral cell. In DNA technology, it is the process of producing multiple copies of a single gene or segment of DNA.

CROSSING OVER. The exchange, during meiosis, of chromosomal material between the paired chromosomes, one of which derives from the mother and one from the father. This process allows for greater variability than if chromosomes were inherited *en bloc*.

CYSTIC FIBROSIS. An autosomal recessive disorder with a high frequency in whites. The major clinical problems are caused by obstruction in the ducts of organs by abnormally thick secretions. The chromosomal location of the gene for this disorder is now known.

DETERMINISM. The theory that, for every human action, there are causal mechanisms such that no other action is possible.

DNA, DEOXYRIBONUCLEIC ACID. A double-stranded molecule, held together by weak bonds between base pairs of nucleotides, that encodes genetic information. There are four nucleotides in DNA: adenosine (A), guanosine (G), cytidine (C) and thymidine (T). Base pairs form only between A and T and between G and C, thus the sequence of each single strand can be deduced from that of its partner. This complementarity is the key to the information-transmitting capabilities of DNA. The information coded by DNA of the gene determines the structure, and thereby the function, of the corresponding protein.

DNA FINGERPRINTING. Laboratory analysis of a person's DNA — so called because, like fingerprints, a person's DNA is unique.

DNA PROBE. See GENE PROBE.

DNA SEQUENCE. The order of base pairs whether in a length of DNA, a gene, or a chromosome.

DOMINANT. Each somatic (body) cell has two copies (alleles) of the gene at any specific locus. An allele that is expressed regardless of the nature of its companion allele is said to be dominant (compare with recessive).

DOUBLE HELIX. The form in which two helical strands of DNA are bound together, looking much like a twisted rope ladder.

DOWN SYNDROME. A chromosomal disorder caused by the presence of an extra 21st chromosome (trisomy 21). The signs are mental disorder, congenital heart defect, a typical facial appearance and a reduced life expectancy. Down syndrome shows an increase in frequency with advancing maternal age.

EUGENICS. Attempts to improve the hereditary qualities of a population by encouraging transmission of traits judged to be desirable (positive eugenics) and discouraging those judged to be undesirable (negative eugenics).

EXPRESSION. See GENE EXPRESSION.

EXPRESSIVITY. The variability with which a given gene is expressed, by outward signs, in different individuals bearing the gene.

GAMETE. A sperm or egg. The mature male or female reproductive cell, which contains one set of chromosomes rather than the two sets found in somatic cells.

GENE. The fundamental physical and functional unit of heredity. A gene is an ordered sequence of nucleotides that make up the DNA located in a particular position on a particular chromosome.

GENE EXPRESSION. The process by which a gene's DNA sequence is converted into the trait that it controls.

GENE MAP. See LINKAGE MAP.

GENE POOL. All of the alleles of all of the individuals in a population.

GENE PROBE. A segment of single-stranded DNA that is labelled with a radioactive or other chemical marker and is used to identify a specific region of the genome.

GENE THERAPY. Insertion of normal DNA directly into cells to correct a genetic defect.

GENETIC MARKER. A readily recognizable genetic difference that occurs frequently enough to be useful in family and population studies.

GENOME. The total genetic material contained in the chromosomes of an individual's cells.

GENOTYPE. The genetic constitution of an individual with respect to a particular gene locus or the entire complement of genes, as contrasted to the outward appearance, the phenotype.

GERM LINE. The cell line that produces gametes (sperm or egg) for reproduction. Any changes to the germ line may be passed on to the next generation.

HAEMOPHILIA. A group of hereditary disorders that causes a condition in which it takes an abnormally long time for blood to coagulate. Classical haemophilia is X-linked. This means that it usually occurs in males and is transmitted to offspring by asymptomatic females, or by an affected male to all of his daughters.

HUNTINGTON'S DISEASE — HUNTINGTON'S CHOREA. A dominantly inherited disease usually manifest between the ages of 30 and 50. It results in slowly progressive degeneration of specific brain tissues and, ultimately, in death. The primary signs are disorders of movement (chorea) and dementia. The chromosome on which the gene is located is now known.

IN VITRO. Manipulations done on biological systems outside the intact organism.

JUSTICE. Generally refers to fair and equal treatment. In ethics, it is the principle that one should act in such a manner that no one bears a disproportionate share of benefits or burdens.

LINKAGE. The tendency of genes at different loci to be inherited together. The closer the loci are on a chromosome, the greater the linkage. The further apart they are, the more likely it is that they will be inherited independently as a result of crossing over during meiosis.

LINKAGE MAP. A map of the chromosomes showing the relative positions of particular genes.

LOCUS. The particular location of a gene on a chromosome.

MARKER. See GENETIC MARKER.

MEIOSIS. Cell division that occurs only in the germ cells during the formation of the egg and sperm. During this process, the number of chromosomes is reduced by half.

MENDELIAN TRAIT OR DISORDER. A trait or disorder that is controlled by a single gene, and that shows a simple pattern of inheritance (dominant or recessive, autosomal or X-linked). It is so named because traits of this sort were first recognized in peas by Gregor Mendel, the Austrian monk whose research laid the basis for modern genetics.

MRNA, MESSENGER RIBONUCLEIC ACID. A molecule that is complementary to the DNA of a specific gene and that moves from the nucleus to the cytoplasm where it serves as a template for the assembly of amino acids into proteins, which are the building blocks and enzymes of cells.

MULTIFACTORIAL. Traits or disorders whose expression results from several genes and environmental factors acting in concert.

MUTATION. A change in the genetic material that results in a new characteristic. When mutation occurs in a germ cell, it can be passed on to subsequent generations.

NATURALISM. The view that an essential element of human beings is that we are a product of chance.

NON-MALEFICENCE. Generally associated with the maxim *primum non nocere*, meaning, above all, do no harm. In ethics, it is the principle that one has a duty not to inflict evil, harm or risk of harm.

NUCLEOTIDE. A sub-unit of DNA or RNA, consisting of a nitrogenous base (adenine, guanine, thymine or cytosine in DNA; RNA has uracil instead of thymine). Thousands of nucleotides are linked to form the DNA or RNA.

PENETRANCE. The frequency with which persons with two recessive alleles or one dominant allele for a disorder show outward signs of the disorder. Where the frequency is less than 100 per cent, penetrance is said to be reduced.

PHENOTYPE. The appearance of an individual that results from the interaction of genes and the environment. This term is also used more narrowly to mean the observable characteristics resulting from a particular genotype.

PKU, PHENYLKETONURIA. An inherited error of metabolism resulting in the inability to convert phenylalanine in the diet to tyrosine in the body. The resulting accumulation of phenylalanine leads to mental disorder. The disorder, which is due to a defective liver enzyme (phenylalanine hydroxylase), can be diagnosed in newborns by a simple test. It can be treated with a diet low in phenylalanine.

POLYGENIC. A trait or characteristic that is determined by more than two genes acting in concert.

POLYMORPHISM. The presence in a population of two or more genetically determined forms of a trait, none of which is rare. Polymorphisms, which are useful for genetic linkage analysis, may result from changes within a gene or in the DNA between genes.

PROBE. See GENE PROBE.

PROTEIN. A molecule composed of a chain of amino acids arranged in a specific sequence that is determined by the sequence of DNA base pairs. Protein molecules determine the structure and function of living organisms.

RECESSIVE. Refers to an allele of a gene that will be expressed only if it is present in two copies, *i.e.*, on both chromosomes (compare with dominant).

RESTRICTION ENZYME. An enzyme that has the ability to recognize a specific nucleotide sequence and cut it at that sequence.

RES NULLIUS. The property of no one. A thing that has no owner, either because a former owner has abandoned it, it has never been appropriated by any person or it is not capable of private ownership.

RFLP, RESTRICTION FRAGMENT LENGTH POLYMORPHISM. A fragment of DNA resulting from cleavage by a restriction enzyme. The length of the fragment depends on whether the restriction site is present. Because these sites are polymorphic they are useful as markers in linkage studies to map the genome.

SEX CHROMOSOMES. The X- and Y-chromosomes, which are responsible for sex determination. XY individuals are male; XX individuals are female.

SICKLE CELL TRAIT. Refers to the phenotype of a person who carries one abnormal allele for sickle cell disease. It can be identified by a simple blood test. The sickle cell mutation has a high frequency in some populations that are subject to malarial infections, such as African blacks. The defective gene is thought to have been maintained in the population because it confers increased resistance to malaria on carriers, even though it kills those with a double dose of the gene. The location and the DNA sequence of the gene are now known.

SINGLE GENE DISORDER. See MENDELIAN TRAIT OR DISORDER.

SOMATIC CELLS. Any cell in the body that does not have the capacity to become a germ cell (egg or sperm).

SPINA BIFIDA. An opening in the spinal canal that is due to a developmental disorder with multifactorial causation.

TAY-SACHS DISEASE. An autosomal recessive disorder resulting in developmental retardation, paralysis, dementia and blindness followed by death, usually before the end of the third year of life. The defective gene codes for an enzyme that would normally degrade certain chemicals in the brain, leading to an accumulation of these undegraded substances in the brain and nervous tissue. The gene is found in highest frequency among Ashkenazic Jews of Eastern European origin. The location of the gene is now known.

THALASSAEMIA. Any of several heritable disorders of haemoglobin resulting from defective genes causing the reduced production of globin, a component of the haemoglobin molecule.

X-LINKED. Any gene found on the X-chromosome or traits determined by such genes.

Table of Cases

Canada

Andrews v. *Law Society of British Columbia*, [1989] 1 S.C.R. 143.
Attorney-General of British Columbia and Astaroff (1983), 6 C.C.C. (3d) 498 (B.C.C.A.).
Borowski v. *Attorney General of Canada*, [1987] 4 W.W.R. 385 (Sask. C.A.).
Dion v. *Attorney General of Canada*, [1986] D.L.Q. 353 (Que. Sup. Ct).
Engstrom v. *Courteau*, [1986] R.J.Q. 3048 (C.S.).
Hunter v. *Southam Inc.*, [1984] 2 S.C.R. 145.
Mills v. *The Queen*, [1986] 1 S.C.R. 863.
Minister of National Revenue v. *Kruger Inc.*, [1984] 2 F.C. 535 (C.A.).
R. v. *Amway of Canada Ltd.*, [1986] 2 F.C. 312 (T.D.).
R. v. *Beare*; *R.* v. *Higgins*, [1988] 2 S.C.R. 387.
R. v. *Big M. Drug Mart Ltd.*, [1985] 1 S.C.R. 295.
R. v. *Dyment*, [1988] 2 S.C.R. 417.
R. v. *Edwards Books*, [1986] 2 S.C.R. 713.
R. v. *Esposito* (1985), 24 C.C.C. (3d) 88 (Ont. C.A.).
R. v. *Jones*, [1986] 2 S.C.R. 284.
R. v. *Legere* (1989), 5 W.C.B. (2d) 384 (N.B.C.A.).
R. v. *Morgentaler*, [1988] 1 S.C.R. 30.
R. v. *Oakes*, [1986] 1 S.C.R. 103.
R. v. *Parent* (1989), 65 A.R. 307 (Q.B.).
R. v. *Pohertsky*, [1987] 1 S.C.R. 945.
R. v. *Therrien* (1982), 67 C.C.C. (2d) 31 (Ont. Co. Ct).
Re Jamieson and The Queen (1982), 70 C.C.C. (2d) 430 (Que. Sup. Ct).
Reference re Public Service Employee Relations Act (Alta.), [1987] 1 S.C.R. 313.
Reference re Section 92(2) of the Motor Vehicle Act, R.S.B.C. 1979, c. 288, [1985] 2 S.C.R. 486.
RWDSU v. *Dolphin Delivery Ltd.*, [1986] 2 S.C.R. 573.
Singh v. *Minister of Employment and Immigration*, [1985] 1 S.C.R. 177.
Tremblay v. *Daigle*, [1989] 2 S.C.R. 530.

United States

Curlender v. *Bio-Science Laboratories*, 165 Cal. Rptr. 477, 106 Cal. App. 3d 811 (1980).

Harbeson v. *Parke-Davis, Inc.*, 656 P. 2d 483, 98 Wash. 2d 460 (Sup. Ct 1983).

Moore v. *Regents of the University of California*, 249 Cal. Rptr. 494 (App. 2 Dist. 1988), reh'g granted 252 Cal. Rptr. 816 (1988).

Procanik v. *Cillo*, 478 A. 2d 755, 97 N.J. 339 (1984).

Siemieniec v. *Lutheran General Hospital*, 480 N.E. 2d 1227 (Ill. App. 1 Dist. 1985).

State v. *Castro*, 545 N.Y.S. 2d 985 (1989) (Bronx Cty).

Turpin v. *Sortini*, 119 Cal. App. 3d 690, 174 Cal. Rptr. 128 (1981), rev'd., 182 Cal. Rptr. 337, 643 P. 2d 954, 31 Cal. 3d 220 (Sup. Ct 1982).

Table of Statutes

Canada

Canadian Charter of Rights and Freedoms, Part I of the *Constitution Act, 1982*, being Schedule B of the *Canada Act 1982* (U.K.), 1982, c. 11.
Charter of Human Rights and Freedoms, R.S.Q., c. C-12.
Cultural Property Act, R.S.Q., c. B-4.
Environmental Quality Act, R.S.Q., c. Q-2.
Sexual Sterilization Act, S.B.C. 1933, c. 59.
The Sexual Sterilization Act, S.A. 1928, c. 37.

United States

An Act (Public Act 86-884, Laws 1989) in relation to sexually transmitted diseases and inherited metabolic diseases amending named Acts, approved 11 September 1989.

France

The French Penal Code, art. 63.

Treaties and International Agreements

African Charter on Human and Peoples' Rights (1981).
American Convention on Human Rights (1969).
Convention for the Protection of Cultural Property in the Event of Armed Conflict (1954).
Convention for the Protection of Human Rights and Fundamental Freedoms (1950).
Convention on the Prevention and Punishment of the Crime of Genocide (1948).
Declaration of Geneva (1948).
Declaration of Helsinki, Recommendations Guiding Physicians in Biomedical Research Involving Human Subjects (1964) (am. Tokyo, 1975; am. Venice, 1983; am. Hong Kong, 1989).
Declaration of Lisbon (1981).
International Covenant on Civil and Political Rights (1966).
International Covenant on Economic, Social and Cultural Rights (1966).
United Nations Convention on the Law of the Sea (1982).
Universal Declaration of Human Rights (1948).

Council of Europe, Parliamentary Assembly

Resolution 808 (1983) on the Return of Works of Art.
Recommendation 934 (1982) on Genetic Engineering.
Recommendation 1046 (1986) on the Use of Human Embryos and Foetuses for Diagnostic, Therapeutic, Scientific, Industrial and Commercial Purposes.
Recommendation 1100 (1989) on the Use of Human Embryos and Foetuses in Scientific Research.

Bibliography

A., J.-G. "Chorée de Huntington: test prédictif offert" (1989) 24:7 Le médecin du Québec 87.

Ad Hoc Committee on DNA Technology, American Society of Human Genetics. "DNA Banking and DNA Analysis: Points to Consider" (1988) 42:5 Am. J. Hum. Genet. 781.

Agich, George J. "Genetic Justice" (1986) 24 U.W.O. L. Rev. 39.

Anderson, Alun. "Judge Backs Technique" (1989) 340:6235 Nature 582.

———. "New Technique on Trial" (1989) 339:6224 Nature 408.

Anderson, Elizabeth. "Values, Risks, and Market Norms" (1988) 17 Phil. Pub. Aff. 54.

Andrews, Lori B. *Medical Genetics: A Legal Frontier*. Chicago: American Bar Foundation, 1987.

Annas, George. J. "Crack, Symbolism, and the Constitution" (1989) 19:3 Hast. Cent. Rep. 35.

Audard, Catherine et al., eds. *Individu et justice sociale: autour de John Rawls*. Paris: Seuil, 1988.

Barreau du Québec. "Rapport du comité sur les nouvelles technologies de reproduction" (1988) 48:2 suppl. R. du B.

Baudouin, Jean-Louis and Catherine Labrusse-Riou. *Produire l'homme: de quel droit?* Paris: P.U.F., 1987.

Benyekhlef, Karim. "Réflexions sur la légalité des tests de dépistage de drogues dans l'emploi" (1988) 48 R. du B. 315.

Blakeslee, S. "New Techniques Help Researchers Track Gene Defects" *International Herald Tribune* (14 September 1989) 7.

Boone, Keith. "Bad Axioms in Genetic Engineering" (1988) 18:4 Hast. Cent. Rep. 9.

Brisson, Jean-Maurice. *Texte annoté de la Charte des droits et libertés de la personne du Québec*. Montreal: SOQUIJ, 1986.

Callahan, Daniel. "Ethical Responsibility in Science in the Face of Uncertain Consequences" (1976) 265 Annals N.Y. Acad. Sci. 1.

Canada, Government of. *A New Perspective on the Health of Canadians* (Lalonde report). Ottawa, 1974.

Canter, Edith F. "Employment Discrimination Implications of Genetic Screening in the Workplace under Title VII and the Rehabilitation Act" (1984-85) 10 Am. J. L. Med. 323

Capron, Alexander M. "The Rome Bioethics Summit" (1988) 18:4 Hast. Cent. Rep. 11.

———. "Tort Liability in Genetic Counseling" (1979) 79 Colum. L. Rev. 618.

Clarke, Angus. "Genetics, Ethics, and Audit" (1990) 335:8698 Lancet 1145.

Commission d'experts pour la génétique humaine et la médecine de la reproduction, *Rapport au Département fédéral de l'intérieur et au Département de la justice et police* (Berne, 19 August 1988).

Congregation for the Doctrine of the Faith. *Instruction on Respect for Human Life in Its Origin and on the Dignity of Procreation*. Vatican City: Vatican Polyglot Press, 1987.

Conseil d'État. *Sciences de la vie : de l'éthique au droit,* 2d ed. Paris: La Documentation française, 1988.

Council of Europe, Ad Hoc Committee of Experts on Progress in the Biomedical Sciences (CAHBI), *Prenatal Genetic Screening, Prenatal Genetic Diagnosis and Associated Genetic Counselling*. Strasbourg: The Council, 1989.

Council of Europe, P.A. *Genetic Engineering: Risks and Chances for Human Rights*, European Parliamentary Hearing, Copenhagen, 25 and 26 May 1981. Strasbourg: The Council, 1981.

Damme, Catherine J. "Controlling Genetic Disease through Law" (1982) 15 U.C. Davis L. Rev. 801.

De Jager, K. "Claims to Cultural Property under International Law" (1988) 1 Leiden J. Int'l L. 183.
de Montigny, Yves. "La protection contre les fouilles, les perquisitions et les saisies abusives: un premier bilan" (1989) 49 R. du B. 53.
Delmas-Marty, Mireille. "Un nouvel usage des droits de l'homme" in *Éthique médicale et droits de l'homme*. Paris: Actes Sud/INSERM, 1988, 313.
Durbin, Paul T., ed. *Technology and Responsibility*. Dordrecht: D. Reidel, 1987.
Edelman, Bernard and Marie-Angèle Hermitte, eds. *L'homme, la nature et le droit*. Paris: Christian Bourgois, 1988.
Edwards, R.G. "Diagnostic Methods for Human Gametes and Embryos" (1987) 2:5 Human Reprod. 415.
Elias, Sherman and George J. Annas. *Reproductive Genetics and the Law*. New York: Yearbook Medical Publications, 1987.
Emery, Alan E.H. and David L. Rimoin. "Nature and Incidence of Genetic Disease" in Alan E.H. Emery and David L. Rimoin, eds. *Principles and Practice of Medical Genetics*, vol. 1. Edinburgh: Churchill Livingstone, 1983.
Engelhardt, H. Tristram. *The Foundations of Bioethics*. New York: Oxford University Press, 1986.
Engelhardt, H. Tristram and Michael A. Rie. "Morality for the Medical-Industrial Complex (1988) 319:16 N. Engl. J. Med. 1086.
Fécondation in vitro, analyse du génome et thérapie génétique (Benda report). Paris: La Documentation française, 1987.
Feinberg, Joel and Hyman Gross, eds. *Philosophy of Law*, 3d ed. Belmont, Calif.: Wadsworth Pub., 1986.
Fletcher, John C. "Ethical and Social Aspects of Risk Predictions" (1984) 25 Clin. Genet. 25.
Fletcher, Joseph. *The Ethics of Genetic Control: Ending Reproductive Roulette*. New York: Anchor, 1974.
Fondation Marangopoulos pour les Droits de l'Homme. *Expérimentation biomédicale et Droits de l'Homme*. Paris: P.U.F., 1988.
Frézal, J. "Les problèmes éthiques en génétique humaine" (1985) 104 Louvain Medical 38.
Gelehrter, Thomas D. and Francis S. Collins. *Principles of Medical Genetics*. Baltimore: Williams & Wilkins, 1990.
"Gene Therapy in Man: Recommendations of the European Medical Research Councils" (1988) 11:8597 Lancet 1271.
Goodfellow, P.N. "Cystic Fibrosis: Steady Steps Lead to the Gene" (1989) 341:6238 Nature 102.
Grobstein, Clifford and Michael Flower. "Gene Therapy: Proceed with Caution" (1984) 14:2 Hast. Cent. Rep. 13.
Hermitte, Marie-Angèle. "L'affaire Moore" (December 1988) 417 Le Monde Diplomatique 20.
———. *Le droit du génie génétique végétal*. Paris: Librairies Techniques, 1987.
Holtzman, Neil A. *Proceed with Caution: Predicting Genetic Risks in the Recombinant DNA Era*. Baltimore: Johns Hopkins University Press, 1989.
———. "Recombinant DNA Technology, Genetic Tests, and Public Policy" (1988) 42:4 Am. J. Hum. Genet. 624.
Huppé, Luc. "La dignité humaine comme fondement des droits et libertés garantis par la Charte" (1988) 48 R. du B. 724.
Jacob, François. *La logique du vivant: une histoire de l'hérédité*. Paris: Gallimard, 1970.
———. *The Statue Within*. New York: Basic Books, 1988.
Jacquard, Albert. *L'héritage de la liberté: de l'animalité à l'humanitude*. Paris: Seuil, 1986.
Kevles, Daniel J. *In the Name of Eugenics: Genetics and the Uses of Human Heredity*. New York: Alfred A. Knopf, 1985.
Keyserlingk, Edward W. "Non-Treatment in the Best Interests of the Child: A Case Commentary of *Couture-Jacquet* v. *Montreal Children's Hospital*" (1987) 32 McGill L.J. 413.
King, M.C. "Genetic Testing of Identity and Relationship" (1989) 44:2 Am. J. Hum. Genet. 178.
Kiss, Alexandre-Charles. "La notion de patrimoine commun de l'humanité" (1982) II, 175 RCADI 99.

Knoppers, Bartha M. ''Comparative Abortion Law: The Living Abortus'' in K. Mason, ed. *Paediatric Medicine*. London: Chapman & Hall, 1989.

———. *Conception artificielle et responsabilité médicale: une étude de droit comparé*. Cowansville, Que.: Yvon Blais, 1986.

———. ''Genetic Screening and Genetic Information in the Workplace'' (Address to the American Society of Human Genetics, October 1986) [unpublished].

———. ''Human Genetics, Predisposition and the New Social Contract'' in International Conference on Bioethics, *The Human Genome Sequencing: Ethical Issues*. Brescia, Italy: Clas International, 1989, 168.

———. ''L'arbitrage du médecin face aux normes régissant la fécondation 'in vitro''' in Christian Byk, ed. *Artificial Procreation: The Present State of Ethics and Law*. Lyon: Lacassagne, 1989, 49.

———. ''L'adoption d'un code de conduite international en matière de technologies de la reproduction,'' in International Law Association. *Report of the Sixty-third Conference*. Warsaw, Poland: The Association, 1988, 879.

———. ''Modern Birth Technology and Human Rights'' (1985) 33 Am. J. Comp. L. 1.

———. ''Reproductive Technology and International Mechanisms of Protection of the Human Person'' (1987) 32 McGill L.J. 336.

Knoppers, Bartha M. and Claude M. Laberge. ''DNA Sampling and Informed Consent'' (1989) 140:9 C.M.A.J. 1023.

Laberge, Claude. ''La révolution biologique'' in Jacques Dufresne, Fernand Dumont and Yves Martin, eds. *Traité d'anthropologie médicale*. Quebec: Presses de l'Université du Québec, 1985.

Langaney, André. ''La diversité génétique humaine: considérable et mal connue'' in *Génétique, procréation et droit*. Paris: Actes Sud, 1985, 349.

Lappé, Marc. ''The Limits of Genetic Inquiry'' (1987) 17:4 Hast. Cent. Rep. 5.

Law Commission, The. *Report on Injuries to Unborn Children*. London: HMSO, 1974.

Law Reform Commission of Canada. *Biomedical Experimentation Involving Human Subjects*, Working Paper 61. Ottawa: The Commission, 1989.

Crimes against the Foetus, Working Paper 58. Ottawa: The Commission, 1989.

Obtaining Forensic Evidence, Report 25. Ottawa: The Commission, 1985.

Omissions, Negligence and Endangering, Working Paper 46. Ottawa: The Commission, 1985.

Lemkin, Raphaël. *Axis Rule in Occupied Europe*. Washington, D.C.: Carnegie Endowment for International Peace, 1944.

Lepage, Henri. ''Destins du droit de propriété'' (1985) Droits (Revue française de théorie juridique) Paris: P.U.F., 1985.

———. *Pourquoi la propriété?* Paris: Hachette, 1985.

Lewin, Roger. ''DNA Typing on the Witness Stand'' (1989) 244:4908 Science 1033.

Lewontin, Richard C., Steven Rose and Leon J. Kamin. *Not in Our Genes*. New York: Pantheon Books, 1984.

Lippman-Hand, A. and F. Clarke Fraser. ''Genetic Counseling — The Postcounseling Period: II. Making Reproductive Choices'' (1979) 4 Am. J. Med. Genet. 73.

Malherbe, Jean-François. *Pour une éthique de la médecine*. Paris: Larousse, 1987.

Manning, Morris. ''Proof of Facts in Constitutional Cases'' in Gérald-A. Beaudoin, ed. *Charter Cases 1986-87*. Cowansville, Que.: Yvon Blais, 1987, 271.

Marx, Jean L. ''DNA Fingerprinting Takes the Witness Stand'' (1988) 240:4859 Science 1616.

———. ''Gene Transfer Is Coming on Target'' (1988) 242:4876 Science 191.

McDougal, Myres S., Harold D. Lasswell and Lung-Chu Chen. *Human Rights and World Public Order: The Basic Policies of an International Law of Human Dignity*. New Haven, Conn.: Yale University Press, 1980.

McKusick, Victor A. *Mendelian Inheritance in Man: Catalogs of Autosomal Dominant, Autosomal Recessive and X-linked Phenotypes*, 9th ed. Baltimore: Johns Hopkins University Press, 1990.

Medical Research Council of Canada. *Guidelines for Research on Somatic Cell Gene Therapy in Humans*. Ottawa: Supply and Services Canada, 1990.

———. *Towards an International Ethic for Research with Human Beings*. Ottawa: Supply and Services Canada, 1988.

Milunsky, Aubrey and George J. Annas, eds. *Genetics and the Law III*. New York: Plenum Press, 1985.

Motulsky, Arno G. "Medical Genetics" (1989) 261:19 JAMA 2855.

Murray, Thomas H. "Warning: Screening Workers for Genetic Risk" (1983) 13:1 Hast. Cent. Rep. 5.

Neel, James V. "Social and Scientific Priorities in the Use of Genetic Knowledge" in Bruce Hilton et al. *Ethical Issues in Human Genetics: Genetic Counseling and the Use of Genetic Knowledge*. New York: Plenum Press, 1973, 353.

"New Tools for Genome Study Being Made" (1988) 24:32 Medical Post 28.

Nichols, Eve K. *Human Gene Therapy*. Cambridge, Mass.: Harvard University Press, 1988.

Nolan, Kathleen and Sara Swenson. "New Tools, New Dilemmas: Genetic Frontiers" (1988) 18:5 Hast. Cent. Rep. 40.

Nora, James J. and F. Clarke Fraser. *Medical Genetics: Principles and Practice*, 3d ed. Philadelphia: Lea & Febiger, 1989.

Palca, Joseph. "Gene Transfer to Humans Approved in the Face of Advice" (1988) 335:6191 Nature 577.

———. "Human Genome Organization Is Launched with a Flourish" (1988) 335:6188 Nature 286.

———. "National Research Council Endorses Genome Project" (1988) 331:6156 Nature 467.

"Preimplantation and Early Post-Implantation Diagnosis" (1987) 2:5 Human Reprod. 399.

Rapport du comité de travail sur les nouvelles technologies de reproduction humaine. Québec: Ministère de la Santé et des Services sociaux, 1988.

Rawls, John. *A Theory of Justice*. Cambridge, Mass.: Belknap Press of Harvard University Press, 1971.

———. "Justice as Fairness: Political Not Metaphysical" (1985) 14 Phil. Pub. Aff. 219.

"Report from Germany, A" (1988) 2:3 Bioethics 254.

Rodgers, Sanda. "Fetal Rights and Maternal Rights: Is There a Conflict?" (1986) 1 C.J.W.L. 456.

Roy, David and Maurice de Wachter. *The Life Technologies and Public Policy*. Montreal: Institute for Research on Public Policy, 1986.

Sass, Hans-Martin. "A Critique of the Enquete Commission's Report on Gene Technology" (1988) 2:3 Bioethics 264.

Schachter, Oscar. "Human Dignity As a Normative Concept" (1983) 77 Am. J. Int'l L. 848.

Schmitz, Cristin. "DNA Fingerprinting" (1989) 48:8 Lawyer's Weekly 1.

Science Council of Canada. *Genetics in Canadian Health Care*. Ottawa: Supply and Services Canada, 1990.

Sève, Lucien. *Recherche biomédicale et respect de la personne humaine: Explication d'une démarche*. Paris: La Documentation française, 1987.

Shaw, Margery W. "Conditional Prospective Rights of the Fetus" (1984) 5 J. Legal Med. 63.

Short, Elizabeth M. "Proposed ASHG Position on Mapping/Sequencing the Human Genome" (1988) 43:1 Am. J. Hum. Genet. 101.

Sieghart, Paul. *The International Law of Human Rights*. Oxford: Clarendon Press, 1983.

Silberner, Joanne. "Finally, Putting Genes into Humans" US News and World Report (17 October 1988) 66.

Special article. "Ethical and Social Issues in Screening for Genetic Disease" (1972) 286:21 N. Engl. J. Med. 1129.

Steinbock, Bonnie. "The Logical Case for 'Wrongful Life'" (1986) 16:2 Hast. Cent. Rep. 15.

Steinbrook, Robert. "In California, Voluntary Mass Prenatal Screening" (1986) 16:5 Hast. Cent. Rep. 5.

Stringer, C.B. and P. Andrews. "Genetic and Fossil Evidence for the Origin of Modern Humans" (1988) 239:4845 Science 1263.

Suzuki, David and Peter Knudtson. *Genethics: The Ethics of Engineering Life*. Toronto: Stoddart, 1988.

Terrenoire, Gwen. "Conseil génétique et eugénisme: le passé du conseil génétique aux États-Unis" (1986) 11 Cahiers Science, technologie et société (Éthique et Biologie) Paris, Éd. du C.N.R.S. 171.

U.S. Congress, Office of Technology Assessment. *Human Gene Therapy: Background Paper*. Washington, D.C.: OTA, 1984.

Mapping Our Genes: Genome Projects — How Big, How Fast? Baltimore: Johns Hopkins University Press, 1988.

Medical Testing and Health Insurance. Washington, D.C.: OTA, 1988.

New Developments in Biotechnology: Ownership of Human Tissues and Cells. Washington, D.C.: U.S. Government Printing Office, 1987.

The Role of Genetic Testing in the Prevention of Occupational Disease. Washington, D.C.: OTA, 1983.

U.S. National Academy of Science. *Genetic Screening: Programs, Principles, and Research*. Washington, D.C.: U.S. Government Printing Office, 1975.

U.S. National Research Council. *Mapping and Sequencing the Human Genome*. Washington, D.C.: National Academy Press, 1988.

U.S. President's Commission for the Study of Ethical Problems in Medicine and Biomedical and Behavioral Research. *Screening and Counseling for Genetic Conditions*. Washington, D.C.: The Commission, 1983.

Splicing Life. Washington, D.C.: The Commission, 1982.

Veatch, Robert M. *A Theory of Medical Ethics*. New York: Basic Books, 1981.

———. *The Foundation of Justice: Why the Retarded and the Rest of Us Have Claims to Equality*. New York: Oxford University Press, 1986.

———. Book Review of *The Foundations of Bioethics* (1986) 105:6 Ann. Intern. Med. 987.

Vogel, Friedrich and Arno G. Motulsky, eds. *Human Genetics: Problems and Approaches*, 2d ed. Berlin: Springer-Verlag, 1986.

Warnock, Mary. "Do Human Cells Have Rights?" (1987) 1:1 Bioethics 1.

Wertz, Dorothy C. and John C. Fletcher, eds. *Ethics and Human Genetics: A Cross-Cultural Perspective*. Berlin: Springer-Verlag, 1989.

World Health Organization and Council for International Organizations of Medical Sciences. *Proposed International Guidelines for Biomedical Research Involving Human Subjects*. Geneva: CIOMS, 1982.

HUMAN DIGNITY AND GENETIC HERITAGE

Protection of Life Series

A Study Paper prepared for the

Law Reform Commission of Canada

by

Bartha Maria Knoppers, B.A., M.A., LL.B., D.É.A., D.L.S., B.C.L., LL.D., Associate Professor, Faculty of Law, University of Montreal

Canadian Cataloguing in Publication Data

Knoppers, Bartha Maria

Human dignity and genetic heritage: study paper

(Protection of life series)
(Study paper)
Text in English and French.
Title on added t.p.: Dignité humaine et patrimoine génétique.
Includes bibliographical references.
ISBN 0-662-58055-9
DSS cat. no. J32-3/44

1. Medical genetics — Law and legislation — Canada.
2. Human genetics — Moral and ethical aspects.
3. Genetic engineering — Law and legislation — Canada. I. Law Reform Commission of Canada. II. Series: Protection of life series. III. Series: Study paper (Law Reform Commission of Canada). IV. Title. V. Title: Dignité humaine et patrimoine génétique.

RB155.K56 1991 344.71′04196 C91-098534-0E

Available by mail free of charge from:

Law Reform Commission of Canada
130 Albert St., 7th Floor
Ottawa, Canada
K1A 0L6

or

Suite 310
Place du Canada
Montreal, Quebec
H3B 2N2

Catalogue No. J32-3/44
ISBN 0-662-58055-9

DIGNITÉ HUMAINE ET PATRIMOINE GÉNÉTIQUE

Série protection de la vie

DIGNITÉ HUMAINE
ET PATRIMOINE GÉNÉTIQUE

Série protection de la vie

Document d'étude préparé à l'intention de la

Commission de réforme du droit du Canada

par

Bartha Maria Knoppers, *B.A.*, *M.A.*, *LL.B.*, *D.É.A.*, *D.L.S.*, *B.C.L.*, *LL.D.*, professeure agrégée, Faculté de droit, Université de Montréal

Données de catalogage avant publication (Canada)

Knoppers, Bartha Maria

Dignité humaine et patrimoine génétique : étude

(Série protection de la vie)
(Document d'étude)
Texte en français et en anglais.
Titre de la p. de t. addit. : Human dignity and genetic heritage.
Comprend des références bibliographiques.
ISBN 0-662-58055-9
N° de cat. MAS J32-3/44

1. Génétique médicale — Droit — Canada. 2. Génétique humaine — Aspect moral. 3. Génie génétique — Droit — Canada. I. Commission de réforme du droit du Canada. II. Coll. : Série protection de la vie. III. Coll. : Document d'étude (Commission de réforme du droit du Canada). IV. Titre. V. Titre : Human dignity and genetic heritage.

RB155.K56 1991 344.71'04196 C91-098534-OF

On peut obtenir ce document gratuitement en écrivant à :

Commission de réforme du droit du Canada
130, rue Albert, 7e étage
Ottawa, Canada
K1A 0L6

ou

Bureau 310
Place du Canada
Montréal (Québec)
H3B 2N2

N° de catalogue J32-3/44
ISBN 0-662-58055-9

Table des matières

Introduction

À l'approche de l'an 2000, l'avenir est porteur de promesses prodigieuses pour la génétique humaine. Mais comme la découverte de l'atome et — plus récemment — la mise au point de la fécondation in vitro, le progrès de cette science recèle la possibilité du bien comme celle du mal. C'est l'essence même du genre humain qui est en jeu. Les potentialités de la génétique humaine résident dans les connaissances qu'elle nous procure. Celles-ci nous forceront inéluctablement à nous interroger sur la nature et le caractère unique de l'espèce humaine, sur les possibilités de transformation qu'elle présente ; et les enjeux revêtiront une importance primordiale. À vrai dire, cette nouvelle ère qui s'annonce nous fournira l'occasion de donner un sens à la dignité inhérente à la personne, nous y contraindra même[1].

Nous ne savons pas exactement où nous mènera la génétique humaine ; cette incertitude suscite de faux espoirs chez certains, en incite d'autres à des dénonciations globales. Les adversaires du génie génétique estiment qu'en recourant à ces techniques, on « empiète sur la nature », « on se prend pour Dieu », on s'engage sur « une pente glissante[2] ». Il ne fait aucun doute que les nouveaux outils offerts par cette science atteignent l'être humain dans sa substance la plus essentielle, les gènes. Mais les résultats peuvent très bien être bénéfiques, pourvu que tous — individus concernés, savants, autorités publiques — agissent de façon responsable et judicieuse dans la recherche et dans l'application de nouvelles connaissances. Pour comprendre ce que l'avenir nous réserve, il nous faut tout d'abord voir comment l'évolution de la génétique moléculaire a modifié l'exercice de la génétique médicale (chapitre premier).

Le Conseil de l'Europe a soutenu dans sa recommandation de 1982 sur l'ingénierie génétique que le droit à la vie et à la dignité humaine comporte le droit à des caractéristiques génétiques inaltérées — c'est-à-dire n'ayant subi aucune manipulation[3]. Il a également proposé d'énoncer expressément ce droit dans la *Convention de*

---

1. *Déclaration universelle des droits de l'homme*, Rés. A.G. 217/A, Doc. off. A.G., 3e session, p. 71, Doc. N.U. A/810 (1948) :

   > Considérant que la reconnaissance de la dignité inhérente à tous les membres de la famille humaine et de leurs droits égaux et inaliénables constitue le fondement de la liberté, de la justice et de la paix dans le monde, [. . .]
   >
   > Considérant que dans la Charte les peuples des Nations Unies ont proclamé à nouveau leur foi dans les droits fondamentaux de l'homme, dans la dignité et la valeur de la personne humaine, dans l'égalité des droits des hommes et des femmes, [. . .] (Préambule).

2. Keith BOONE, « Bad Axioms in Genetic Engineering » (1988), 18:4 *Hast. Cent. Rep.* 9.

3. Conseil de l'Europe, A.P., 33e sess., IIIe partie, *Textes adoptés*, *Recommandation 934 (1982) relative à l'ingénierie génétique*, al. 4(i).

sauvegarde des droits de l'homme et des libertés fondamentales[4]. Le Conseil n'a cependant pas précisé ce qu'il entendait par « caractéristiques génétiques » et « patrimoine génétique », ni indiqué les protections juridiques susceptibles d'être établies en la matière. Or, les progrès réalisés en biologie moléculaire depuis 1982 et leurs effets sur la génétique humaine nous obligent à définir le patrimoine génétique. S'agit-il du pool génique, ou du génome individuel[5] ? La réponse est indispensable à la détermination des qualités inhérentes à la dignité humaine qui méritent d'être juridiquement protégées (chapitre deux).

La notion de dignité inhérente à la personne humaine, considérée comme fondamentale, n'a pourtant pas encore reçu d'interprétation claire dans le contexte des droits de la personne. Nul ne conteste, toutefois, que le respect de l'être humain comporte nécessairement le respect du corps, du bagage génétique et des origines de chaque individu. Les cellules humaines, et l'information génétique qu'elles recèlent, ne sont pas qu'un support temporaire de l'existence humaine, elles sont une composante de la dignité humaine. Le Conseil de l'Europe a lié le droit à la protection du patrimoine génétique au droit à la vie et à la dignité humaine, mais sans exclure l'intervention thérapeutique. En fait, le rapport préliminaire qu'il a préparé renferme une proposition surprenante : la liberté de reproduction des personnes susceptibles de transmettre certaines affections génétiques graves pourrait être assujettie à ce qu'elles consentent à la pratique d'une thérapie génique visant à réduire le risque de transmission de ces affections aux générations suivantes. Ainsi, le droit à un patrimoine génétique « sain », établi au départ pour protéger la dignité humaine, risque paradoxalement d'y porter atteinte, en restreignant les libertés individuelles (chapitre trois).

Bien que la signification de la dignité humaine en droit international des droits de l'homme ne soit pas entièrement fixée, la notion peut quand même servir de fondement à l'interprétation des droits de la personne dans le contexte du droit constitutionnel. Elle est du reste considérée comme le fondement du droit à la vie, à la liberté et à la sécurité de la personne, du droit à la protection contre les fouilles, les perquisitions et les saisies abusives, du droit à l'égalité et du droit à la protection contre la discrimination énoncés dans la *Charte canadienne des droits et libertés*[6]. On peut alors se demander si, dans le cadre d'un société libre et démocratique comme le Canada, ces garanties constitutionnelles sont directement applicables aux problèmes que soulève la nouvelle génétique humaine. Pensons par exemple à l'éventuelle instauration du dépistage obligatoire de maladies ou de l'état de porteur au sein de certains groupes ; à la possibilité d'obliger les parents à faire subir à leurs enfants des tests de dépistage de maladies pour lesquelles il existe un traitement ; à l'utilisation de prélèvements d'ADN à des fins non autorisées (chapitre quatre).

---

4. (1955) 213 R.T.N.U. 223 (ci-après Convention européenne des droits de l'homme).

5. Pour la définition des termes techniques, voir le glossaire, p. 85.

6. Partie I de la *Loi constitutionnelle de 1982* [annexe B de la *Loi de 1982 sur le Canada* (1982, R.-U., ch. 11)] art. 7, 8 et 15.

L'amélioration des capacités de traitement ou de modification du génome et le dépistage génétique visant à déterminer les risques de maladies futures peuvent jeter l'opprobre sur les individus concernés. Par exemple, [TRADUCTION] « [d]ans une perspective sociale, on peut faire un rapprochement entre la sonde génique de la psychose maniaco-dépressive et le dépistage des anticorps anti-SIDA : dans les deux cas, les tests entraînent la découverte d'un marqueur[7] », lequel est capable de prédire (avec plus ou moins de précision) l'apparition de la maladie. Or, cette prédiction s'accompagne d'un risque considérable de stigmatisation sociale.

Notre conception de la nature humaine est intimement liée à cette stigmatisation ainsi qu'à notre attitude face à la nouvelle génétique. Si nous concevons les conséquences génétiques comme inévitables et certaines, il est possible que nous penchions pour l'élimination des personnes présentant des déficiences génétiques plutôt que pour la recherche de mesures d'intégration sociale. Ce faisant, nous décidons de ce qui est « normal » et acceptable. Nous pouvons, par exemple, soumettre tous les travailleurs à un dépistage et exclure ceux qui présentent une prédisposition génétique, plutôt que d'essayer de réduire le risque de maladie en assainissant les lieux de travail. Nous pouvons nous abstenir de mettre en question un système politique qui réduit les possibilités d'assurance des personnes présentant des déficiences génétiques. Nous pouvons exercer des pressions pour que les gens prennent, en matière de reproduction, des décisions conformes à nos critères de normalité, et promouvoir l'élimination, par l'avortement, des handicapés génétiques plutôt que de leur rendre le monde plus accueillant. Par contre, si nous considérons la diversité de notre constitution génétique comme une chose naturelle et une caractéristique essentielle de l'humanité, nous pourrions nous opposer à toute intervention génétique, indépendamment de ses justifications morales (chapitre cinq).

Les répercussions de la science moderne sur l'être humain peuvent être appréciées au regard de trois principes moraux : les principes d'autonomie, de bienfaisance et de non-malfaisance. Dans le contexte de la biologie moléculaire et de la génétique prévisionnelle modernes, comme dans celui de la médecine en général, il peut y avoir opposition entre le principe d'autonomie, d'une part, et les principes de bienfaisance et de non-malfaisance, d'autre part. Quel cadre ces principes tracent-ils pour une future action législative ?

À l'échelle gouvernementale, l'application d'une analyse coûts-avantages et de son fondement utilitariste pourrait être une très forte incitation à l'utilisation des tests. Elle pourrait forcer les gens à prendre connaissance de leurs prédispositions génétiques, à en informer autrui et à agir en conséquence, de façon que les « choix opportuns » qu'ils feront permettent à la société d'éviter les coûts à long terme de maladies invalidantes. De telles incitations économiques pourraient mener à une nouvelle eugénique, fondée non pas sur des caractéristiques indésirables, mais sur la réduction des coûts — une forme de justice sociale économique plutôt qu'une « justice génétique ». Devant ces choix, la justice génétique suppose, d'une part, une meilleure

---

7. Marc LAPPÉ, « The Limits of Genetic Inquiry » (1987), 17:4 *Hast. Cent. Rep.* 5, p. 7.

communication des connaissances dans le contexte protégé de la relation entre médecin et patient et, d'autre part, l'attribution à celui-ci de la responsabilité de divulguer à sa famille les renseignements utiles dont elle a intérêt à disposer (chapitre six).

L'élaboration d'une théorie de la « justice génétique » requiert un examen approfondi des droits de la personne dans le contexte des milieux de travail, de l'assurance et des rapports entre le médecin et ses patients. Il faudra également étudier avec la plus grande rigueur d'autres questions : le droit de regard de l'individu sur l'utilisation de ses tissus corporels ou de ses cellules et de l'information génétique qu'elles contiennent ; la diffusion de l'information génétique aux membres de la famille ; l'accès à des services de consultation et à des services d'éducation génétique adéquats[8]. C'est dès aujourd'hui, cependant, qu'il faut définir les valeurs et les principes fondamentaux qui sont en jeu.

Nous tentons dans cette étude de faire le point sur les connaissances philosophiques et scientifiques fondamentales — et en pleine évolution — qui sous-tendent les progrès de la génétique humaine. Nous examinerons les répercussions que ces connaissances auront sur la définition et sur la protection juridique du patrimoine génétique humain. Il importe de situer la notion de patrimoine génétique, et les mécanismes de protection possibles, dans une analyse de la dignité humaine. Ceci nous permettra d'envisager la formulation d'un concept révisé d'« a-normalité » génétique dans le contexte d'un nouveau concept de « justice génétique ».

La nouvelle génétique nous touche individuellement et collectivement dans notre structure sociale, politique et économique. Pourtant, les tribunaux n'ont pas encore donné une interprétation exhaustive de la dignité humaine, reconnue dans les pactes internationaux et les constitutions nationales. La présente étude fait valoir que la reconnaissance de la dignité de chaque être humain et de l'humanité dans son ensemble passe par la protection de notre patrimoine génétique, fondée sur des principes de respect de la vie humaine axés sur la médecine. Nous entendons démontrer que la vie humaine, au sens génétique, n'est pas fixée dans le temps et ne saurait se réduire à un pool génique immuable. Il est possible, croyons-nous, de susciter le respect de la complexité, de la variabilité et du caractère unique de l'être humain, ainsi que la reconnaissance de l'égalité dans la différence génétique, par la généralisation de l'éducation génétique du public et du corps médical. Sans cette diffusion de l'information, on risque de voir les connaissances génétiques employées à mauvais escient pour des fins discriminatoires, et aussi d'assister à l'apparition de la dangereuse rhétorique des « droits génétiques », avec le cortège des revendications et des obligations juridiques qui en découlent. Bref, la présente étude vise d'une part à préciser le sens de la dignité humaine dans le contexte des nouveaux choix qu'offre la génétique, et d'autre part à en proposer des interprétations qui consacrent l'indivisibilité de la nature génétique de la personne dans le cadre d'une éthique sociale commune, celle d'une justice génétique.

---

8. Voir, en général, Neil A. HOLTZMAN, *Proceed with Caution: Predicting Genetic Risks in the Recombinant DNA Era*, Baltimore, Johns Hopkins University Press, 1989 et Lori B. ANDREWS, *Medical Genetics: A Legal Frontier*, Chicago, American Bar Foundation, 1987.

CHAPITRE PREMIER

Aperçu de génétique

I. Introduction

L'humanité a depuis des millénaires une connaissance intuitive de la transmission héréditaire des caractères physiques. Ainsi, les agriculteurs ont amélioré le rendement des animaux domestiques et des cultures au cours des siècles en choisissant pour la reproduction les spécimens qui présentaient des caractéristiques supérieures. Mais il a fallu attendre jusqu'à il y a un peu plus d'un siècle avant d'entrevoir le fondement biologique de l'hérédité grâce aux travaux du moine autrichien Gregor Mendel. Ce dernier a pu établir l'existence d'unités d'hérédité qui se transmettent de génération en génération selon des règles mathématiques simples. En d'autres mots, on pouvait prédire le patrimoine génétique.

Le début du vingtième siècle a été témoin d'une explosion de travaux de recherche en génétique qui s'inspiraient des travaux de Mendel. On a d'abord établi que les unités d'hérédité décrites par Mendel sont localisées sur les chromosomes. Dans les années 1940, on a découvert la composition du matériel génétique ; on a établi qu'une substance, appelée acide désoxyribonucléique (ADN), renferme l'information génétique de chaque cellule. Il restait alors à savoir comment cette information est transmise d'une cellule à l'autre. En 1953, James Watson et Francis Crick ont découvert que la molécule d'ADN a une structure pouvant remplir cette fonction (la fameuse double hélice). Cette découverte leur a valu le prix Nobel.

Depuis lors, la génétique humaine a connu une révolution grâce aux progrès de la science appelée biologie moléculaire[9] ; nous en décrirons un certain nombre. Mais auparavant, nous expliquerons brièvement comment les différences génétiques se produisent et quels types de différences peuvent modifier l'aspect physique ou les fonctions de l'organisme humain. Nous examinerons ensuite comment les progrès de la biologie moléculaire ont modifié la pratique de la génétique médicale.

---

9. Claude LABERGE, « La révolution biologique », dans Jacques DUFRESNE, Fernand DUMONT et Yves MARTIN (dir.), *Traité d'anthropologie médicale*, Québec, Presses de l'Université du Québec, 1985, p. 201.

II. Fondement structural des différences génétiques[10]

Les caractères héréditaires sont transmis par les gènes, disposés le long des filaments de chromosomes. Il y a vingt-trois paires de chromosomes dans chaque cellule de l'organisme[11]. Un chromosome de chaque paire provient de l'ovule de la mère et l'autre, du spermatozoïde du père. L'ovule et le spermatozoïde (appelés également cellules germinales ou gamètes) sont formés respectivement dans les ovaires de la femme et les testicules de l'homme grâce à un processus appelé méiose. Au cours de la méiose, les paires de chromosomes s'alignent côte à côte, s'échangent de l'information génétique par recombinaison, puis se séparent. Il s'ensuit que les cellules germinales ont vingt-trois chromosomes au lieu de vingt-trois paires et que chaque cellule germinale renferme un mélange du matériel génétique des chromosomes parentaux.

Chaque cellule germinale renferme vingt-deux autosomes — les chromosomes qui se retrouvent chez les deux sexes — ainsi qu'un chromosome sexuel. Dans l'ovule, ce chromosome sexuel est toujours un X ; dans le spermatozoïde, ce peut être un X ou un Y. L'union de l'ovule avec un spermatozoïde donne un embryon de sexe féminin lorsque le spermatozoïde porte un chromosome X, et de sexe masculin lorsqu'il porte un chromosome Y. Après cette union (la fécondation), la division cellulaire donne naissance aux cellules du corps proprement dites que l'on appelle cellules somatiques, lesquelles, comme on l'a déjà dit, renferment deux jeux de chromosomes.

L'unité de l'hérédité est le gène, lequel est composé chimiquement d'ADN. L'ADN est constitué de deux brins enroulés, reliés entre eux par des bases, les nucléotides[12], à la manière des échelons d'une échelle tordue (c'est la fameuse double hélice).

On peut déduire la séquence des bases d'un brin à partir de celle de l'autre. Cette complémentarité entre les deux brins d'ADN est la clé du pouvoir de transmission de l'information de celui-ci. La séquence de nucléotides du gène est transcrite dans une molécule qui agit comme messager : l'acide ribonucléique messager (ARNm). Cette molécule d'ARNm, qui a été élaborée dans le noyau de la cellule, passe dans le cytoplasme où sa séquence de nucléotides sert de matrice pour l'assemblage d'acides aminés en une protéine. Ainsi, l'ADN détermine la séquence des bases de l'ARNm, qui déterminent la séquence des acides aminés ; celle-ci détermine quant à elle la structure de la protéine. Chaque protéine est donc déterminée par un gène spécifique.

---

10. N.A. HOLTZMAN, *op. cit.*, note 8.

11. Sauf dans le cas du spermatozoïde et de l'ovule qui comptent chacun vingt-trois chromosomes non appariés.

12. Il y a quatre types de nucléotides dans l'ADN : l'adénosine (A), la guanosine (G), la cytidine (C) et la thymine (T). L'adénosine ne se lie qu'à la thymine et la guanosine, qu'à la cytidine. Les nucléotides de l'ARNm sont complémentaires de ceux de l'ADN, sauf que l'ARN renferme de l'uracile (U) à la place de la thymine.

Toutefois, l'ADN présent dans le noyau de la cellule ne sert pas uniquement à la synthèse des protéines. Une quantité importante de l'ADN réparti parmi ou entre les gènes producteurs de protéines sert à réguler l'activité des gènes eux-mêmes ou remplit une fonction encore inconnue[13].

L'ensemble complet des gènes d'un individu s'appelle le génome. Chaque gène est situé à un locus particulier sur l'un des chromosomes. Nous avons tous deux gènes à chaque locus, un sur chacun des chromosomes de la paire (sauf dans la cellule germinale mâle où les chromosomes sexuels sont X et Y).

Les gènes appariés situés à un locus donné peuvent porter une information identique ou différente. On appelle allèles les formes différentes d'un même gène. Les allèles proviennent d'une modification spontanée de l'ADN ; dans la situation la plus simple, il s'agit d'un changement dans une seule paire de nucléotides. Cette différence peut modifier un acide aminé dans la protéine. Lorsqu'une mutation se produit dans une cellule germinale, elle peut alors être transmise aux enfants et aux générations suivantes. Les mutations, responsables des variations génétiques au sein de l'espèce, permettent l'évolution, au cours de laquelle l'allèle le plus favorable est sélectionné. Certaines mutations semblent neutres, c'est-à-dire qu'elles semblent ne pas présenter plus d'avantages ou d'inconvénients que d'autres. Les gènes neutres peuvent présenter plusieurs allèles à un site donné, dont aucun n'est rare. Ces types d'allèles sont qualifiés de polymorphiques. Le polymorphisme se produit également dans l'ADN entre deux gènes et, comme on pourra le constater, constitue un outil précieux dans la cartographie du génome.

Bien que certaines mutations soient avantageuses pour l'organisme et que certaines soient neutres, la plupart sont nuisibles. Ce sont ces gènes nuisibles qui peuvent provoquer des maladies ou des dysfonctionnements.

III. Affections génétiques

On estime que dix pour cent des Canadiens présentent des affections génétiques qui entraînent la mort ou sont une cause de maladie, d'invalidité ou de handicap. Les maladies à composante génétique sont responsables de trente à cinquante pour cent des admissions dans les hôpitaux pédiatriques[14]. Les connaissances concernant la

---

13. Voir Arno G. MOTULSKY, « Medical Genetics » (1989), 261:19 *JAMA*, 2855.

14. Pour des renseignements généraux, consulter GOUVERNEMENT DU CANADA, *Nouvelle perspective de la santé des Canadiens* (rapport Lalonde), Ottawa, 1974. Voir aussi les données divergentes contenues dans Alan E.H. EMERY et David L. RIMOIN, « Nature and Incidence of Genetic Disease », dans Alan E.H. EMERY et David L. RIMOIN (dir.), *Principles and Practice of Medical Genetics*, vol. 1, Édimbourg, Churchill Livingstone, 1983, p. 1.

pathogenèse de ces maladies et les traitements sont toutefois limitées, et l'on ne connaît le locus du gène responsable que dans trois pour cent seulement des cas[15].

Les affections génétiques peuvent se diviser en trois catégories : les aberrations chromosomiques, les affections monogéniques et les affections multifactorielles[16].

A. Aberrations chromosomiques

En 1959, on a découvert que les enfants atteints du syndrome de Down (mongolisme, trisomie 21) avaient quarante-sept chromosomes au lieu du nombre normal de quarante-six. Peu après, on s'est rendu compte que d'autres maladies étaient associées à une trop grande ou à une trop faible quantité de matériel chromosomique. Dans les années 1970, de nouvelles techniques de coloration histologique ont permis une meilleure étude des chromosomes sous le microscope et ont révélé l'existence d'aberrations chromosomiques jusqu'alors inconnues.

L'absence ou l'excès de matériel chromosomique peut toucher tout le chromosome ou une partie seulement. La plupart des anomalies proviennent d'erreurs au moment de la séparation des chromosomes à la méiose. Un enfant né vivant sur deux cents est victime d'une aberration chromosomique. La plupart d'entre eux souffrent de troubles mentaux et d'un retard de croissance ; ils présentent souvent des malformations.

On peut déceler les aberrations chromosomiques avant la naissance. Les tests sont généralement offerts aux femmes de trente-cinq ans et plus[17], aux couples qui ont déjà eu un enfant présentant une aberration chromosomique et à ceux dont l'un des membres a subi un remaniement chromosomique équilibré.

B. Affections monogéniques

Les affections génétiques appartenant à la deuxième catégorie sont souvent qualifiées de « mendéliennes » car leur transmission suit les règles établies par Gregor Mendel. Nous connaissons maintenant l'existence de plus de quatre mille traits mendéliens, dont environ trois mille peuvent être responsables de maladies et de dysfonctionnements[18]. L'affection est qualifiée de dominante si elle s'exprime lorsqu'un

---

15. NATIONAL RESEARCH COUNCIL, *Mapping and Sequencing the Human Genome*, Washington (D.C.), National Academy Press, 1988, p. 28.

16. Pour une étude plus détaillée des affections génétiques, voir James J. NORA et F. Clarke FRASER, *Medical Genetics: Principles and Practice*, 3e éd., Philadelphie, Lea & Febiger, 1989.

17. Plus une femme est âgée, plus elle court le risque d'avoir un enfant atteint du syndrome de Down.

18. Victor A. MCKUSICK, *Mendelian Inheritance in Man: Catalogs of Autosomal Dominant, Autosomal Recessive and, X-linked Phenotypes*, 9e éd., Baltimore, Johns Hopkins University Press, 1990.

seul allèle de la paire est défectueux. Ces affections peuvent s'exprimer à différents degrés selon les individus (expressivité variable). Dans certains cas, la maladie ne s'exprime même pas (pénétrance réduite). Pour ces raisons, et parce que l'affection peut ne se manifester qu'à un âge avancé, il s'avère difficile de prédire la gravité et l'âge du début de la maladie chez un individu donné.

L'affection est qualifiée de récessive lorsque les deux allèles doivent être défectueux pour que la maladie s'exprime. Dans ce cas, les parents qui portent tous les deux l'allèle mutant peuvent être extérieurement normaux. Il est possible de dépister les porteurs de certaines de ces affections (par exemple dans le cas de la drépanocytose), c'est-à-dire d'identifier les individus d'une population qui ont ce gène dans leur bagage génétique. Lorsque ce dépistage est impossible, les parents n'apprennent qu'ils sont porteurs de l'allèle défectueux que lorsqu'ils donnent naissance à un enfant atteint de la maladie.

Dans le cas de certaines affections génétiques, on peut prévenir les conséquences du gène anormal en modifiant le régime de vie. Par exemple, chez les individus atteints de phénylcétonurie, le gène défectueux donne une enzyme inactive qui normalement devrait transformer la phénylalanine en tyrosine. L'accumulation de phénylalanine qui s'ensuit produit des troubles mentaux. On peut toutefois prévenir cette accumulation en contrôlant rigoureusement l'apport alimentaire de phénylalanine à partir de la période néonatale et au moins jusqu'à la fin de la petite enfance, de façon à limiter les effets à long terme.

Le dernier type d'affection monogénique est la maladie récessive liée au chromosome X. À l'instar des maladies autosomiques récessives, elle ne s'exprime pas lorsqu'un allèle normal est présent sur l'autre chromosome. Ainsi, une femme n'ayant qu'un chromosome X défectueux sera normale. Toutefois, si son fils hérite du chromosome X défectueux, celui de l'hémophilie, par exemple, il aura la maladie car il ne possède pas de deuxième chromosome X pour le protéger.

On peut déceler plus de cinquante affections monogéniques avant la naissance à l'aide d'épreuves biochimiques réalisées sur des cellules fœtales prélevées dans le liquide amniotique de la mère.

C. Affections multifactorielles

Les affections multifactorielles forment la dernière catégorie des affections génétiques. Il est quelque peu arbitraire de les qualifier de génétiques, étant donné que les facteurs environnementaux peuvent avoir autant d'importance que les gènes défectueux dans leur cause et leur expression.

Les affections multifactorielles comprennent des maladies courantes comme l'hypertension, les maladies cardio-vasculaires, l'athérosclérose et le diabète ainsi que des malformations congénitales comme le spina-bifida. Parfois, des études familiales peuvent nous faire soupçonner une composante génétique (dans le cas du spina-bifida, par exemple). D'autres fois, on a repéré un gène qui augmente la prédisposition à une maladie[19]. La plupart des affections génétiques courantes sont complexes et hétérogènes. Une maladie ou une malformation donnée peut avoir différentes causes selon les familles ou les individus.

IV. Progrès technologiques en biologie moléculaire

Les progrès technologiques réalisés en biologie moléculaire sont importants dans la mesure où ils peuvent nous aider à cartographier le génome humain, c'est-à-dire à localiser la position du gène qui cause une affection génétique sur un chromosome donné, et par rapport à d'autres gènes adjacents.

Le Congrès américain a approuvé un projet de détermination de la séquence du génome complet[20], auquel se sont associés d'autres pays (projet HUGO)[21]. Ces travaux nous fourniront des données qui pourraient nous aider à éviter ou à prévenir les affections génétiques et même à les traiter et à les guérir[22].

Voyons quels sont les principaux progrès ayant rendu cette initiative possible[23]. La cartographie génétique a connu une percée importante grâce à la découverte du polymorphisme des sites de restriction — RFLP, de l'anglais « restriction fragment length polymorphism » — dans les années 1980. Les enzymes de restriction, dont plusieurs centaines sont connues à l'heure actuelle, coupent l'ADN en fragments aux deux extrémités d'une séquence de nucléotides déterminée. La longueur des fragments est spécifique à chaque enzyme. Lorsqu'une mutation se produit à un site de coupure, l'enzyme ne coupe pas à cet endroit et la longueur du fragment d'ADN résultant n'est pas la même. Ainsi, lorsque le fragment en question est marqué à l'aide d'une sonde et

---

19. M. LAPPÉ, *loc. cit.*, note 7, p. 10. Par exemple, la spondylarthrite ankylosante est associée à l'allèle B-27 au locus du gène codant pour les antigènes d'histocompatibilité humains (système HLA). Ce ne sont toutefois pas tous les individus porteurs du gène en question qui vont manifester la maladie, et la maladie se déclare parfois chez des individus dépourvus de ce gène.

20. Joseph PALCA, « National Research Council Endorses Genome Project » (1988), 331:6156 *Nature* 467.

21. Joseph PALCA, « Human Genome Organization is Launched with a Flourish » (1988), 335:6188 *Nature* 286 ; G. Christopher ANDERSON, « Genome Project: Howard Hughes gets HUGO Off the Ground » (1990), 345:6271 *Nature* 100. Fait intéressant à noter, l'information contenue dans les trois milliards de paires de base de la séquence du génome humain remplirait [TRADUCTION] « 200 volumes de la taille de l'annuaire téléphonique de Manhattan », « New Tools for Genome Study Being Made » (1988), 24:38 *Medical Post* 28.

22. En 1988, on connaissait l'emplacement de plus de 1 215 gènes sur les chromosomes humains (on pense que le génome humain se compose d'environ 100 000 gènes). CONGRESS OF THE UNITED STATES, OFFICE OF TECHNOLOGY ASSESSMENT [ci-après OTA], *Mapping Our Genes: Genome Projects — How Big, How Fast?*, Baltimore, Johns Hopkins University Press, 1988, p. 4.

23. Pour plus de détails, voir Thomas D. GELEHRTER et Francis S. COLLINS, *Principles of Medical Genetics*, Baltimore, Williams & Wilkins, 1990.

que les fragments sont séparés sur gel selon leur longueur, le fragment provenant de l'individu portant l'allèle mutant migre sur le gel à une position différente de celle des fragments de l'ADN normal. La variation de la longueur d'un fragment donné qui en résulte est due au polymorphisme des sites de restriction.

Ces allèles polymorphiques sont transmis aux descendants selon les lois de Mendel. Étant donné qu'il existe de nombreux RFLP, dont beaucoup sont courants, ils sont très utiles pour établir la cartographie des loci des affections génétiques.

Lorsqu'on peut montrer qu'un RFLP est étroitement lié au locus d'une affection génétique, le marqueur peut être utilisé dans une famille pour déterminer la probabilité qu'un individu de cette famille soit porteur du gène responsable de cette affection. Ainsi, lorsque la probabilité d'une affection autosomique dominante est de cinquante pour cent selon les lois de Mendel, la probabilité qu'une personne soit réellement porteuse du gène peut être révisée à la baisse ou à la hausse selon le type de polymorphisme que l'on trouve lié à ce gène. Il arrive que le RFLP soit situé au sein du gène et qu'on puisse prédire la présence de celui-ci avec une quasi-certitude.

V. Évolution de la génétique médicale

L'information obtenue de la cartographie du génome peut être utilisée dans un certain nombre de situations. Dans le cas des affections mendéliennes, on peut y recourir avant la naissance pour déterminer si le fœtus est atteint[24]. Après la naissance, on peut s'en servir pour confirmer un diagnostic ou déceler la présence d'une maladie avant qu'elle ne se manifeste par des symptômes (épreuve pré-symptomatique). Par exemple, on utilise cette méthode pour déceler les porteurs de la chorée de Huntington[25] qui, s'ils vivent assez longtemps, finiront par manifester les symptômes. Les épreuves permettent également de déceler les couples normaux dont les partenaires sont tous les deux porteurs d'une maladie récessive. Les conjoints peuvent ainsi utiliser cette information pour prendre des décisions en matière de procréation. Enfin, elles peuvent servir à déterminer qu'un individu porte un marqueur génétique d'une maladie multifactorielle, auquel cas la probabilité que cet individu contracte la maladie augmente.

Dans le passé, peu de maladies étaient associées à des structures géniques connues permettant de confirmer la présence ou l'absence d'un gène mutant. Ainsi, ce sont les études familiales qui ont d'abord permis de déterminer qu'une maladie était de type mendélien. On pouvait alors prédire, d'après les lois de Mendel, la probabilité que

---

24. L'objet du diagnostic prénatal est de permettre aux couples ou aux individus qui sont à risque de transmettre une maladie héréditaire d'entreprendre la création d'une famille. En ce qui a trait à la fibrose kystique, voir S. BLAKESLEE, « New Techniques Help Researchers Track Gene Defects », *International Herald Tribune* (14 septembre 1989), p. 7 et P.N. GOODFELLOW, « Cystic Fibrosis: Steady Steps Lead to the Gene » (1989), 341:6238 *Nature* 102.

25. Voir J.-G. A., « Chorée de Huntington : test prédictif offert » (1989), 24:7 *Le Médecin du Québec* 87.

l'enfant d'une personne atteinte d'une maladie ou de deux parents porteurs soit atteint. Dorénavant, la possibilité de localiser un gène ou un marqueur situé près du gène responsable de la maladie augmentera grandement la précision de ces prédictions, et ceci, d'autant plus que le marqueur est situé à proximité du gène. La génétique médicale en sera profondément changée car les nombreux autres loci génétiques qui seront découverts pourront servir à effectuer des épreuves prénatales et présymptomatiques et être utilisés comme outils de dépistage systématique, sans que les maladies concernées soient nécessairement graves. Par ailleurs, des incertitudes subsisteront forcément : celles qui sont attribuables à l'expressivité variable, à la pénétrance réduite et à la complexité générale d'affections multifactorielles courantes.

VI. Thérapie génique

Lorsqu'on connaît la séquence des bases de l'ADN, on peut modifier cette séquence d'une façon déterminée. Cela nous permettra un jour de traiter ou de guérir les maladies génétiques. On peut isoler les gènes, ainsi que l'ADN voisin qui renferme l'information régulatrice importante. Il sera alors possible d'insérer des gènes « normaux » dans les cellules d'un patient qui en est dépourvu ou dont les gènes sont anormaux. À l'heure actuelle, la thérapie génique ne se pratique que sur les cellules somatiques ; ces modifications, contrairement à celles qui touchent les cellules germinales, ne sont pas transmises aux générations suivantes[26]. Même s'il n'est pas encore possible de modifier la lignée des cellules germinales chez les humains, il existe un faible risque que cela se produise par inadvertance dans l'application d'une thérapie somatique. Celle-ci, rappelons-le, en est encore au stade expérimental ; on l'envisage uniquement pour le traitement des individus atteints de quelques affections qui semblent se prêter tout particulièrement à ce type d'intervention[27]. Il pourrait un jour être possible d'appliquer la thérapie génique aux embryons au stade de préimplantation (pendant la période de quatorze jours qui suit la fécondation) — mais cela pose des difficultés pratiques considérables[28].

En avril 1988, les délégués des sept pays occidentaux les plus industrialisés ont participé à la Cinquième Conférence internationale sur la bioéthique qui portait sur la cartographie du génome humain. Ils sont arrivés à la conclusion qu'il n'y a pas de limite intrinsèque à l'acquisition des connaissances sur le génome humain et que la

---

26. OTA, *Human Gene Therapy: Background Paper*, Washington (D.C.), OTA, 1984, p. 6.

27. Joseph PALCA, « Gene Transfer to Humans Approved in the Face of Advice » (1988), 335:6191 *Nature* 577 ; Joanne SILBERNER, « Finally, Putting Genes Into Humans », *US News and World Report* (17 octobre 1988), p. 66, où l'on a signalé que les sujets cancéreux en phase terminale pourraient recevoir bientôt une version modifiée de leurs cellules antitumorales. Jean L. MARX, « Gene Transfer is Coming on Target » (1988), 242:4876 *Science* 191 ; Diane GERSHON, « Genetic Engineering : Transfer Study Expands » (1990), 344:6266 *Nature* 483.

28. De façon générale, voir « Preimplantation and Early Post-Implantation Diagnosis » (1987), 2:5 *Human Reprod.* 399 ; R.G. EDWARDS, « Diagnostic Methods for Human Gametes and Embryos » (1987), 2:5 *Human Reprod.* 415.

recherche dans ce domaine doit être vivement encouragée. Ils ont également déclaré que la thérapie génique des cellules somatiques doit être évaluée selon les mêmes critères que les autres traitements médicaux au stade expérimental. Toutefois, ils ont souligné qu'il n'y a, à l'heure actuelle, aucune justification médicale ou éthique à la manipulation génétique intentionnelle des cellules de la lignée germinale humaine[29]. Le Conseil de recherches médicales du Canada reconnaît dans son document de travail la spécificité de ces travaux scientifiques, qui ne sauraient être assimilés aux autres recherches sur les humains. Il a adopté la position suivante à l'égard des protocoles de recherche sur la thérapie génique des cellules somatiques humaines : « le transfert de gènes dans les cellules somatiques ne devrait être envisagé que dans le cas des maladies qui répondent à tous les critères suivants : elles sont attribuables à une anomalie touchant un gène unique ; elles entraînent pour un être humain né vivant une maladie gravement débilitante ou une mort prématurée ; [et] elles ne peuvent être traitées avec succès d'aucune autre façon[30] ». Le comité du Conseil qui s'est penché sur cette question a conclu qu'il n'existe actuellement aucun indice donnant lieu de croire que la thérapie des cellules de la lignée germinale humaine ou quelque autre type de transfert génétique permettent l'amélioration des fonctions, et non pas seulement la guérison de maladies causant de graves infirmités[31]. Cette position concorde avec celles des commissions américaines qui ont étudié la thérapie génique humaine[32] et de la commission présidentielle établie en 1982 pour étudier les problèmes éthiques en médecine et en recherches sur le comportement[33]. Plus récemment, le Conseil des sciences du Canada mettait sur pied un groupe multidisciplinaire d'experts pour étudier les progrès de la génétique humaine et leurs implications, dans le but d'élaborer une politique nationale sur la médecine génétique[34].

Les pays d'Europe continentale sont beaucoup plus prudents lorsqu'il est question de modification des gènes. Les conseils européens de recherches médicales ont, il est vrai, approuvé la thérapie génique de la lignée somatique[35]. Mais comme nous le

---

29. Alexander M. CAPRON, « The Rome Bioethics Summit » (1988), 18:4 *Hast. Cent. Rep.* 11, p. 12. Voir également INTERNATIONAL CONFERENCE ON BIOETHICS, *The Human Genome Sequencing: Ethical Issues*, Brescia (Italie), Clas International, 1989, p. 291.

30. CONSEIL DE RECHERCHES MÉDICALES DU CANADA, *Lignes directrices concernant la recherche sur la thérapie génique somatique chez les humains*, Ottawa, Approvisionnements et Services Canada, 1990, pp. 10 et 11.

31. *Ibid.*

32. *Op. cit.*, notes 15 et 26.

33. PRESIDENT'S COMMISSION FOR THE STUDY OF ETHICAL PROBLEMS IN MEDICINE AND BIOMEDICAL AND BEHAVIORAL RESEARCH (ci-après PRESIDENT'S COMMISSION), *Splicing Life*, Washington (D.C.), La Commission, 1982 ; voir également PRESIDENT'S COMMISSION, *Screening and Counseling for Genetic Conditions*, Washington (D.C.), La Commission, 1983.

34. CONSEIL DES SCIENCES DU CANADA, *La génétique et les services de santé au Canada*, Ottawa, Approvisionnements et Services Canada, 1990.

35. Voir « Gene Therapy in Man: Recommendations of the European Medical Research Councils » (1988), 11:8597 *Lancet* 1271, p. 1272, où l'on indique que seule doit être envisagée la thérapie génique des cellules somatiques qui entraîne des changements non héréditaires à certains tissus de l'organisme. La thérapie de la lignée germinale, visant à introduire des modifications génétiques transmissibles, n'est pas acceptable ; *Contra* : COMMISSION DES COMMUNAUTÉS EUROPÉENNES, *Proposition modifiée de décision du*

verrons plus loin (dans les chapitres consacrés à la dignité humaine et à la notion de « normalité » génétique[36]), des pays européens comme la France[37], la Suisse[38] et l'Allemagne de l'Ouest[39] sont en faveur d'une application plus restrictive des nouvelles découvertes de la génétique humaine.

VII. Conclusion

Cet aperçu montre que l'application de la biologie moléculaire à la recherche sur les affections génétiques ne nous met pas seulement en face de nouveaux choix : elle sème aussi l'incertitude. L'explosion des connaissances a élargi le fossé entre notre capacité d'identifier les affections génétiques, et notre capacité de les comprendre et d'y remédier.

Conseil : Analyse du Génome Humain, COM (89) 532 final, 13 novembre 1989, au par. 4.4.4 : « Le développement et l'application de thérapies génétiques somatiques ne sont pas prévues dans le cadre du présent programme. » Non seulement des fonds ne seront pas accordés pour la thérapie de la lignée somatique, mais « [. . .] les parties contractantes prennent l'engagement contraignant de s'abstenir de tout travail de recherche visant à modifier la constitution génétique d'êtres humains par altération des cellules germinales ou de tout stade de développement embryonnaire qui puisse rendre ces altérations héréditaires ».

36. La notion de « normalité » est étudiée dans le cinquième chapitre.

37. CONSEIL D'ÉTAT, *Sciences de la vie : De l'éthique au droit*, 2e éd., Paris, La Documentation française, 1988, p. 84. Le Conseil est d'avis que toute modification de la lignée germinale devrait être interdite. Il a également recommandé d'interdire le diagnostic génétique au moyen d'une biopsie de l'embryon chez des embryons préimplantés. Cette position recoupe celle qu'a prise le Comité national d'éthique dans son *Avis relatif aux recherches sur les embryons humains in vitro et à leur utilisation à des fins médicales et scientifiques* de décembre 1986 (reproduit dans COMITÉ CONSULTATIF NATIONAL D'ÉTHIQUE POUR LES SCIENCES DE LA VIE ET DE LA SANTÉ, *Avis de recherche sur l'embryon*, Vendome, France, Actes du Sud et INSERM, 1987, p. 73). Voir également G. HUBER, *Patrimoine génétique et droits de l'humanité* (Livre blanc des recommandations), Paris, Osiris, 1990.

38. COMMISSION D'EXPERTS POUR LA GÉNÉTIQUE HUMAINE ET LA MÉDECINE DE LA REPRODUCTION (ci-après COMMISSION D'EXPERTS), *Rapport au Département fédéral de l'intérieur et au Département de la justice et police*, Berne, le 19 août 1988, p. 97. L'organisme estime que la thérapie génique somatique devrait être limitée aux cas d'affections héréditaires graves. Toute thérapie de la lignée germinale sera interdite sur les gamètes et sur les embryons ; les manipulations génétiques non thérapeutiques seront également prohibées. Cette opinion est particulièrement intéressante car elle est fondée sur l'équation que fait le Conseil de l'Europe entre le droit à la dignité et le patrimoine génétique (voir le chapitre trois).

39. *Fécondation in vitro, analyse du génome et thérapie génétique* (rapport Benda), Paris, La Documentation française, 1987. La Commission considérait la thérapie des cellules somatiques comme une technique encore au stade expérimental et donc soumise aux règles et protocoles obligatoires sur l'expérimentation humaine. Elle estimait que la recherche sur la lignée germinale n'était pas justifiée car elle exigeait l'utilisation d'embryons et leur destruction éventuelle au cours d'expériences. La Commission a recommandé d'interdire les expériences ou les traitements portant sur la lignée germinale. Cette position a été réaffirmée dans le récent rapport de l'Enquete Commission au Bundestag de la République fédérale allemande (ci-après ENQUETE COMMISSION), *Prospects and Risks of Gene Technology*, dans « A Report from Germany » (1988), 2:3 *Bioethics* 254, dans lequel, à la page 257, on énonçait que le développement naturel des êtres humains est un reflet de leur degré d'« humanité ». Comme dans la *Loi sur la protection des embryons* proposée en 1986, on y exclut rigoureusement toute expérimentation, même thérapeutique, sur la lignée germinale humaine (p. 261) ; voir également Hans-Martin SASS, « A Critique of the Enquete Commission's Report on Gene Technology » (1988), 2:3 *Bioethics* 264, p. 273.

Le nombre d'affections susceptibles d'être dépistées grâce à une épreuve prénatale ou pré-symptomatique croît rapidement. Avec la possibilité de déceler la présence de loci génétiques qui augmentent la prédisposition à contracter des maladies courantes ou le risque d'avoir des enfants qui vont les contracter, il pourrait arriver que la grande majorité d'entre nous soit soumise au dépistage génétique. Il est urgent de bien renseigner les professionnels de la santé et la population si l'on veut éviter les retombées néfastes d'un tel contrôle[40].

40. Neil A. HOLTZMAN, « Recombinant DNA Technology, Genetic Tests, and Public Policy » (1988), 42:4 *Am. J. Hum. Gen.* 624.

CHAPITRE DEUX

Le génome et le pool génique

I. Introduction

L'Assemblée parlementaire du Conseil de l'Europe, on l'a vu[41], a recommandé en 1982 au Comité des Ministres de faire en sorte que la Convention européenne des droits de l'homme reconnaisse explicitement le droit à un patrimoine génétique n'ayant subi aucune manipulation, sauf en application de principes reconnus pleinement compatibles avec le respect des droits de l'homme[42]. On ne trouve de définition du patrimoine génétique ni dans le rapport de l'audition[43] qui a précédé la rédaction de la recommandation, ni dans la recommandation elle-même. Ce terme désigne-t-il le génome (le matériel génétique d'une personne) ou le pool génique (la somme des génomes de la population) ? Voyons ce que l'on entend par patrimoine génétique dans le langage courant, dans le langage scientifique et en droit.

---

41. Recommandation 934, *supra*, note 3.

42. *Id.*, al. 7*b*). Les manipulations génétiques sont exceptionnellement permises à des fins de prévention ou de thérapie, lorsqu'il y a des raisons évidentes et scientifiques d'y recourir. Voir le chapitre trois. De la même façon, Sa Sainteté le pape Jean-Paul II, bien qu'elle ait condamné la plupart des formes de recherche sur les techniques de reproduction et le génie génétique ainsi que leurs applications cliniques, a spécifiquement approuvé, dans son *Instruction* de 1987, la possibilité de traiter *in utero* les maladies génétiques, si cela est dans l'intérêt de l'enfant à naître. CONGRÉGATION POUR LA DOCTRINE DE LA FOI, *Instruction sur le respect de la vie humaine naissante et la dignité de la procréation*, Cité du Vatican, Typographie Polyglotte Vaticane, 1987, p. 14 :

> [Le diagnostic prénatal] est licite si les méthodes utilisées, avec le consentement des parents convenablement informés, sauvegardent la vie et l'intégrité de l'embryon et de sa mère, sans leur faire courir de risques disproportionnés.

Et aux pp. 15-16, sur l'embryon humain :

> Une intervention strictement thérapeutique qui se fixe comme objectif la guérison de diverses maladies, comme celles dûes [*sic*] à des déficiences chromosomiques, sera, en principe, considérée souhaitable, pourvu qu'elle tende à la vraie promotion du bien-être personnel de l'homme, sans porter atteinte à son intégrité ou détériorer ses conditions de vie. Une telle intervention se situe en effet dans la logique de la tradition morale chrétienne.

43. CONSEIL DE L'EUROPE, A.P., *Genetic Engineering: Risks and Chances for Human Rights*, European Parliamentary Hearing, Copenhague, 25 et 26 mai 1981, Strasbourg, Le Conseil, 1981.

II. Patrimoine : sens ordinaire

Pour le commun des mortels, le patrimoine est un ensemble de biens, que l'on a hérités de ses ascendants. Cette conception individualiste du patrimoine comme objet de propriété est la plus répandue. Étymologiquement, le mot comporte pourtant un sens figuré comprenant la notion de patrimoine commun de l'humanité et pouvant viser des choses comme les découvertes scientifiques ou encore la culture ou l'économie d'une nation. Même dans son sens ordinaire, le mot patrimoine admet en outre une définition biologique désignant les caractères héréditaires d'une personne tels qu'ils s'expriment dans son apparence extérieure (le phénotype)[44].

III. Patrimoine : sens scientifique

Pour le biologiste, la notion de patrimoine a à la fois une portée individuelle et collective, puisque le pool génique de la population est constitué des génomes individuels. Il y a également un élément temporel reliant le pool génique et le génome. La diversité du pool génique s'est en effet élaborée, avec les siècles, par le processus de la mutation. De plus, la diversité individuelle s'accroît à l'intérieur de chaque génération par suite du processus de recombinaison qui se produit pendant la méiose. L'ovule ou le spermatozoïde produit par la méiose contient, on s'en souvient, un mélange du matériel chromosomique des parents[45]. Les processus biologiques de la mutation et de la méiose font de chaque individu un être unique, différent de ses parents.

Il existe pourtant un lien spatial et temporel entre le génome et le pool génique. Cette filiation ancestrale et universelle fait que le pool génique a à la fois une expression individuelle et une origine supranationale[46]. Cela revêt une grande importance pour la compréhension des effets de la thérapie génique de la lignée germinale et celle de la lignée somatique[47]. La première mènerait à des changements

44. De façon générale, voir *Larousse de la langue française : lexis*, Paris, Librairie Larousse, 1979, 1989, p. 896 : « 2. Ce qui est transmis par les parents, par la génération antérieure » et Paul ROBERT, *Petit Robert I : dictionnaire alphabétique et analogique de la langue française*, Paris, Le Robert, 1988, p. 1378 : « Biol. *Le patrimoine héréditaire de l'individu*, l'ensemble des caractères hérités. »

45. Voir le chapitre premier.

46. André LANGANEY, « La diversité génétique humaine : considérable et mal connue », dans *Génétique, procréation et droit*, Paris, Actes Sud, 1985, p. 349. Voir également C.B. STRINGER et P. ANDREWS, « Genetic and Fossil Evidence for the Origin of Modern Humans » (1988), 239:4845 *Science* 1263.

47. *Human Gene Therapy*, *op. cit.*, note 26, p. 31.

héréditaires. Elle pourrait ainsi avoir des répercussions sur la population future[48]. La thérapie de la lignée somatique n'agit que sur l'individu concerné ; elle n'a pas d'effets directs ni immédiats sur le mélange des gènes dans la population humaine[49]. Cependant, les réussites de cette dernière forme de thérapie génique pourraient, en définitive, se traduire par la survie de patients qui autrement auraient péri. En permettant à ces personnes de transmettre leurs gènes à la génération suivante, elles augmenteront ainsi la fréquence du gène mutant[50]. Et lorsque la même maladie frappera certains de leurs descendants, ceux-ci devront également être traités. Ainsi, si la thérapie de la lignée germinale modifie directement le pool génique, celle de la lignée somatique le modifie indirectement.

IV. Patrimoine : sens juridique

La diversité des interprétations marque aussi les notions juridiques relatives au concept de patrimoine. Traditionnellement, ce concept ne vise, en droit privé, que des biens à valeur pécuniaire, et en droit public, que des biens d'intérêt commun. Mais la notion de domaine public, qui a fini par acquérir une portée plus universelle, embrasse notamment, en droit international, les biens qui constituent le patrimoine commun de l'humanité.

A. Le droit privé

Dans le domaine du droit privé, le droit romain protégeait le « patrimonium » familial. Bien que les codes civils québécois et français ne définissent pas formellement le « patrimoine », le terme désigne une universalité de droits et de biens à valeur pécuniaire dans laquelle l'actif et le passif sont indissociables. Le patrimoine est indivisible et intransmissible entre vifs. Chaque personne ne possède qu'un patrimoine, dont la nature est principalement pécuniaire. En outre, les droits patrimoniaux ont souvent été associés à la possession ou à la propriété physique, par opposition aux droits extra-patrimoniaux, comme les droits personnels, les droits innés et les actions judiciaires relatives à l'état civil[51].

---

48. *Ibid.* Cela pourrait causer une perte de diversité génétique. Toutefois, cet effet n'aurait pas une portée énorme, car la plupart des maladies sont multifactorielles, et la thérapie de la lignée germinale ne peut s'appliquer qu'à certaines affections monogéniques, affections qui sont rares. La perte de diversité du fond génétique commun serait davantage attribuable au [TRADUCTION] « relâchement des pressions sélectives historiques qui s'exercent sur la population humaine, par suite de changements environnementaux et des progrès de l'hygiène et des soins médicaux » qu'à des interventions délibérées pratiquées à l'échelle individuelle.

49. Voir le chapitre premier.

50. Bien sûr, on peut en dire autant des thérapies classiques applicables aux maladies à base génétique.

51. Voir, de façon générale, CENTRE DE RECHERCHE EN DROIT PRIVÉ ET COMPARÉ DU QUÉBEC, *Private Law Dictionary and Bilingual Lexicon*, Montréal, Le Centre, 1988 ; *Dictionnaire de droit privé*, Montréal,

Toutefois, comme pour les notions de biens réels et de biens personnels en common law, le concept juridique de patrimoine ne se restreint plus nécessairement aujourd'hui aux biens transmis par succession ou aux biens à caractère économique. Il ne se distingue plus autant, non plus, des droits personnels, ainsi qu'en témoigne l'émergence, dans les deux systèmes de droit, de droits mixtes tels les droits relatifs à la propriété intellectuelle (les brevets et les droits d'auteur, par exemple). Nous verrons néanmoins que l'adoption des concepts du droit privé, qui dicte l'attribution à chacun d'un droit de propriété sur son génome, n'est pas sans causer des problèmes.

B. Le droit public

La notion classique de biens publics englobe les choses du domaine public ou réputées en fiducie dans l'intérêt public (*public trust*), les choses sans maître (*res nullius*) et les choses qui appartiennent à tous (*res communis*). L'air, la mer et l'espace, en particulier, sont depuis longtemps tenus pour des choses communes, à savoir, non susceptibles d'appropriation individuelle, et partant indivisibles, imprescriptibles et inaliénables[52]. L'État, par sa réglementation, a considérablement restreint la portée de ces notions classiques[53]. Nous tenterons de montrer que le recours aux concepts du droit public à l'égard du matériel et de l'information génétiques pose lui aussi des difficultés.

C. Le droit international

Une théorie du droit international dont la formulation remonte au XIXe siècle fournit une autre interprétation du concept de propriété en droit public. Elle propose la notion de propriété commune ou d'intérêt public au regard du « patrimoine commun de l'humanité ». Cette notion, fondée sur les travaux de Grotius, a été d'abord appliquée à la mer, celle-ci étant ainsi considérée comme une chose commune et les pays riverains ne jouissant d'une servitude que sur leurs eaux territoriales. En droit international moderne, le respect du patrimoine commun de l'humanité implique le

---

Le Centre, 1985 et *Lexique de droit privé et Supplément au Dictionnaire de droit privé (1985)*, Montréal, Le Centre, 1988. Voir aussi Henry Campbell BLACK (dir.), *Black's Law Dictionary*, 5e éd., St.Paul (Minn.), West Publishing, 1979, p. 1015 : « Patrimonium [TRADUCTION] : Ce qui peut être reçu en héritage. Ce dont une personne est propriétaire à titre privé et exclusif, ses possessions [. . .] »

52. OTA, *New Developments in Biotechnology: Ownership of Human Tissues and Cells*, Washington (D.C.), U.S. Government Printing Office, 1987 ; Marie-Angèle HERMITTE, « Histoires juridiques extravagantes : la reproduction végétale » et « Le concept de diversité biologique et la création d'un statut de la nature » et Catherine LABRUSSE-RIOU, « Servitude, servitudes », dans Bernard EDELMAN et Marie-Angèle HERMITTE (dir), *L'homme, la nature et le droit*, Paris, Christian Bourgois, 1988, respectivement aux pp. 40, 238 et 308.

53. De façon générale, voir Henri LEPAGE, *Pourquoi la propriété ?*, Paris, Hachette, 1985 et « Destins du droit de propriété » (1985), *Droits (Revue française de théorie juridique)*, Paris, P.U.F., 1985.

partage entre les nations et la protection des ressources pour les générations à venir[54]. Les principes fondamentaux sont les suivants : utilisation pacifique du patrimoine commun ; accessibilité à ceux qui y ont droit, sous réserve du respect du droit des autres ; partage égal ; administration des choses sans maître en conformité avec le bien public, vu leur caractère indivisible[55]. Cette notion d'internationalité découle de la nécessité d'empêcher l'appropriation privée des choses d'intérêt commun et de préserver les choses d'intérêt international pour l'avenir. Comme l'institution de la fiducie en droit privé (qui, auparavant, ne s'appliquait qu'aux « choses » [*res*] et qui, maintenant, vise également les droits), elle peut être assimilée à la notion de fiducie dans l'intérêt public. La fiducie favorise la transmission des biens et des droits d'une génération à l'autre.

Les conventions internationales sur le droit de la mer[56] et sur le patrimoine culturel ou naturel de l'humanité[57] ont reconnu le principe de la contribution et des intérêts communs des peuples ou des pays et de la nécessité de partager et de protéger ces patrimoines. Ce « capital » peut demeurer dans le domaine public ou privé, mais il incombe à l'État de définir, de désigner, de protéger et de préserver ces biens pour les générations futures[58]. Ainsi, l'on considère que le patrimoine culturel de l'humanité embrasse même une notion aussi vague que celle des « biens culturels, à quelque peuple qu'ils appartiennent[59] ». En Europe, l'Assemblée parlementaire du Conseil de l'Europe a demandé aux gouvernements des États membres de reconnaître « que le patrimoine culturel européen appartient à tous les Européens[60] ». Selon l'UNESCO, « [l]e patrimoine culturel en tant que témoignage du génie créateur et de l'histoire des peuples constitue un élément fondamental de leur identité ; la pleine jouissance de ce patrimoine est pour chaque peuple une condition indispensable de son épanouissement[61] ». En pratique, toutefois, le concept se limite souvent à la protection juridique nationale du patrimoine culturel[62]. De toute façon, l'imprécision évidente de la notion de patrimoine culturel rend très difficile l'application d'obligations juridiques définitives aux États. Au niveau international, le concept demeure donc largement « politique[63] ».

---

54. Alexandre-Charles KISS, « La notion de patrimoine commun de l'humanité » (1982) II, 175 *RCADI* 99.

55. *Ibid.* ; voir également K. DE JAGER, « Claims to Cultural Property Under International Law » (1988), 1 *Leiden J. Int'l L.* 183.

56. *Convention des Nations Unies sur le droit de la mer,* N.U. Doc A/Conf.62/122 (1982).

57. K. DE JAGER, *loc. cit.*, note 55.

58. A.-C. KISS, *loc. cit.*, note 54, p. 129 et suiv.

59. *Convention pour la protection des biens culturels en cas de conflit armé* (La Haye, 1954) (1956), 249 R.T.N.U. 241.

60. Conseil de l'Europe, A.P., 35e sess., IIe partie, *Textes adoptés*, *Résolution 808 (1983) relative au retour des objets d'art*, art. 10.

61. UNESCO, Comité d'experts chargé d'étudier la question de la restitution des œuvres d'art, Venise, 1976, SHC-76/CONF. 615/5, art. 18.

62. Voir, par exemple, la *Loi sur les biens culturels*, L.R.Q. , ch. B-4.

63. Voir K. De Jager, *loc. cit.*, note 55 citant Larschan et Brennan, p. 191.

La notion internationale de patrimoine commun, bien qu'elle n'ait d'abord visé que la protection de la flore et de la faune[64], pourrait englober aussi le « patrimoine génétique » humain. Traditionnellement, les plantes et les animaux étaient considérés comme *res nullius*, et donc comme des choses susceptibles d'être détruites, que chacun pouvait s'approprier. Il fallait donc les protéger et les gérer dans l'intérêt commun[65]. L'humanité, au sens global du terme, devient donc le fiduciaire de ces ressources, même si des organismes internationaux peuvent établir les principes devant être mis en œuvre par les États signataires. Cette protection contre la dégradation, l'exploitation et le gaspillage du patrimoine naturel n'est limitée ni dans le temps ni dans l'espace, car elle s'applique sans égard aux frontières géographiques et politiques et touche les générations futures[66].

Le Conseil de l'Europe, dans sa recommandation de 1982 sur l'ingénierie génétique appliquée aux micro-organismes végétaux ou animaux, a étendu ce concept aux êtres humains. Est-il possible de protéger le patrimoine génétique humain en recourant soit au concept de patrimoine commun élaboré en droit international, soit aux règles du droit privé ou du droit public ?

D. Une conception intégrée

L'application à la génétique humaine de ce concept de patrimoine commun de l'humanité peut soulever des difficultés. Premièrement, elle suppose la reconnaissance du génome humain (individuel) ou du pool génique (collectif) comme *res communis* (chose appartenant à tous) ou comme *res nullius* (chose sans maître). Deuxièmement, l'idée de participation commune à la gestion du patrimoine suscite certaines difficultés sur les plans conceptuel et politique, surtout en l'absence de propriété partagée. Dans l'ordre génétique, l'intégration est naturelle ; l'apartheid procède de l'ignorance culturelle. Enfin, on ne peut déterminer ce qui constitue une utilisation paisible et ce qui constitue une pratique abusive, sans définir les objectifs de la génétique humaine à l'échelle de la collectivité[67]. Il faut donc établir [TRADUCTION] « dans quelle mesure le pool génique est un bien public que nous détenons en fiducie pour les générations

---

64. On a initialement décidé de protéger la flore et la faune parce que l'on craignait que la création de nouveaux micro-organismes ou d'organismes hybrides ou synthétiques entraîne la disparition de matériel « original » dont on ignorait encore la valeur génétique.

65. Par exemple, voir la *Loi sur la qualité de l'environnement*, L.R.Q., ch. Q-2, et de façon générale, Marie-Angèle HERMITTE, *Le droit du génie génétique végétal*, Paris, Librairies Techniques, 1987.

66. *Convention pour la protection des biens culturels en cas de conflit armé*, précitée, note 59, p. 240.

67. Voir les chapitres cinq et six. Voir aussi (Septembre 1988) *FORUM* (Conseil de l'Europe), le numéro spécial consacré à la génétique (animale, végétale, environnementale et médicale).

futures, et dans quelle mesure sa subdivision en lots génétiques très individualisés empêche de le traiter comme une ressource publique[68]. »

En 1987, l'*Office of Technology Assessment* (OTA) des États-Unis a évoqué la possibilité de la reconnaissance par le Congrès du principe suivant lequel toute lignée cellulaire devrait être réputée appartenir au domaine public, ce qui empêcherait toute revendication du droit de propriété sur ces produits[69]. Un comité du *National Research Council* des États-Unis a, pour sa part, recommandé en 1988 que [TRADUCTION] « les séquences du génome humain soient considérées comme un *public trust* et ne puissent de ce fait être assujetties au droit d'auteur[70]. » La possibilité a aussi été mentionnée par le *Committee on Mapping and Sequencing* de l'*American Society of Human Genetics*, lorsqu'il a demandé à ses membres leur point de vue sur l'idée que les séquences du génome humain constitueraient un *public trust* et échapperaient en conséquence à tout droit d'auteur[71]. Par contre, le *Ad Hoc Committee on DNA Technology* de cette même société a conclu que [TRADUCTION] « sauf disposition contraire, l'ADN mis en banque appartenait au déposant[72] ». Il n'y a pas nécessairement de contradiction entre les deux positions. En fait, il est possible de soutenir que le droit de regard d'une personne sur l'utilisation de ses tissus ou de ses cellules n'est pas incompatible avec l'idée voulant que le génome humain lui-même constitue un « public trust ». Il devrait y avoir moyen de concilier les notions de droit de regard individuel et de gestion publique du pool génique ou du génome humain sans avoir recours aux règles du droit de propriété. Cette orientation répond du reste à l'union biologique, dans chaque personne, des caractéristiques individuelles et de la source du pool génique.

V. Conclusion

Les difficultés que pose l'application, à la génétique humaine, du concept de patrimoine commun de l'humanité tel qu'il est connu en droit privé, en droit public ou même en droit international, tiennent au fait que ces notions s'inscrivent dans un contexte historique et culturel bien précis. La génétique humaine a des répercussions tant sur le domaine privé que sur le domaine public ; et avec la cartographie du génome, le domaine international est lui aussi touché. C'est pourquoi il nous faut

68. James V. NEEL, « Social and Scientific Priorities in the Use of Genetic Knowledge », dans Bruce HILTON, Daniel CALLAHAN, Maureen HARRIS, Peter CONDLIFFE et Burton BERKLEY (dir.), *Ethical Issues in Human Genetics: Genetic Counseling and the Use of Genetic Knowledge*, New York, Plenum Press, 1973, p. 353, à la page 358.

69. *New Developments in Biotechnology*, *op. cit.*, note 52, p. 17.

70. *Mapping and Sequencing the Human Genome*, *op. cit.*, note 15, p. 100.

71. Elizabeth M. SHORT, « Proposed ASHG Position on Mapping/Sequencing the Human Genome » (1988), 43:1 *Am. J. Hum. Genet.* 101, p. 102.

72. AD HOC COMMITTEE ON DNA TECHNOLOGY, AMERICAN SOCIETY OF HUMAN GENETICS, « DNA Banking and DNA Analysis: Points to Consider » (1988), 42:5 *Am. J. Hum. Genet.* 781, p. 782.

envisager le concept de patrimoine dans une perspective originale, qui respecte la personne dans son intégralité et comme membre de la société.

Ce choix doit être fait tant à l'échelon provincial qu'à l'échelon national. En outre, les notions de droit de regard individuel et de fiducie dans l'intérêt public (*public trust*) doivent être compatibles avec les principes internationaux. Le concept de patrimoine génétique humain pourra ainsi acquérir la spécificité qui lui permettra de constituer une protection réelle et efficace.

Comme nous l'avons signalé, l'Assemblée parlementaire du Conseil de l'Europe a recommandé la protection du patrimoine génétique. Nous avons exploré le concept de patrimoine génétique et avons vu qu'il comporte à la fois un aspect individuel, le génome, et un aspect collectif, le pool génique.

Nous allons maintenant voir pourquoi le patrimoine génétique doit être protégé. L'Assemblée parlementaire du Conseil de l'Europe a jugé que cela est nécessaire à la protection de la dignité humaine. Nous étudierons donc, dans les deux prochains chapitres, la signification de la dignité dans le contexte de la génétique humaine, d'abord sur le plan du droit international, ensuite sur le plan constitutionnel.

CHAPITRE TROIS

Dignité humaine et génétique : le contexte international

I. Introduction

« Considérant que la reconnaissance de la dignité inhérente à tous les membres de la famille humaine et de leurs droits égaux et inaliénables constitue le fondement de la liberté, de la justice et de la paix dans le monde ». C'est mue par ces idéaux nobles et stimulants que l'Assemblée générale des Nations Unies a proclamé la *Déclaration universelle des droits de l'homme*, le 10 décembre 1948. L'article premier de ce document énonce : « [t]ous les êtres humains naissent libres et égaux en dignité et en droits » ; et l'article 27 : « [t]oute personne a le droit de [...] participer au progrès scientifique et aux bienfaits qui en résultent[73] ». Le préambule de la Convention européenne des droits de l'homme (1950) et le *Pacte international relatif aux droits économiques, sociaux et culturels* (1966)[74] reconnaissent les mêmes principes fondamentaux. Le dernier texte énonce que tous ces droits découlent de la dignité inhérente à la personne humaine[75]. Bien que le Canada ait signé ces deux pactes internationaux, la Charte canadienne ne reprend pas les termes qui y sont employés et ne fait pas expressément mention de la notion de dignité humaine. En revanche, la *Charte des droits et libertés de la personne* du Québec dispose, à l'article 4, que « [t]oute personne a droit à la sauvegarde de sa dignité[76] », sans plus de précisions.

Aucune institution internationale indépendante et compétente ne s'est encore prononcée sur l'interprétation ou l'application des dispositions précitées relatives à la dignité humaine[77]. En fait, il ressort clairement du libellé même des textes

---

73. Précitée, note 1.

74. (1976) 993 R.T.N.U. 13.

75. Voir également le préambule similaire du *Pacte international relatif aux droits civils et politiques* adopté en 1966 (1976), 999 R.T.N.U. 187 (« Reconnaissant que ces droits découlent de la dignité inhérente à la personne humaine ») ; la *Convention américaine relative aux droits de l'homme* (1969), par. 11(1) : « Toute personne a droit au respect de son honneur et à la reconnaissance de sa dignité » et la *Charte africaine des droits de l'homme et des peuples* (1981), art. 5 : « Tout individu a droit au respect de la dignité inhérente à la personne humaine », les textes de la convention américaine et de la charte africaine sont reproduits dans CONSEIL DE L'EUROPE, *Droits de l'homme en droit international : Textes de base*, Strasbourg, Le Conseil, 1985, respectivement aux pp. 179 et 211.

76. L.R.Q., ch. C-12. Pour l'étude du droit constitutionnel canadien, voir le chapitre quatre.

77. Paul SIEGHART, *The International Law of Human Rights*, Oxford, Clarendon Press, 1983, p. 309. Pour ce qui est de la Charte québécoise, voir Jean-Maurice BRISSON, *Texte annoté de la Charte des droits et libertés de la personne du Québec*, Montréal, SOQUIJ, 1986.

internationaux susmentionnés que le respect de la dignité humaine est considéré comme une condition sine qua non de l'élaboration et de l'interprétation de tous les autres droits fondamentaux de l'homme. Peut-être, en raison de son caractère aussi fondamental et du fait qu'elle est la source de tous les droits de l'homme, n'a-t-on pas jugé nécessaire de garantir ou de restreindre la notion de dignité humaine[78]. Tous les droits de l'homme découlent du respect de cette dignité inhérente.

La doctrine confirme cette interprétation. En effet, les auteurs, définissant les principes fondamentaux du droit international relatif à la dignité humaine, affirment qu'il faut aborder la question dans une perspective reposant [TRADUCTION] « sur une conception de l'univers dont la clé de voûte est formée par la personnalité morale de l'être humain, par sa dignité et par ses droits[79] ».

En outre, contrairement aux autres règles juridiques de nature technique, les droits de l'homme, énoncés en termes généraux, tirent leur force de leur dimension éthique et morale. Ils constituent une sorte de point de rencontre des domaines juridique, éthique et politique, dont résulte une forme de droit naturel qui constitue le cadre principal de cette rencontre. La réalisation du concept de dignité humaine varie donc selon les besoins nationaux et culturels et selon les différences d'interprétation[80].

Finalement, la reconnaissance des droits de l'homme dans les constitutions nationales et internationales ne vise pas seulement à [TRADUCTION] « conférer une forme d'immunité individuelle par rapport aux autorités ou à obliger celles-ci à nous protéger contre les actions d'autres citoyens[81] » ou d'autres organisations de citoyens, mais aussi à [TRADUCTION] « favoriser la mise en place de certaines conditions concrètes permettant la jouissance effective des droits de l'homme[82]. »

Dans le domaine médical, l'Association médicale mondiale a adopté en 1949, au cours de sa troisième assemblée générale, un *Code International d'Éthique Médicale*[83]. L'Assemblée a conclu que l'un des devoirs impératifs du médecin est de prodiguer des

---

78. Il faut signaler, toutefois, qu'au par. 10(1) du *Pacte international relatif aux droits civils et politiques*, précité, note 75, le respect de la dignité inhérente à la personne humaine est expressément lié à la protection des personnes privées de leur liberté.

79. Myres S. McDOUGAL, Harold D. LASSWELL et Lung-Chu CHEN, *Human Rights and World Public Order: The Basic Policies of an International Law of Human Dignity*, New Haven (Conn.), Yale University Press, 1980, citant M. Muskowitz à la p. 373.

80. Mireille DELMAS-MARTY, « Un nouvel usage des droits de l'homme », dans *Éthique médicale et droits de l'homme*, Paris, Actes Sud/INSERM, 1988, p. 313.

81. B. ELMQUIST, « Genetic Engineering: Risks and Chances for Human Rights — Legal Aspects: Possibilities of New Legislative Steps at National and International Level », dans CONSEIL DE L'EUROPE, *op. cit.*, note 43, p. 203, à la page 207.

82. P. LEUPRECHT, intervention à l'audition parlementaire, CONSEIL DE L'EUROPE, *op. cit.*, note 43, p. 115. L'établissement de telles conditions concrètes est évident lorsqu'un État, par exemple, crée un poste d'ombudsman ou met sur pied des programmes d'action positive.

83. Reproduit dans « Medical Ethics Declarations » (1984), 31:3 *World Medical Journal* (voir la couverture arrière). Ce code s'inspire de la *Déclaration de Genève* de 1948. Il a été révisé au cours de la trente-cinquième assemblée de l'Association médicale mondiale, en 1983, à Venise.

services médicaux suffisants « avec compassion et dans le respect de la dignité humaine[84] ». La Déclaration de Lisbonne sur les droits du patient, adoptée en 1981, fait mention du droit de mourir dans la dignité[85]. Quant à la *Déclaration d'Helsinki* (révisée)[86] sur la recherche biomédicale touchant des sujets humains, elle ne fait pas expressément état d'un droit à la dignité ; mais, comme pour les directives postérieures plus précises du Conseil des organisations internationales des sciences médicales (CIOMS), adoptées en 1982[87], le fondement même des mesures de protection des sujets humains consiste dans la dignité inhérente à la personne humaine.

Selon les principes du droit international relatif aux droits de l'homme, la dignité humaine et le patrimoine génétique concernent le statut, la protection et l'accessibilité du matériel génétique humain ainsi que les usages qu'on peut en faire. Ces notions peuvent donc mettre en jeu le droit de disposer de soi-même, le droit de se marier et de fonder une famille, le droit à la vie, le droit à la santé, le droit de ne pas être soumis à des traitements inhumains et dégradants, le droit au respect de la vie privée et de la famille. Ces droits ont été interprétés d'une façon large, s'agissant du problème de l'avortement[88]. Mais comme on peut le constater dans le contexte des techniques de reproduction et dans celui de la protection du matériel génétique humain (gamètes et embryons, par exemple), le recours à la protection que confèrent ces droits, en droit international public, ne peut être qu'indirect, incomplet et vraisemblablement inadéquat[89]. De fait, comme nous allons le voir, certains des arguments invoqués par l'Assemblée parlementaire du Conseil de l'Europe témoignent de la nécessité de décrire avec précision les droits de l'homme touchant spécifiquement les techniques de reproduction et la génétique humaine[90].

---

84. *Ibid.* Voir les dispositions similaires de l'AMERICAN MEDICAL ASSOCIATION, *Principles of Ethics*, Chicago, L'Association, 1980.

85. Reproduite dans « WMA's Declarations and Statements » (1982), 29:6 *World Medical Journal* 91. La déclaration a été adoptée lors de la trente-quatrième assemblée mondiale de la santé, à Lisbonne, au Portugal, en 1981. Voir aussi ASSOCIATION MÉDICALE CANADIENNE, *Code de déontologie*, Ottawa, L'Association, 1990, art. 18.

86. Recommandations destinées à guider les médecins dans les recherches biomédicales, 1964 (modifiée à Tokyo en 1975 ; à Venise en 1983 et à Hong Kong en 1989), la déclaration est reproduite dans « L'Association médicale mondiale adopte une version révisée de la Déclaration d'Helsinki » (1990), 41:3 *Rec. int. Lég. sanit.* 579.

87. ORGANISATION MONDIALE DE LA SANTÉ et CONSEIL DES ORGANISATIONS INTERNATIONALES DES SCIENCES MÉDICALES, *Directives internationales proposées pour la recherche biomédicale impliquant des sujets humains*, Genève, CIOMS, 1982. Voir aussi CONSEIL DE RECHERCHES MÉDICALES DU CANADA, *Pour une éthique internationale en recherche sur des sujets humains*, Ottawa, Approvisionnements et Services Canada, 1988, p. 66, sur la nécessité d'intensifier la surveillance relative à la protection de la dignité et de la vie privée dans les recherches épidémiologiques.

88. Voir *infra*, note 129.

89. Voir Bartha M. KNOPPERS, « Reproductive Technology and International Mechanisms of Protection of the Human Person » (1987), 32 *R.D. McGill* 336, pp. 350-356 et la suite donnée à cet article par l'auteure dans « L'adoption d'un code de conduite international en matière de technologies de la reproduction », dans ASSOCIATION DE DROIT INTERNATIONAL, *Report of the Sixty-Third Conference*, Varsovie, Pologne, L'Association, 1988, p.879.

90. Voir *infra*, notes 103 à 108.

II. Droits relatifs au patrimoine génétique

La recommandation de 1982 de l'Assemblée parlementaire du Conseil de l'Europe constitue la première tentative pour situer la notion de dignité inhérente à la personne dans la perspective de l'ingénierie génétique humaine[91]. Elle énonce que « les droits à la vie et à la dignité humaine garantis par les articles 2 et 3 de la Convention européenne des droits de l'homme impliquent le droit d'hériter des caractéristiques génétiques n'ayant subi aucune manipulation[92] ». Pour éviter toute ambiguïté, l'Assemblée a recommandé que ce droit soit expressément énoncé dans le cadre de la Convention précitée[93].

Pendant les auditions parlementaires qui ont précédé la formulation de la recommandation, on s'est mis d'accord sur l'idée que tous les droits découlent de la dignité inhérente et contribuent à sa signification. Le rapport des auditions, sur ce point, est ainsi rédigé :

> [TRADUCTION]
> Parmi les droits fondamentaux de l'homme énoncés dans cette convention, priorité absolue est donnée aux droits à la vie (article 2) et à l'intégrité de la personne (article 3) ; ces droits, ainsi que les règlements prévus à la Convention et à son protocole signé à Paris, le 20 mars 1952, forment un concept très élaboré de la dignité humaine qui a inspiré aux États membres signataires de cet instrument international le respect de ces droits et la participation active à leur développement[94].

Les progrès considérables de la génétique humaine et de la technologie relative à l'ADN, ainsi que les applications envisageables, ont semble-t-il incité l'Assemblée à proposer, à la Recommandation 934, une description plus spécifique de la dignité en tant que droit de l'homme[95].

En 1986, l'Assemblée a adopté la Recommandation 1046 sur l'utilisation d'embryons et de fœtus humains à des fins diagnostiques, thérapeutiques, scientifiques, industrielles et commerciales. La recommandation — conforme à la plupart des

---

91. Recommandation 934, précitée, note 3, al. 4(i). Voir aussi, B.M. KNOPPERS, « Reproductive Technology », *loc. cit.*, note 89 ; bien que nous ne traitions pas du droit d'hériter des caractéristiques génétiques, nous avons soutenu que des textes internationaux ont reconnu le droit à la vie, à l'intégrité et à l'inviolabilité de la personne humaine. Voir aussi Bartha M. KNOPPERS et Claude M. LABERGE, « DNA Sampling and Informed Consent » (1989), 140:9 *Journal de l'Association médicale canadienne* 1023, où nous avons affirmé que l'avènement de la thérapie génique des lignées germinale et somatique ne change rien à la nécessité de protéger l'inviolabilité et de respecter l'intégrité de la personne en obtenant le consentement éclairé du sujet visé, avant la thérapie ou avant toute utilisation de matériel génétique. En fait, l'application des techniques de la biologie moléculaire en génétique humaine élargit l'objet du consentement éclairé nécessaire.

92. Recommandation 934, précitée, note 3, al. 4(i).

93. *Id.*, al. 4(ii).

94. Intervention par D. CUCCHIARA à l'audition parlementaire, CONSEIL DE L'EUROPE, *op. cit.*, note 43, p. 81.

95. Précitée, note 3.

rapports nationaux portant sur le respect des embryons humains[96] — énonce que les embryons et les fœtus humains doivent être traités avec le respect dû à la dignité humaine[97], quel que soit leur statut juridique. L'article premier affirme en outre la nécessité de reconnaître le « droit à un patrimoine génétique qui ne soit pas manipulé artificiellement, à l'exception de fins thérapeutiques[98] ». Finalement, l'Assemblée parlementaire a réitéré son appui aux propositions contenues dans les recommandations antérieures en adoptant, en 1989, la Recommandation 1100 sur l'utilisation des embryons et fœtus humains dans la recherche scientifique[99].

La Recommandation 1046 du Conseil de l'Europe précise qu'il est nécessaire d'interdire légalement les abus de l'ingénierie génétique humaine, notamment le clonage, le choix du sexe, la création de chimères, la fécondation entre espèces et d'autres manipulations génétiques non thérapeutiques[100]. Cette recommandation a reçu l'appui unanime des autres commissions gouvernementales européennes chargées d'étudier les questions soulevées par les techniques de reproduction et le génie génétique humain[101].

III. Effets des droits relatifs au patrimoine génétique

L'Assemblée parlementaire a confirmé, dans les recommandations qu'elle a formulées en 1989, ses propositions antérieures touchant le droit à un patrimoine génétique n'ayant subi aucune manipulation[102]. Au cours des auditions précédant l'adoption de la recommandation de 1981, les parlementaires ont précisé que ce droit appartiendrait [TRADUCTION] « aux générations futures[103] » et notamment, sans doute,

---

96. Voir B.M. KNOPPERS, *loc. cit.*, note 89.

97. Conseil de l'Europe, A.P., 38e sess., IIe partie, *Textes adoptés, Recommandation 1046 (1986) relative à l'utilisation d'embryons et fœtus humains à des fins diagnostiques, thérapeutiques, scientifiques, industrielles et commerciales.*

98. *Id.*, art. 1.

99. Conseil de l'Europe, A.P., 40e sess., IIIe partie, *Textes adoptés, Recommandation 1100 (1989) sur l'utilisation des embryons et fœtus humains dans la recherche scientifique.* L'article 2 est ainsi rédigé : « Se référant à la Recommandation 934 (1982) de l'Assemblée parlementaire du Conseil de l'Europe, qui demande que les applications du génie génétique se fassent dans le respect du patrimoine génétique de l'humanité sur lequel on ne pourra intervenir chez l'individu qu'à des fins préventives ou thérapeutiques établies de façon claire et scientifique ».

100. *Id.*, al. 14(iv).

101. Rapport Benda, *op. cit.*, note 39, p. 48 : « L'utilisation des méthodes qui viennent d'être décrites constitue une atteinte particulièrement grave à la dignité de l'être humain.
Résolution : Quelle que soit la méthode employée, le clonage d'êtres humains est inadmissible. L'est également la création de chimères et d'hybrides d'homme et d'animal. » Voir également *supra*, note 35 et *infra*, chapitre cinq.

102. Voir Recommandation 1100, précitée, note 99.

103. B. ELMQUIST, *loc cit.*, note 81, p. 208. C'est-à-dire les gamètes emmagasinées *ex utero* ou dans les gonades.

aux enfants déjà conçus mais non encore nés, aux embryons ou aux gamètes gardés in vitro ou stockés ou aux enfants non encore conçus ».

Qui pourrait s'adresser aux tribunaux pour faire valoir le droit de ces personnes non existantes à un patrimoine génétique inaltéré ? Selon le rapporteur, [TRADUCTION] « peut-être [cela revient-il] aux autorités et, en tout cas, aux personnes elles-mêmes, une fois qu'elles sont nées, si elles jugent qu'elles ont fait l'objet de manipulations génétiques illégales[104] ».

La recommandation sur l'ingénierie génétique formulée en 1982 par le Conseil de l'Europe reconnaît spécifiquement une exception à l'interdiction générale proposée à l'égard des manipulations génétiques visant les êtres humains. Cette exception consiste dans les interventions préventives ou thérapeutiques dont la nécessité est « établi[e] de façon claire et scientifique[105] ». Des précisions s'imposaient manifestement. La Recommandation 1046 de 1986 propose l'établissement d'un répertoire « des maladies pour lesquelles la thérapeutique dont il est fait état dispose de moyens diagnostiques fiables et présente de bonnes possibilités de succès. Cette liste des maladies devrait être renouvelée périodiquement en fonction de nouvelles connaissances et de nouveaux progrès scientifiques[106]. »

Le rédacteur du rapport de 1981 préalable à l'adoption de la Recommandation 934 a précisé que l'inclusion d'une maladie au répertoire susmentionné nécessiterait l'assentiment général[107]. Il a également déclaré qu'à l'égard des maladies inscrites au répertoire, [TRADUCTION] « la possibilité d'imposer un traitement de génie génétique autorisé devrait peut-être être envisagée [. . .] On pourrait aussi se contenter d'exiger que la personne concernée consente à un traitement de génie génétique pour être autorisée à avoir des enfants[108]. »

Les propositions comportent donc deux aspects : d'abord, empêcher les manipulations génétiques non souhaitables et ensuite, faire en sorte qu'on ne se livre à des manipulations génétiques que si la transmission de gènes susceptibles de causer une maladie grave résulterait de l'absence d'intervention.

Il importe incontestablement d'établir des limites légales afin de prévenir les abus possibles du génie génétique. C'est ce que vise la recommandation de l'Assemblée parlementaire préconisant l'interdiction de certaines formes d'expérimentation génétique à des fins non thérapeutiques[109]. Toutefois, assurer une telle protection en lui donnant

---

104. *Id.*, p. 209.

105. Recommandation 1100, précitée, note 99, art. 2. Cette recommandation a été approuvée dans la recommandation de 1986 relative à l'utilisation d'embryons et fœtus humains.

106. Précitée, note 97, Annexe B(iv).

107. B. ELMQUIST, *loc. cit.*, note 81. L'article 10 de la Recommandation 1046 renvoie à l'alinéa B (iv) de l'Annexe.

108. B. ELMQUIST, *loc. cit.*, note 81, p. 208.

109. Recommandation 1046, précitée, note 97.

la forme d'un « droit » de ne pas hériter certains gènes pourrait entraîner des conséquences effrayantes. L'adoption de l'interprétation proposée dans le rapport de 1981 pourrait donner lieu, entre autres, à des pressions scientifiques ou individuelles visant à inclure certaines maladies dans le répertoire ou à en exclure, au dépistage de l'incompatibilité génétique chez les couples, au traitement obligatoire des maladies inscrites au répertoire et à des poursuites contre des parents actuels ou potentiels. Quels types de maladies peuvent être jugées suffisamment sérieuses pour qu'il soit nécessaire de recourir au génie génétique ? Faut-il assujettir le « privilège » de procréer à l'acceptation de traitements offerts par le génie génétique ? Serait-il possible de poursuivre des parents ou l'État parce que, en s'abstenant de recourir au génie génétique, ils n'ont pas tenu compte de l'intérêt de l'enfant[110] ? Vu les rapports entre le droit d'hériter un génome inaltéré, la dignité inhérente à la personne humaine et la définition d'une forme de protection juridique, ces questions sont indissociables.

IV. Critique des droits génétiques

Actuellement, les choix préalables à la conception sont laissés aux couples, sous réserve de la réglementation établie par l'État et dans la mesure où l'information et les services médicaux sont accessibles[111]. On estime d'une manière générale que pendant la grossesse, le recours à l'avortement ou à des traitements médicaux de même que le choix du mode de vie relèvent du droit à la liberté et à la vie privée des femmes[112]. L'intérêt de l'État à la protection des « personnes potentielles » s'apprécie en regard de ces droits. Toutefois, lorsque le fœtus devient viable, cet intérêt se manifeste par la surveillance accrue de la mère et une plus grande protection de l'enfant à naître[113]. Enfin, dans les cas de fécondation in vitro, la question de l'intervention directe de l'État afin d'assurer la protection de l'embryon est encore objet de débat[114].

---

110. Cela pourrait sembler la conclusion logique du rapport de 1981 (CONSEIL DE L'EUROPE, *op. cit.*, note 43). Certains auteurs américains soutiennent également cette position, voir Margery W. SHAW, « Conditional Prospective Rights of the Fetus » (1984), 5 *J. Legal Med.* 63.

111. Bartha M. KNOPPERS, « Modern Birth Technologies and Human Rights » (1985), 33 *Am. J. Comp. Law* 1, B.M. KNOPPERS, *loc. cit.*, note 89 et *Conception artificielle et responsabilité médicale : une étude de droit comparé*, Cowansville (Qc), Yvon Blais, 1986.

112. Sanda RODGERS, « Fetal Rights and Maternal Rights: Is There a Conflict ? » (1986), *R.J.F.D.* 456 ; voir également le chapitre cinq.

113. S. RODGERS, *loc. cit.*, note 112. Voir également Jean-Louis BAUDOUIN et Catherine LABRUSSE-RIOU, *Produire l'homme : de quel droit ?*, Paris, P.U.F., 1987 et COMMISSION DE RÉFORME DU DROIT DU CANADA, *Les crimes contre le fœtus*, Document de travail n° 58, Ottawa, La Commission, 1989. Le droit privé protège aussi, indirectement, le fœtus. Ainsi, si des professionnels de la santé font preuve de négligence en ne divulguant pas aux parents les risques reproductifs qu'ils courent ou en les informant mal, ces derniers ou leur enfant né handicapé à cause de cela pourront intenter une action pour les préjudices causés aux parents ou à l'enfant. Voir *infra*, chapitre cinq et *supra*, note 111.

114. B.M. KNOPPERS, *loc. cit.*, note 89.

Bien que certaines formes d'expérimentation génétique non thérapeutique eussent été universellement condamnées[115], le droit à la dignité n'avait jamais été invoqué pour conclure à l'existence du droit à un patrimoine génétique inaltéré, avant l'établissement des Recommandations 934 et 1046 de l'Assemblée parlementaire. Compte tenu des interprétations auxquelles un tel droit peut donner naissance, il y a lieu de mettre en question son fondement ; une discussion et une analyse sérieuses s'imposent avant toute reconnaissance définitive.

Il importe également de considérer d'autres points avant de faire quelque nouvelle recommandation. Premièrement, la thérapie génique de la lignée somatique ou, éventuellement, de la lignée germinale, ne visera qu'un nombre relativement restreint de maladies, car elle n'est applicable qu'aux affections monogéniques dont le locus est connu. Or, la plupart des maladies sont imputables à plus d'un gène. Deuxièmement, lorsqu'une intervention directe devient possible, il se peut qu'elle prenne la forme d'une préfécondation, d'une préimplantation ou d'une sélection génétique *in utero* plutôt que d'une thérapie génique. C'est donc dans la diffusion, la communication et l'utilisation de l'information génétique, dans la liberté des choix de procréation ainsi que dans les mesures de protection souhaitables à l'égard de la mise en banque de l'ADN qu'il importera de respecter la dignité inhérente à la personne humaine et, à de rares occasions seulement, dans les manipulations génétiques elles-mêmes. Or dans tous ces domaines importants, des choix devront être exercés, à la lumière de l'information que suppose une décision éclairée. Il est donc nécessaire, pour assurer l'individualité de la personne et la continuité de l'espèce humaine, d'accorder une protection juridique à la liberté de choix génétique, car la dignité humaine repose sur le libre choix de chacun[116].

Enfin, le respect de la personne passe par le respect de la dignité humaine dans son substrat — le gène[117]. Il est possible de distinguer au sein de l'être humain les

---

115. *Supra*, notes 94 et 97. Voir J. DAUSSET « Éditorial : Les droits de l'Homme face à la science » (1989), 3:3 *Cahiers du M.U.R.S.*, à l'article X : [M.U.R.S. (Mouvement Universel de la Responsabilité Scientifique) propose un ajout à la *Déclaration universelle des droits de l'homme*] « Les connaissances scientifiques ne doivent être utilisées que pour servir la dignité, l'intégrité et le devenir de l'Homme. Nul ne peut en entraver l'acquisition. »

  Le M.U.R.S. propose aussi que l'Organisation des Nations Unies adopte les principes suivants :

  - toute source d'énergie ne doit être utilisée qu'au bénéfice de l'Homme sans atteinte à la biosphère,
  - le patrimoine génétique de l'homme, dans l'état actuel de nos connaissances, ne doit pas être modifié de façon héréditaire.*
  - le corps humain dans tous ses éléments, cellules, tissus et organes n'a pas de prix et ne peut donc être source de profit.

  * Ce qui n'exclut pas le traitement des maladies génétiques par modification du patrimoine génétique des cellules non reproductrices d'un malade.

116. Oscar SCHACHTER, « Human Dignity as a Normative Concept » (1983), 77 *Am. J. Int'l L.* 848.

117. CONGRÉGATION POUR LA DOCTRINE DE LA FOI, *op. cit.*, note 42, pp. 7-9.

dimensions organique, psychique et symbolique[118]. Ces dimensions du corps, de l'esprit et de l'âme supposent une nécessité de réciprocité et de partage, spécifique au genre humain, et cette indispensable réciprocité est à la base de la solidarité de tous les membres de la Famille de l'Homme. La personne humaine ne peut se concevoir sans cette triple dimension de la dignité, intemporelle et inestimable.

V. Conclusion

Nous avons vu, dans le contexte international, les risques d'une interprétation du concept de dignité humaine qui entraînerait la reconnaissance du « droit » à un patrimoine génétique inaltéré[119]. Cette interprétation, prétendument protectrice, mènerait à la sélection, par dépistage, des sujets aptes à procréer et, ultimement, à des poursuites judiciaires au sein des familles et entre les générations. Il faut aborder autrement la définition de la dignité comme principe fondamental des droits de l'homme dans le contexte de la génétique humaine. La dignité ne saurait se dissocier de l'individualité. Si nous tenons pour acquis que le gène humain, avec l'information qu'il renferme, n'est pas simplement le substrat de l'existence de la personne, alors la liberté de l'individu d'en contrôler l'expression pendant sa vie deviendra le principe essentiel de la dignité humaine.

Au Canada, les tribunaux n'ont pas étudié les implications du concept de dignité dans le contexte de la génétique humaine. Ils l'ont néanmoins interprété dans la perspective plus vaste des droits de la personne prévus par le droit constitutionnel canadien. L'examen de cette interprétation peut nous indiquer des directions nouvelles.

---

118. Jean-François MALHERBE, *Pour une éthique de la médecine*, Paris, Larousse, 1987 ; Mary WARNOCK, « Do Human Cells Have Rights ? » (1987), 1:1 *Bioethics* 1 ; Lucien SÈVE, *Recherche biomédicale et respect de la personne humaine : Explication d'une démarche*, Paris, La Documentation française, 1987. Voir également le chapitre six.

119. Pour une interprétation générale du droit international et des droits de l'homme en matière de procréation et de techniques de reproduction, voir B.M. KNOPPERS, *loc. cit.*, note 89.

CHAPITRE QUATRE

Dignité humaine et génétique : la *Charte canadienne des droits et libertés*

I. Introduction

Ainsi que nous l'avons mentionné, toute recommandation sur la politique de l'État en matière génétique peut avoir de profondes répercussions sur l'individu dans ce qu'il a de plus intime. Nul ne conteste qu'il faudra légiférer pour protéger la dignité inhérente et la valeur personnelle des êtres humains au regard de leur patrimoine génétique. Cependant, les lois ainsi adoptées devront être conformes à la *Charte canadienne des droits et libertés*. Quelle aide pouvons-nous tirer de l'économie de la Charte et des décisions de la Cour suprême du Canada touchant à la question qui nous occupe ? Commençons l'examen des incidences possibles de la Charte sur l'élaboration d'une politique législative future en analysant le champ d'application des dispositions de ce document constitutionnel.

La Charte permet de contester les lois ou les autres actions des autorités publiques portant atteinte aux droits qu'elle garantit. L'article 32 interdit tout acte inconstitutionnel de la part des gouvernements fédéral, provinciaux et territoriaux ou des instances gouvernementales. Autrement dit, la Charte protège les Canadiens contre toute atteinte des pouvoirs publics aux droits et libertés qui y sont énoncés[120]. Elle ne s'applique cependant pas aux organismes privés. Lorsqu'une personne allègue qu'une autre personne, une personne morale ou un employeur a violé ses droits, ce sont généralement les lois provinciales sur les droits de la personne qui s'appliquent.

Bien que la Charte canadienne n'en fasse pas expressément mention, le thème fondamental qui la sous-tend est celui de la dignité humaine. Or, la liberté de prendre des décisions constitue un élément important de cette dignité. Il s'ensuit que l'État a l'obligation de respecter les choix individuels[121].

Le thème de la dignité humaine s'exprime dans les droits et libertés garantis par la Charte. Nous en examinerons plusieurs : la liberté de conscience, de religion et d'association (article 2), le droit à la vie, à la liberté et à la sécurité de la personne et

---

120. *SDGMR* c. *Dolphin Delivery Ltd.*, [1986] 2 R.C.S. 573.

121. Luc HUPPÉ, « La dignité humaine comme fondement des droits et libertés garantis par la Charte » (1988), 48 *R. du B.* 724.

le droit à ce qu'il n'y soit porté atteinte qu'en conformité avec les principes de justice fondamentale (article 7), le droit à la protection contre les fouilles, les perquisitions ou les saisies abusives (article 8) et enfin, le droit à l'égalité devant la loi, à l'égalité de bénéfice et à la protection égale de la loi indépendamment de toute discrimination (article 15). Ces droits peuvent, dans le domaine de la génétique humaine, être invoqués à l'encontre de dispositions législatives fédérales ou provinciales, ou de politiques établies par des organismes publics.

Nous allons examiner brièvement, à la lumière de quelques arrêts de la Cour suprême du Canada, la portée attribuée à chacun de ces droits, pour voir ensuite, à l'aide d'exemples, comment ils pourraient être interprétés dans le domaine de la génétique humaine. Il faut signaler enfin que des dispositions législatives qui portent atteinte à un droit énoncé à la Charte peuvent tout de même résister à une contestation judiciaire si le tribunal y voit (pour reprendre les termes de l'article premier) une limite raisonnable dont la justification peut se démontrer dans le cadre d'une société libre et démocratique.

II. Liberté d'association, de conscience et de religion

La protection conférée à l'article 2 de la Charte s'applique notamment à la liberté d'association, de conscience et de religion. La Cour suprême a établi que la liberté d'association comprenait les « activités collectives qu'on pourrait qualifier de fondamentales dans notre culture et selon nos traditions et qui, d'un commun accord, méritent protection[122] ». Elle a également indiqué qu'une institution fondamentale comme celle du mariage « pourrait fort bien être protégée par la combinaison de la liberté d'association et d'autres droits et libertés[123] ». En conséquence, le fait de lier la délivrance d'un permis de mariage au statut génétique, dans le but de prévenir la transmission de maladies héréditaires, pourrait porter atteinte à cette protection.

La Cour a donné une interprétation large des libertés de conscience et de religion. Elle en décrit ainsi la portée :

> La liberté peut se caractériser essentiellement par l'absence de coercition ou de contrainte. Si une personne est astreinte par l'État ou par la volonté d'autrui à une conduite que, sans cela, elle n'aurait pas choisi d'adopter, cette personne n'agit pas de son propre gré et on ne peut pas dire qu'elle est vraiment libre. L'un des objectifs importants de la *Charte* est de protéger, dans des limites raisonnables, contre la coercition et la contrainte. La coercition comprend non seulement la contrainte flagrante exercée, par exemple, sous forme d'ordres directs d'agir ou de s'abstenir d'agir sous peine de sanction, mais également les formes indirectes de contrôle qui permettent de déterminer ou de restreindre les possibilités d'action d'autrui[124].

---

122. *Renvoi relatif à la Public Service Employee Relations Act (Alb.)*, [1987] 1 R.C.S. 313, p. 401.

123. *Id.*, p. 406.

124. Le juge en chef Dickson dans *R.* c. *Big M. Drug Mart Ltd.*, [1985] 1 R.C.S. 295, pp. 336-337.

D'autres décisions ont étendu cette liberté aux manifestations du mode de vie individuel choisi[125] et aux choix faits par les parents à l'égard de leurs enfants, dans le domaine de l'éducation par exemple[126].

La vaste liberté reconnue aux parents l'emporterait-elle sur des dispositions prescrivant des examens génétiques préalables à la procréation ? S'il y avait moyen de prédire avec certitude la naissance d'un enfant présentant de graves malformations, est-ce que des fidèles d'une religion donnée pourraient encore procréer librement en application des préceptes de leur foi ? Et en dehors du contexte religieux, pourrait-on faire valoir que toute restriction de la liberté de procréer dans l'institution du mariage enfreint le droit à la liberté d'association ?

III. Droit à la vie, à la liberté et à la sécurité de la personne

L'application de l'article 7 de la Charte se fait en deux temps. Il faut établir d'abord qu'il y a eu atteinte au droit « à la vie, à la liberté et à la sécurité de sa personne » et, ensuite, que cette atteinte est contraire aux principes de justice fondamentale. La Cour suprême a déclaré que les trois éléments distincts énumérés à l'article 7 — vie, liberté et sécurité de la personne — sont des droits indépendants qui doivent recevoir chacun leur propre signification[127]. Toutefois, le Parlement pourrait restreindre l'exercice de l'un ou l'autre d'entre eux, dans le respect des principes de justice fondamentale.

On peut difficilement imaginer de quelle façon le droit à la vie pourrait être invoqué dans le contexte de la génétique humaine. Il a été jugé que le droit de « chacun » à la vie ne s'appliquait pas au fœtus[128]. On voit donc mal comment le génome, les gamètes ou les embryons pourraient être protégés par le droit à la vie établi à l'article 7.

Le droit à la liberté ou le droit à la sécurité de la personne pourraient plus vraisemblablement fonder la contestation d'interventions gouvernementales dans le domaine de la génétique humaine. S'exprimant sur la portée du droit à la liberté, madame la juge Wilson, de la Cour suprême du Canada, a déclaré qu'il comprenait « [. . .] le droit de prendre des décisions personnelles fondamentales sans intervention de l'État[129]. » Les décisions relatives à la santé génétique d'une personne ou à celle de

125. *Attorney-General of British Columbia and Astaroff* (1983), 6 C.C.C. (3d) 498 (C.A. C.-B.).

126. *R.* c. *Jones*, [1986] 2 R.C.S. 284.

127. *Singh* c. *Ministre de l'Emploi et de l'Immigration*, [1985] 1 R.C.S. 177.

128. *Borowski* c. *Attorney General of Canada*, [1987] 4 W.W.R. 385 (C.A. Sask.). On trouve dans cet arrêt un excellent résumé du point de vue similaire adopté par les tribunaux de nombreux pays. Le 16 novembre 1989, la Cour suprême du Canada a jugé, dans *Tremblay* c. *Daigle*, [1989] 2 R.C.S. 530, que le fœtus n'était pas une personne aux yeux du droit civil du Québec.

129. *R.* c. *Morgentaler*, [1988] 1 R.C.S. 30, p. 166.

ses enfants seraient certainement considérées comme des décisions personnelles. Obliger les adultes ou les adolescents à se soumettre à des tests visant à déterminer s'ils sont porteurs de maladies génétiques enfreindrait donc incontestablement ce droit et porterait atteinte à la dignité de ces personnes, à leur respect de soi. Il y aurait contravention à l'article 7, parce que de telles dispositions « oblige[raie]nt une personne [. . .] à subir une procédure d'identification sous peine [d'une sanction], en cas de refus d'obtempérer[130] ».

Par ailleurs, y aurait-il violation du droit à la liberté des parents si l'État imposait l'examen de tous les nouveau-nés afin de détecter des désordres pour lesquels il existe un traitement[131] ? Puisqu'il existe une obligation de traiter lorsque cela est dans l'intérêt véritable de l'enfant[132], n'est-il pas obligatoire par le fait même de déterminer si un traitement est nécessaire ? Une loi pénale interdisant toute modification génétique thérapeutique, sur la lignée germinale ou sur la lignée somatique, constituerait-elle une atteinte à la liberté ? La réponse n'est pas claire.

Selon le juge en chef Dickson, le droit à la sécurité de la personne prévu à la Charte constitutionnalise le principe de l'inviolabilité de la personne humaine, suivant lequel le corps humain est protégé contre les atteintes d'autrui. Ce droit ne se limite pas au concept du pouvoir de décision sur son corps, il englobe également la protection contre « la stigmatisation de l'accusé, l'atteinte à la vie privée, la tension et l'angoisse résultant d'une multitude de facteurs, y compris éventuellement les perturbations de la vie familiale, sociale et professionnelle, les frais de justice[133] ». Ainsi, non seulement l'article 7 serait opposable à l'atteinte minime à l'intégrité corporelle que suppose le prélèvement obligatoire de sang ou de tissus corporels en vue d'analyses génétiques, mais il protégerait également l'intégrité psychologique de la personne[134]. Et dans le contexte de la génétique médicale, il peut constituer une garantie contre les atteintes injustifiées à l'autonomie et à la vie privée de la personne.

---

130. *R.* c. *Beare* ; *R.* c. *Higgins*, [1988] 2 R.C.S. 387, pp. 388-389, la Cour n'a pas remis en cause la décision de la Cour d'appel de la Saskatchewan, mais elle a jugé qu'aux termes de l'article 1, la prise des empreintes digitales des suspects constituait une atteinte justifiable, dans le contexte « criminel » particulier de l'affaire.

131. *Splicing Life*, *op. cit.* note 33, p. 66 et suiv. et *Screening and Counseling*, *op. cit.*, note 33.

132. Edward W. Keyserlingk, « Non-Treatment in the Best Interests of the Child: A Case Commentary of *Couture-Jacquet* v. *Montreal Children's Hospital* » (1987), 32 *R.D. McGill* 413.

133. *R.* c. *Morgentaler*, précité, note 129, p. 55, citation extraite des motifs du juge Lamer dans *Mills* c. *La Reine*, [1986] 1 R.C.S. 863. Voir également *Dion* c. *Procureur général du Canada*, [1986] D.L.Q. 353 (C.S.), p. 358 où l'on a jugé que le prélèvement aléatoire d'urine auprès de prisonniers afin d'identifier les utilisateurs de drogue contrevenait à l'article 7 (« Le droit à l'intimité, à la discrétion et au secret des actes de la vie privée est une composante du droit à la sécurité de la personne »). Bien qu'il puisse être difficile de justifier le recours aux analyses d'urine lorsqu'on n'a pas établi l'existence de motifs raisonnables, il est possible que les tests de sang ne soient pas considérés aussi abusifs puisqu'ils sont [Traduction] « sûrs, indolores et d'usage courant ». Georges J. Annas, « Crack, Symbolism, and the Constitution » (1989), 19:3 *Hast. Cent. Rep.* 35.

134. Dans *R.* c. *Morgentaler*, précité, note 129, le juge en chef Dickson a étudié la notion de stress psychologique imposé par l'État au regard de la sécurité de la personne, tandis que la juge Wilson l'a étudiée au regard de la liberté.

Le législateur, nous l'avons déjà mentionné, pourrait décider de restreindre les droits énoncés à l'article 7 pourvu qu'il le fasse d'une manière conforme aux principes de justice fondamentale[135]. Cette conformité s'apprécie en examinant la loi attaquée afin de déterminer si, concrètement, son application et son économie administrative et procédurale font qu'elle est si manifestement injuste qu'elle viole les principes de justice génétique[136]. Même si un tribunal conclut à la violation des droits prévus à l'article 7, il peut donc juger l'atteinte conforme aux principes de justice fondamentale.

C'est ce qui s'est passé dans une affaire où la Cour suprême a conclu que le fait d'obliger, sous peine d'emprisonnement, une personne à se soumettre à la prise de ses empreintes digitales contrevenait à l'article 7, tout en jugeant cette atteinte conforme aux principes de justice fondamentale[137]. Pour la Cour, une personne accusée, sur la foi de motifs raisonnables et probables, d'avoir commis un crime grave doit s'attendre, en raison de sa mise sous garde, à une atteinte importante à sa vie privée[138].

La jurisprudence relative aux empreintes digitales est applicable aux « empreintes génétiques d'ADN »[139], l'expression utilisée pour désigner l'analyse en laboratoire de l'ADN d'une personne. L'ADN de chaque personne est unique[140], c'est pourquoi l'analyse de cette substance (la prise d'empreintes génétiques d'ADN) peut, si le nombre de marqueurs examinés est suffisant et si les techniques sont correctement appliquées[141], permettre l'identification avec une certitude virtuellement absolue. On a

---

135. Les principes de justice fondamentale sont des « éléments essentiels d'un système d'administration de la justice fondé sur la foi en la dignité et la valeur de la personne humaine et en la primauté du droit » : *Renvoi relatif au par. 92(2) de la B.C. Motor Vehicle Act, R.S.B.C. 1979, chap. 288*, [1985] 2 R.C.S. 486, p. 512.

136. Voir *R.* c. *Jones*, précité, note 126.

137. *R.* c. *Beare* ; *R.* c. *Higgins*, précité, note 130. La Cour a conclu que la prise d'empreintes digitales ne constituait pas une forme de fouille, de perquisition ou de saisie abusive visée à l'article 8. Voir également Yves DE MONTIGNY, « La protection contre les fouilles, les perquisitions et les saisies abusives : un premier bilan » (1989), 49 *R. du B.* 53.

138. *R.* c. *Beare* ; *R.* c. *Higgins*, précité, note 130, p. 413.

139. Bien que la Cour suprême ne se soit pas prononcée sur l'identification génétique, il y a beaucoup de jurisprudence sur la prise d'empreintes digitales ; voir *R.* c. *Amway du Canada Ltée.*, [1986] 2 C.F. 312 (Div. 1re inst.), *R.* c. *Therrien* (1982), 67 C.C.C. (2d) 31 (C. comté Ont.) ; *R.* c. *Esposito* (1985), 24 C.C.C. (3d) 88 (C.A. Ont.) ; *Re Jamieson and The Queen* (1982), 70 C.C.C. (2d) 430 (C.S.Q.). Les tribunaux n'ont pas jugé que cette mesure violait le droit de ne pas être contraint de témoigner contre soi-même, garanti à l'alinéa 11*c*). Relativement aux empreintes génétiques d'ADN, voir également Gilles LÉTOURNEAU et André A. MORIN, « Technologie nouvelle et droit pénal » (1989), 49 *R. du B.* 821.

140. A.G. MOTULSKY, *loc. cit.*, note 13, p. 2855. La seule exception réside dans le cas des jumeaux identiques.

141. M.C. KING, « Genetic Testing of Identity and Relationship » (1989), 44:2 *Am. J. Hum. Genet.* 178 ; Roger LEWIN, « DNA Typing on the Witness Stand » (1989), 244:4908 *Science* 1033 ; Alun ANDERSON, « New Technique on Trial » (1989), 339:6224 *Nature* 408 et Alun ANDERSON, « Judge Backs Technique » (1989), 340:6235 *Nature* 582 (reconnaissance de la validité de l'utilisation de l'ADN dans l'expertise judiciaire). Il faut signaler toutefois que dans *State* c. *Castro*, 545 N.Y.S. 2d 985 (1989) (Bronx Cnty), la Cour n'a pas admis la preuve, car le laboratoire chargé de l'analyse ne s'était pas conformé aux normes scientifiques. La technique de la prise d'empreintes génétiques d'ADN est

eu recours à ces techniques pour disculper ou identifier des personnes soupçonnées d'avoir commis un crime. De petites quantités de sang ou de sperme, et même un seul cheveu, suffisent pour une identification positive[142].

À la lumière de la jurisprudence sur la prise d'empreintes digitales traditionnelles, il est permis de croire que l'utilisation des « empreintes génétiques d'ADN » pourrait être jugée conforme aux principes de justice fondamentale, mais seulement dans le contexte des affaires criminelles. Et même là, le recours à ces techniques — et l'admissibilité des résultats en preuve — serait assujetti à certaines limites. Premièrement, il faut établir la fiabilité des méthodes en cause[143], et deuxièmement, il faut déterminer si « leur utilisation est susceptible de déconsidérer l'administration de la justice », suivant les termes du paragraphe 24(2) de la Charte[144].

IV. Fouilles, perquisitions ou saisies abusives

L'article 8 de la Charte interdit les fouilles, perquisitions ou saisies abusives. La Cour suprême a jugé qu'il ne fallait pas confiner cette protection dans les étroites classifications légalistes, relevant de la notion de propriété, qui ont été élaborées dans le passé pour défendre cette valeur fondamentale[145]. Elle a décidé aussi que l'article 8 ne fait pas qu'interdire les fouilles, les perquisitions ou les saisies abusives, mais garantit aussi le droit à la protection contre de telles interventions[146]. Selon la Cour, la vie privée « est au cœur de [la notion de] liberté dans un État moderne », et sa protection constitutionnelle « revêt [. . .] une importance capitale sur le plan de l'ordre public[147] ».

---

maintenant utilisée au Canada. Voir Cristin SCHMITZ, « DNA Fingerprinting » (1989), 48:8 *Lawyers Weekly* 1. Voir également *R.* c. *Parent* (1989), 65 A.R. 307 (B.R.).

142. La conservation de ces données soulève des questions relevant des libertés publiques puisqu'il est théoriquement possible d'identifier tous les membres d'une population à partir d'échantillons prélevés pour d'autres fins, et que ces échantillons renferment des renseignements sur des prédispositions à certaines maladies. Voir Jean L. MARX, « DNA Fingerprinting Takes the Witness Stand » (1988), 240:4859 *Science* 1616. On a également eu recours à ces techniques pour établir la filiation dans des demandes de pension alimentaire ou d'immigration. Il faut signaler que la contestation de la prise d'empreintes digitales traditionnelles fondée sur l'al. 11*c*) de la Charte (le droit de ne pas être contraint de témoigner contre soi-même) a échoué. Voir *supra*, note 139.

143. Dans l'affaire *Castro*, précitée, note 141, le ministère public s'était appuyé sur des épreuves ne satisfaisant pas aux normes scientifiques, et cette preuve a été écartée.

144. Voir *R.* c. *Dyment*, [1988] 2 R.C.S. 417.

145. Voir *Hunter* c. *Southam Inc.*, [1984] 2 R.C.S. 145, p. 160. La décision établit que l'article 8 vise à « protéger les particuliers contre les intrusions injustifiées de l'État dans leur vie privée ».

146. *Ministre du Revenu national* c. *Kruger Inc.*, [1984] 2 C.F. 535 (C.A.).

147. *R.* c. *Dyment*, précité, note 144, p. 427 ; la Cour se réfère à Alan WESTIN, *Privacy and Freedom* :

> Fondée sur l'autonomie morale et physique de la personne, la notion de vie privée est essentielle à son bien-être. Ne serait-ce que pour cette raison, elle mériterait une protection constitutionnelle, mais elle revêt aussi une importance capitale sur le plan de l'ordre public.

C'est pourquoi la Cour a conclu que le prélèvement d'un échantillon du sang d'un patient inconscient constituait une atteinte à l'intégrité physique de celui-ci et un grave affront à la dignité humaine[148]. En outre, même lorsqu'il n'y a pas « fouille ou perquisition » au sens de prélèvement d'échantillons de sang ou de tissus, « l'utilisation du corps d'une personne, sans son consentement, en vue d'obtenir des renseignements à son sujet, constitue une atteinte à une sphère de la vie privée essentielle au maintien de sa dignité humaine[149] ». La Cour suprême a donc dit clairement que, même si le sujet consent au prélèvement de l'échantillon ou à l'examen, l'information recueillie ne devrait servir qu'aux fins médicales ayant fait l'objet du consentement. Elle a affirmé que « [c]ela est évidemment nécessaire si l'on considère la vulnérabilité de l'individu dans de telles circonstances. Il est forcé de divulguer les renseignements les plus intimes et d'autoriser les atteintes à son intégrité physique s'il veut protéger sa vie ou sa santé[150]. » La Cour est allée plus loin, déclarant qu'il faut une nécessité urgente ou l'autorisation préalable du patient pour prélever du sang ou d'autres substances corporelles à des fins secondaires[151]. Selon elle, la vie privée ne s'entend pas qu'au sens physique, et la saisie pratiquée en l'occurrence constituait une violation de la dignité humaine[152]. Cette décision, même si elle relève du domaine pénal, a des conséquences importantes sur la question qui nous occupe.

Les analyses génétiques ainsi que la mise en banque et l'utilisation de l'ADN et de l'information qu'il contient peuvent très bien se faire à l'insu du sujet — par exemple, lorsqu'il a consenti à un prélèvement de sang pour d'autres raisons. Cela pourrait constituer une violation de l'article 8 de la Charte.

L'exigence de l'autorisation préalable à toute utilisation de matériel ou d'information génétiques est une mesure importante pour assurer le respect de la dignité humaine dans le contexte médical[153]. Mais la difficulté provient du fait que, contrairement aux traitements et aux diagnostics médicaux ordinaires, les examens génétiques portent souvent sur toute la famille — et quelquefois sur les parents éloignés. Ils peuvent donc s'étendre sur une longue période et sur plusieurs générations. Afin de respecter le consentement initial, il faut par conséquent communiquer avec les membres de la famille du participant de départ et obtenir une autorisation pour l'utilisation des prélèvements à des fins autres que celles sur lesquelles le consentement

148. *R.* c. *Pohoretsky*, [1987] 1 R.C.S. 945. Dans cette affaire, un médecin, acquiesçant à la demande de la police, avait prélevé du sang d'un patient en état de délire.

149. *R.* c. *Dyment*, précité, note 144, pp. 431-432.

150. *Id.*, p. 433. La Cour a signalé également que « la confiance du public dans l'administration des services médicaux serait mise à rude épreuve si l'on devait autoriser la circulation libre et informelle de renseignements, et particulièrement de substances corporelles, des hôpitaux vers la police » (p. 439). Cette confiance est essentielle à la participation du public aux programmes de médecine préventive.

151. *Id.* pp. 430 et 436. Voir également *R.* c. *Légère* (1989), 5 W.C.B. (2d) 384 (C.A. N.-B.).

152. *R.* c. *Dyment*, précité, note 144, p. 439. La Cour s'est également inspirée d'un rapport de la COMMISSION DE RÉFORME DU DROIT DU CANADA, *Les techniques d'investigation policière et les droits de la personne*, Rapport n° 25, Ottawa, La Commission, 1985, p. 1.

153. Voir B.M. KNOPPERS et C.M. LABERGE, *loc. cit.*, note 91, p. 1024.

portait[154]. Nous verrons, dans les chapitres qui suivent, que le respect du choix et le maintien de « la confiance du public dans l'administration des services médicaux[155] » dépendent de l'élaboration d'un nouveau contrat social et de l'élaboration du concept de justice génétique.

V. Droits à l'égalité

Le dernier des droits garantis à la Charte qu'il est opportun d'examiner au regard du patrimoine génétique est le droit à l'égalité devant la loi et à la protection de la loi. Les motifs de discrimination interdits comprennent la race, l'origine nationale ou ethnique, la couleur, la religion, le sexe, l'âge et les déficiences mentales ou physiques. Qu'en est-il de la discrimination qui serait fondée sur le génome ?

La Cour suprême a inclus dans les droits consacrés à l'article 15 la protection contre tout effet discriminatoire de la loi[156]. Seraient ainsi jugées discriminatoires des distinctions qui, reposant sur les caractéristiques spécifiques de personnes ou de groupes, auraient pour effet de leur imposer des obligations ou des désavantages auxquels les autres ne seraient pas assujettis ou de leur refuser des avantages accordés aux autres. Certes, le fait de tenir une personne pour génétiquement différente et de la traiter en conséquence ne semble pas pouvoir, à première vue, être relié à un motif de discrimination interdit. Toutefois, la Cour a envisagé la possibilité d'élargir les catégories de minorités protégées en vertu de l'article 15[157] ; théoriquement donc, les personnes présentant un handicap ou une déficience génétiques pourraient former une de ces nouvelles catégories.

La Cour suprême a considéré que les motifs énumérés à l'article 15 visent des caractéristiques inhérentes aux individus, et non des traits qu'ils peuvent acquérir par choix — ou en raison de leurs mérites ou de leurs capacités. La Charte protégerait ainsi contre la discrimination fondée sur le génome, que celle-ci soit qualifiée de discrimination du fait de la race, de l'origine ethnique ou d'une déficience. Des dispositions législatives imposant des examens génétiques pourraient donc être considérées comme discriminatoires si, délibérément ou fortuitement, elles prévoyaient des mesures particulières à l'égard de groupes raciaux ou ethniques porteurs de certains

154. *Ibid.*, p. 1026.

155. *R.* c. *Dyment*, précité, note 144, p. 439.

156. Antérieurement à la décision *Andrews* c. *Law Society of British Columbia*, [1989] 1 R.C.S. 151, la plupart des causes portant sur le droit à l'égalité se résolvaient par l'application du critère de la « situation analogue ». D'autres se décidaient sur la base du critère de la « discrimination injuste ». La Cour a rejeté ces deux critères dans *Andrews*. Elle a jugé le premier sérieusement vicié en raison de son formalisme et du fait qu'il ne permettait pas de prendre en ligne de compte la nature de la règle de droit, et conclu que le second confondait les paragraphes (1) et (2) de l'article 15. Il était donc suffisant que le plaignant établisse l'existence d'une distinction discriminatoire entraînant « un préjudice ou un désavantage ».

157. *Ibid.*

traits génétiques. De la même façon, obliger les femmes enceintes à subir des examens génétiques pourrait aussi constituer une infraction à l'article 15. Toute intervention de l'État visant, au moyen d'un dépistage génétique, à déterminer l'admissibilité à un emploi[158] ou à d'autres avantages dans une industrie soumise à l'application de la Charte, ou encore à limiter le droit au mariage ou à la procréation, pourrait être considérée comme de la discrimination fondée sur des déficiences physiques ou mentales.

Toutefois, l'inclusion de la notion de handicap génétique dans la notion générale de handicap n'est sans doute pas souhaitable. En effet, on pourrait en conclure, du fait qu'il n'est pas toujours aisé de distinguer la « différence » et le « handicap », que le fait d'être génétiquement différent constitue une déficience. Il est préférable de considérer plutôt que tous les êtres humains sont égaux *parce que* chacun d'eux diffère génétiquement des autres. La différence génétique pourrait donc constituer l'assise d'un nouveau contrat social reposant sur cette égalité génétique[159].

VI. Limites raisonnables

Une éventuelle intervention législative touchant les examens génétiques serait-elle tenue pour raisonnable et justifiable dans le cadre d'une société libre et démocratique ? Des dispositions portant atteinte à un droit garanti par la Charte résisteront à une contestation constitutionnelle si cette atteinte se situe dans « des limites qui soient raisonnables et dont la justification puisse se démontrer dans le cadre d'une société libre et démocratique » (article premier). Il appartient à la législature concernée de faire cette démonstration[160].

Selon la Cour suprême, non seulement la justification des restrictions apportées aux droits garantis par la Charte doit pouvoir se démontrer, mais les moyens mis en œuvre doivent être raisonnables[161]. Il faut donc que l'objet de toute loi ou de toute disposition législative soit « suffisamment important [. . .] pour justifier la suppression

---

158. Edith F. CANTER, « Employment Discrimination Implications of Genetic Screening in the Workplace under Title VII and the Rehabilitation Act » (1984-1985), 10 *Am. J. L. Med.* 323. Voir également Karim BENYEKHLEF, « Réflexions sur la légalité des tests de dépistage de drogues dans l'emploi » (1988), 48 *R. du B.* 315.

159. Voir le chapitre six.

160. Cette preuve peut être tirée de données des sciences sociales, de rapports préparés par des commissions royales ou des comités parlementaires et de lois adoptées par d'autres sociétés libres et démocratiques ainsi qu'en font foi les traités de droit comparé et les pactes internationaux. La partie qui conteste la loi doit alors réfuter la preuve en démontrant qu'elle n'est [TRADUCTION] « ni décisive ni convaincante ou que la Couronne n'a pas fait la preuve des conséquences découlant de l'application ou de la non-application de la restriction ». Morris MANNING, « Proof of Facts in Constitutional Cases », dans Gérald-A. BEAUDOIN (dir.), *Causes invoquant la Charte 1986-1987*, Cowansville (Qc), Yvon Blais, 1987, p. 271, à la page 284.

161. *R.* c. *Oakes*, [1986] 1 R.C.S. 103.

d'un droit ou d'une liberté garantis par la Constitution[162] ». Le critère de la restriction raisonnable vise à garantir que les moyens législatifs sont proportionnés aux objectifs poursuivis[163]. Les moyens retenus doivent être rationnels, équitables et ne pas laisser place à l'arbitraire. Ils doivent porter le moins possible atteinte au droit ou à la liberté en cause, et l'effet de la restriction imposée ne doit pas être disproportionné avec l'objectif visé[164]. Finalement, la Cour a répété que parmi les valeurs d'une société libre et démocratique figurent « le respect de la dignité inhérente de l'être humain, la promotion de la justice et de l'égalité sociales, l'acceptation d'une grande diversité de croyances, le respect de chaque culture et de chaque groupe et la foi dans les institutions sociales et politiques qui favorisent la participation des particuliers et des groupes dans la société[165] ».

Il est douteux qu'une forme quelconque de dépistage ou d'examen génétique obligatoire puisse survivre à l'application du critère final que constitue l'article premier.

VII. Conclusion

La protection de la Charte connaît des limites quant à sa portée et à son application. L'interprétation que la Cour suprême a donnée des droits qui y sont énumérés donne à penser que la liberté de choix génétique peut être protégée en vertu des droits fondamentaux suivants : la liberté d'association, de conscience et de religion, le droit à la vie, à la liberté et à la sécurité de la personne, le droit à la protection contre les fouilles, les perquisitions et les saisies abusives et le droit à l'égalité. On pourrait trouver dans ces droits des outils puissants pour préserver la dignité inhérente à la personne dans le domaine de la génétique humaine.

Les généticiens, en s'imposant eux-mêmes des règles, ont pris des mesures en ce sens. Le dépistage n'est tenu pour acceptable que lorsque la maladie est grave et les résultats précis. Il faut de plus qu'une thérapie ou une intervention efficace soit possible et que le coût du dépistage soit proportionné aux gains visés[166]. Les garanties juridiques ou scientifiques générales évoquées au présent chapitre suffisent-elles, face à une génétique humaine en expansion qui permet de prédire de plus en plus de maladies touchant de plus en plus de gens ? Quelles maladies graves, identifiables et pour

---

162. *R.* c. *Big M. Drug Mart Ltd.*, précité, note 124, p. 352.

163. *R.* c. *Oakes*, précité, note 161, pp. 139-140.

164. *R.* c. *Edwards Books*, [1986] 2 R.C.S. 713.

165. *R.* c. Oakes, précité, note 161, p. 136.

166. NATIONAL ACADEMY OF SCIENCE, *Genetic Screening: Programs, Principles, and Research*, Washington (D.C.), U.S Government Printing Office, 1975, confirmé dans les rapports de la PRESIDENT'S COMMISSION, *op. cit.*, note 33. En 1976, l'*Academy*, compte tenu de l'état des connaissances, a conclu qu'il n'y avait pas de rapport entre les mesures obligatoires de santé publique applicables aux maladies contagieuses et celles qui visaient les maladies génétiques. Voir également Robert STEINBROOK, « In California, Voluntary Mass Prenatal Screening » (1986), 16:5 *Hast. Cent. Rep.* 5.

lesquelles il existe un traitement est-il possible de dépister de façon rentable sans porter atteinte aux droits et aux libertés constitutionnels[167] ?

Nous avons vu que la Charte offre sans doute la liberté de choix nécessaire à la protection du concept de dignité humaine qui sous-tend ses dispositions. Mais vu les préjugés sociaux actuels relatifs à la maladie, est-il possible de s'appuyer sur les droits généraux qui y sont énoncés pour assurer la protection de la liberté de choix génétique ?

Les nouvelles connaissances que nous tirons de la génétique nous imposent des choix difficiles. La capacité d'identifier des maladies pour lesquelles il n'existe encore aucune cure, l'application à de nouvelles maladies (par exemple la fibrose kystique) des tests de dépistage des porteurs, la mise en banque de l'ADN en vue de recherches futures (sur des individus non encore identifiés, pour des maladies encore indéterminées) et la détection, d'une rentabilité douteuse, de maladies rares vont obliger la communauté scientifique à réévaluer les critères traditionnels applicables au dépistage et aux examens médicaux[168]. Peut-être n'est-il pas possible, pour cette raison, de s'en remettre exclusivement aux droits fondamentaux décrits au présent chapitre. Il faudra sans doute se demander ce que, comme société, nous considérons comme génétiquement « normal », et voir ensuite s'il y a lieu d'élargir ou de restreindre l'intervention législative en matière de génétique médicale.

---

167. Actuellement, seul le dépistage de la phénylcétonurie et d'autres troubles du métabolisme, chez les nouveau-nés, satisfont à ces critères et il ne fait l'objet d'aucune sanction législative. Ce sont les règles générales de la common law relatives au consentement éclairé qui s'appliquent.

168. Kathleen NOLAN et Sara SWENSON, « New Tools, New Dilemmas: Genetic Frontiers » (1988), 18:5 *Hast. Cent. Rep.* 40. Les auteures soutiennent que les quatre critères traditionnels justifiant le dépistage (maladie grave, test précis, possibilité de traitement ou d'intervention utile, coût raisonnable) ne sont plus aussi clairement applicables dans le domaine de la génétique moderne. Voir Bartha M. KNOPPERS et Claude M. LABERGE, « Genetic Screening: From Newborns to DNA Typing », dans Bartha M. KNOPPERS et Claude M. LABERGE (dir.), *Genetic Screening: From Newborns to DNA Typing*, Amsterdam, Excerpta Medicine, 1990, p. 379.

CHAPITRE CINQ

« A-normalité » génétique

I. Introduction

Les choix sociaux peuvent être fonction de la conception que l'on se fait de la nature humaine — tout particulièrement dans le domaine de la génétique. Inversement, la façon dont on conçoit la génétique humaine peut influer sur l'idée que l'on se fait de la nature humaine et sur les choix sociaux envisageables. Si l'on considère que les gènes déterminent la personne, le fait de savoir qu'un individu est porteur de tel ou tel trait génétique prendra, aux yeux de certains, l'aspect de la fatalité. Dans ce cas, les choix possibles seront axés sur l'élimination ou sur la manipulation du gène, puisque le sujet et sa maladie sont tenus pour biologiquement déterminés. Si l'on perçoit la diversité aléatoire des caractéristiques génétiques comme naturelle, si l'on y voit comme l'essence de l'humanité, on pourra s'opposer à toute intervention génétique, quels qu'en soient les motifs. Par contre, si l'on estime que l'être humain est déterminé par des forces sociales, environnementales et historiques, on pourra utiliser le savoir tiré de la génétique pour combattre ces forces ou les canaliser en fonction de l'idéologie politique du moment.

Dans le présent chapitre, il sera question des notions de déterminisme, de naturalisme, de discrimination et de perfectionnisme génétiques. Nous allons également signaler certaines des incidences juridiques possibles des choix sociaux relatifs aux génomes « normaux » ou « sains ».

II. Déterminisme génétique

Les tenants du déterminisme biologique ou génétique croient que « tout comportement humain — et, par voie de conséquence, toute société humaine — est commandé par une chaîne de déterminations qui va du gène à l'individu et à la société (conçue comme la somme des comportements de tous les individus). Donc, pour les déterministes, la nature humaine est fixée par nos gènes[169]. » Le déterminisme génétique est, on le voit, une théorie réductionniste qui explique la nature humaine par sa biologie ou par ses gènes.

---

169. Richard C. LEWONTIN, Steven ROSE et Leon J. KAMIN, *Nous ne sommes pas programmés : Génétique, hérédité, idéologie*, Paris, La Découverte, 1985, p. 22.

Dans leur ouvrage intitulé *Nous ne sommes pas programmés*, R.C. Lewontin et ses collègues font l'historique de cette conception[170]. Le démantèlement de l'organisme vivant a commencé par la démonstration du fait que les lois physiques régissaient les choses animées aussi bien que les choses inanimées et l'hypothèse que les deux mondes étaient constitués de la même façon. Cette hypothèse, toutefois, ne laissait pas d'être paradoxale. S'il y avait similitude de constitution, il aurait dû être possible de créer la vie à partir de ses composantes inanimées. Or, Pasteur avait démontré que la vie ne pouvait surgir que de la vie.

Charles Darwin a proposé, dans ses travaux, une explication de l'émergence de la vie. Selon lui, la matière vivante a évolué, à travers les âges, par un processus de sélection naturelle agissant sur une surabondance de descendants présentant chacun divers degrés d'adaptabilité. La dimension temporelle de cette théorie a permis à Darwin de formuler l'hypothèse que la première étape du processus avait été la formation de la vie à partir de substances inanimées. Ainsi, la biologie matérialiste substituait la science à Dieu comme facteur de l'ordre social[171].

Cependant, la théorie darwinienne n'expliquait pas comment, au sein d'une population, se maintenaient les variations acquises sur lesquelles agissaient les forces de sélection. Mendel, par sa théorie du gène comme unité héréditaire, a répondu à la question, mais il a fallu attendre les travaux de Watson et de Crick qui, en 1950, ont élucidé le code génétique, pour que soit décrite la transmission d'information entre le gène et les produits cellulaires. On en est finalement arrivé à assimiler à une chaîne de montage la production de protéines par la cellule à partir de l'ARNm et de l'ADN, pour conclure que « l'organisme, après tout, n'est que le moyen pour l'ADN de faire une autre molécule d'ADN[172]. »

Peu après l'élaboration de la théorie de Darwin sur l'évolution, Galton tenta de réduire le comportement à des normes quantifiables et d'en attribuer l'origine à une hérédité ancestrale[173]. Sa thèse erronée voulant que la maladie mentale et la criminalité soient, en grande partie, déterminées biologiquement, a alimenté le mouvement eugénique qu'il avait fondé et qui fut à l'origine de politiques d'immigration restrictives, de programmes de stérilisation et, finalement, de l'extermination, par les Nazis, des personnes jugées indésirables.

Les horreurs de l'holocauste n'ont malheureusement pas sonné le glas du déterminisme génétique. La théorie a ressurgi, comme explication de phénomènes sociaux, avec la publication du traité d'Arthur Jensen sur le quotient intellectuel. Ce dernier y soutenait, selon une méthode dont on a depuis démontré les failles[174], que les

---

170. *Id.*, ch. 3.

171. *Id.*, pp. 68-69.

172. *Id.*, p. 77.

173. *Id.*, p. 75.

174. *Id.*, p. 146.

différences observées entre les races au chapitre du quotient intellectuel s'expliquaient en grande partie par des différences génétiques. Par la suite, la théorie sociobiologique de la nature humaine exposée dans les travaux de E.O. Wilson a attiré l'attention de la presse populaire. Cette théorie, dont on a critiqué les fondements de manière systématique[175], postulait que de nombreuses caractéristiques humaines comme le tribalisme, la xénophobie et l'altruisme se retrouvaient également chez l'animal. Wilson tentait de démontrer que ces comportements, à l'instar des caractères physiques, étaient le résultat des forces de l'évolution. Les caractéristiques sociales, telles que nous les connaissons, étaient donc sinon inévitables, du moins prévisibles.

Lewontin et ses collègues, par contre, ont défendu une vision large de la complexité des forces à l'œuvre dans la formation des individus et de la société, une vision qui donnerait un sens à la liberté :

> Ce qui caractérise le développement et les actions de l'homme, c'est qu'ils résultent d'un immense ensemble de causes qui interagissent et interfèrent. Nos actions ne sont pas aléatoires ou indépendantes par rapport à la totalité de ces causes comme système en interaction, car nous sommes des êtres matériels dans un monde causal. Mais dans la mesure où elles sont libres, nos actions sont indépendantes de ces multiples trajectoires causales (ou d'un ensemble d'entre elles, même petit) : telle est la signification précise de la liberté dans un monde causal.
>
> [. . .]
>
> Pour le déterminisme biologique, nous ne sommes pas libres parce que notre vie est contrainte par un nombre relativement petit de causes internes, les gènes qui amènent des comportements spécifiques ou la prédisposition à ces comportements. Mais cela passe à côté de l'essence même de la différence entre la biologie humaine et celle d'autres organismes. Nos cerveaux, nos mains, nos langues nous ont rendus indépendants de nombreuses caractéristiques du monde extérieur. Notre biologie a fait de nous des créatures qui recréent constamment leur propre environnement psychique et matériel, et dont la vie individuelle résulte d'une multiplicité extraordinaire de trajectoires causales qui se recoupent. En ce sens, c'est notre biologie qui nous rend libres[176].

Albert Jacquard s'est lui aussi élevé contre la conception réductionniste de l'homme, en cherchant, dans ses travaux, à établir la spécificité de l'être humain. Tout en reconnaissant l'interaction et l'influence réciproque des gènes et du milieu en général, il a fait intervenir une influence environnementale particulière, à savoir celle de la culture spécifique dans une société donnée. Cette influence culturelle peut agir au hasard ou même avoir des effets inconnus. Selon Jacquard, la dialectique de tous ces facteurs démontre la complexité génétique individuelle. C'est de cette complexité que procède la possibilité de passer de l'« animalité », fondée sur le déterminisme biologique, à l'« humanitude ». L'humanitude repose sur la foi en la contribution active de chaque personne à la constitution et à la complexité futures de la personne humaine,

---

175. *Id.*, ch. 9. Les auteurs réfutent la théorie de Wilson sous plusieurs rapports : description de la nature humaine, caractères retenus pour démontrer qu'elle procède d'une action des gènes, tentative d'établir que ces caractères sont le résultat des forces évolutives de la sélection naturelle.

176. *Id.*, p. 361. Voir aussi François JACOB, *La logique du vivant : une histoire de l'hérédité*, Paris, Gallimard, 1970 et *La statue intérieure*, Paris, Seuil, 1987.

individuellement et collectivement[177]. Ainsi, chaque être humain est un agent actif de la définition de ce que sont et de ce que seront l'être humain et la société. Le concept collectif de normalité influera à son tour sur l'action qu'exerce l'individu sur le savoir génétique.

En dépit des vigoureuses critiques dont il a été l'objet, le déterminisme biologique semble sous-tendre certains arguments avancés pour justifier les compressions budgétaires en matière d'aide sociale et d'éducation, étayer certaines politiques restrictives en matière d'immigration et faire obstacle à l'égalité dans l'emploi[178]. Selon cette théorie, en effet, la hiérarchie en place est naturelle et inévitable, puisqu'elle est l'expression de facteurs héréditaires intrinsèques. Raison de plus pour faire appel au système de justice et à l'ordre politique pour redresser les inégalités[179].

Ce survol rapide du déterminisme génétique, s'il ne prétend pas à l'exhaustivité philosophique, illustre du moins la relation qui existe entre la connaissance scientifique et la compréhension que nous avons des origines et de la nature humaines. Il fait également ressortir les possibles applications politiques des thèses du déterminisme biologique. Voilà autant d'éléments qui doivent être pris en considération dans la recherche de solutions aux problèmes soulevés par le progrès de la génétique humaine.

Un auteur fait remarquer, par exemple, que si les généticiens sont en mesure de comprendre que le milieu contribue tout autant que les gènes à l'expression, [TRADUCTION] « pour le commun des mortels, les gènes sont les émissaires du destin biologique[180] ». Il s'ensuit que [TRADUCTION] « les épreuves génétiques peuvent acquérir un statut trompeur dans l'arsenal médical, comme indicateurs d'un nouveau type de déterminisme biologique[181]. » Cela met en relief la nécessité pressante de faire de l'éducation dans ce domaine. La personne humaine n'est ni programmée ni programmable ; la composition génétique de tout être humain peut même être changée[182].

III. Naturalisme génétique

Selon les tenants du déterminisme génétique, personne ne peut changer sa condition sociale, celle-ci étant inscrite dans les gènes. Les naturalistes soutiennent,

---

177. Albert JACQUARD, *L'héritage de la liberté : de l'animalité à l'humanitude*, Paris, Seuil, 1986, pp. 178-179.

178. R.C. LEWONTIN, S. ROSE et L.J. KAMIN, *op. cit.*, note 169.

179. *Ibid.*

180. M. LAPPÉ, *loc. cit.*, note 7, p. 8.

181. *Id.*, p. 10.

182. David SUZUKI et Peter KNUDTSON, *Genethics: The Ethics of Engineering Life*, Toronto, Stoddart, 1988.

eux, que la constitution génétique est naturelle, que ce fait détermine le genre humain ; et qu'il faut, partant, éviter toute intervention sur le matériel génétique.

On retrouve cette conception naturaliste dans le rapport présenté par une commission d'enquête au *Bundestag* de la République fédérale d'Allemagne[183]. Les auteurs y affirment : [TRADUCTION] « l'essence de l'humanité repose sur le développement naturel [. . .] La dignité des êtres humains réside essentiellement dans le fait qu'ils sont nés et dans le caractère naturel de leurs origines[184] ». Pour eux, l'un des éléments primordiaux de ce caractère naturel provient du fait que l'homme est un [TRADUCTION] « produit du hasard », ce qui [TRADUCTION] « garantit l'indépendance de chacun vis-à-vis des autres ». Toute manipulation qui porte atteinte à la loi du hasard serait ainsi [TRADUCTION] « incompatible avec l'essence de l'être libre[185]. » Cette conception a amené la commission allemande à recommander l'interdiction de toute technique génétique qui toucherait la lignée germinale humaine.

Cet aspect du rapport, notamment, a fait l'objet de critiques sévères de la part de Hans-Martin Sass[186]. Il soutient que, loin d'être des « produits du hasard », nous infléchissons le cours de nos vies de bien des façons, sur les plans social et culturel. D'autres auteurs ont convenu que cette conception tenait le hasard pour la seule cause de notre unicité, ce qui rendait son immuabilité et son intangibilité dignes d'être protégées. Cette crainte de la suppression de l'action du hasard et de la disparition de l'authenticité de la personne humaine repose sur la perception erronée voulant que, fondamentalement, nous ne soyons rien de plus que notre matériel génétique[187]. Autrement dit, le naturalisme génétique, comme le déterminisme génétique, exprime une conception réductionniste de l'humanité.

Boone fait valoir que la notion de caractère naturel [TRADUCTION] « devrait procéder d'une conception humaine de la nature et non d'une définition naturaliste de ce qui est humain[188] ». Sass, pour sa part, affirme que même lorsqu'on souscrit à une vision naturaliste de la nature humaine, on peut se poser cette question : [TRADUCTION] « les humains sont-ils naturellement des êtres biologiques, ou des êtres transformateurs », autrement dit, qu'est-ce qui leur est naturel, protéger leur nature ou agir sur elle[189] ? [TRADUCTION] « La question n'est pas de savoir si la dignité humaine permet ou non les manipulations de la lignée germinale, mais de déterminer les formes de

---

183. ENQUETE COMMISSION, *op. cit.*, note 39. Voir également CONSEIL D'ÉTAT, *op. cit.*, note 37 ; B. EDELMAN et M.A. HERMITTE (dir.), *op. cit.*, note 52 ; COMMISSION D'EXPERTS, *op. cit.*, note 38.

184. ENQUETE COMMISSION, *op. cit.*, note 39, p. 257.

185. *Ibid.*

186. *Loc. cit.*, note 39.

187. Wolfgang SCHIRMACHER, « *Homo Generator*: The Challenge of Gene Technology », dans Paul T. DURBIN (dir.), *Technology and Responsibility*, Dordrecht, D. Reidel, 1987, p. 203.

188. *Loc. cit.*, note 2, p. 11.

189. *Loc. cit.*, note 39, p. 270.

manipulations de la lignée germinale (ou, à vrai dire, de toute autre manipulation) qui sont moralement acceptables et celles qui ne le sont pas[190] ».

Il y a donc deux problèmes à examiner. Le premier est celui de la nature de l'humanité et de la dignité humaine ; le second, celui des changements susceptibles d'être moralement acceptables à partir du moment où l'humain n'est pas considéré comme un être biologique naturel et inaltérable.

Le droit international et la *Charte canadienne des droits et libertés* reposent sur le concept de dignité humaine[191], qui n'a jamais été véritablement défini, mais seulement interprété. Or, [TRADUCTION] « si nous n'avons pas une idée raisonnablement claire de ce que signifie ce concept, nous ne pourrons facilement réfuter les utilisations spécieuses qui en sont faites[192] ». Sass estime que [TRADUCTION] « la signification concrète de la dignité humaine doit être analysée et jaugée dans le cadre de discussions d'ordre moral et de débats publics, par des citoyens instruits, en leur qualité de premiers agents moraux, par des organismes professionnels et aussi par les autorités législatives ou réglementaires, mais elle ne peut être prédéterminée [. . .] par référence à d'obscurs concepts de droit naturel[193] ».

Le respect de la dignité de l'homme a toujours fait partie du nombre restreint des droits absolus[194], et l'on a toujours vu dans l'affirmation et la proclamation des droits de la personne eux-mêmes le refus de se soumettre aux interprétations que l'humanité pouvait faire des lois de la nature[195]. Il serait, en conséquence, paradoxal de restreindre le respect de la dignité à une conception biologique naturaliste de la personne humaine[196].

Dans le cas où la thèse du naturalisme génétique serait rejetée, il nous faudra décider, en deuxième lieu, quand il est moralement permis de procéder à des interventions. La conception naturaliste écarte les effrayants scénarios d'interventions immorales : elle interdit carrément toute action médicale touchant les gènes. Pourtant, la question [TRADUCTION] « n'est pas de savoir si nous devons ou non modifier le code génétique humain, mais bien de savoir si nous le faisons d'une manière pleinement consciente[197] ». Devant le défi que pose la nouvelle génétique, un auteur propose

---

190. *Id.*, p. 269.

191. Voir les chapitres trois et quatre.

192. SCHACHTER, *loc. cit.*, note 116, p. 849.

193. *Loc. cit.*, note 39, p. 272.

194. Mireille DELMAS-MARTY, « Droits de l'homme et conditions de validité d'un droit de l'expérimentation humaine », p. 155 et Patrick VERSPIEREN, « Le respect de la dignité humaine », dans FONDATION MARANGOPOULOS POUR LES DROITS DE L'HOMME, *Expérimentation biomédicale et Droits de l'Homme*, Paris, P.U.F., 1988, p. 147.

195. M. DELMAS-MARTY, *loc. cit.*, note 194, p. 155.

196. C.M. LABERGE, *loc. cit.*, note 9, p. 231.

197. W. SCHIRMACHER, *loc. cit.*, note 187, p. 214.

l'établissement du principe de [TRADUCTION] « l'imagination morale » ; il s'agirait, pour décider de ce qui est acceptable dans le domaine scientifique, de tenter de prévoir les conséquences de nos actes[198].

IV. Discrimination génétique

La discrimination fondée sur le génotype peut être conçue comme un moyen, soit d'orienter la prise de décisions personnelles, soit d'imposer des décisions prises par autrui[199]. Nous examinerons trois domaines où des personnes peuvent faire l'objet de mesures discriminatoires à la suite d'un dépistage génétique : le travail, l'assurance et la procréation.

A. Dépistage dans le milieu de travail

Le dépistage génétique dans le milieu de travail vise notamment à identifier la cause de certains problèmes médicaux (pour déterminer, par exemple, s'ils sont d'origine génétique ou environnementale) et à prévenir la maladie en décelant une prédisposition génétique. En cela, il peut s'avérer aussi bénéfique pour l'employé que pour l'employeur. En effet, l'information génétique, vu son caractère individuel, peut fournir à l'employé (ou au candidat) des renseignements qui lui permettront de faire des choix salutaires quant à son emploi, à son milieu et à son mode de vie. À l'employeur, elle donne le pouvoir d'exclure ou de surveiller le sujet ; cependant, ces connaissances lui imposent en même temps une responsabilité accrue à l'égard de la santé et de la sécurité de l'employé[200].

Le dépistage génétique peut être légitime s'il a directement rapport aux qualités reliées au travail ou s'il est nécessaire à la sécurité de l'employé. Toutefois, on pourrait faire valoir qu'il ne devrait y avoir refus d'embauche ou congédiement qu'en fonction des aptitudes actuelles de l'employé et non en fonction d'une invalidité future prévisible[201].

Étant entendu que l'employé devrait avoir accès à tout renseignement le concernant, le dépistage en milieu de travail soulève par ailleurs un problème particulier

---

198. Daniel CALLAHAN, « Ethical Responsibility in Science in the Face of Uncertain Consequences » (1976), 265 *Annals N.Y. Acad. Sci.* 1.

199. D. SUZUKI et E.P. KNUDTSON, *op. cit.*, note 182, ch. 7, p. 160.

200. Voir Bartha M. KNOPPERS, « Genetic Screening and Genetic Information in the Workplace » (Allocution prononcée devant l'American Society of Human Genetics, octobre 1986) [non publié].

201. *Ibid.* L'auteure soutient que les employeurs devraient pouvoir exiger le dépistage génétique seulement lorsqu'il permet de mesurer effectivement la probabilité d'un risque de maladie afin de déterminer s'il y a lieu de retenir le candidat.

de confidentialité médicale. L'employeur dispose en effet d'informations qui normalement relèvent du secret professionnel du médecin. On peut en particulier s'inquiéter des possibilités de manquement aux règles de la confidentialité lorsqu'il y a informatisation des renseignements personnels[202].

En 1982, l'*Office of Technology Assessment* des États-Unis a effectué une enquête nationale sur le dépistage génétique en milieu de travail. Le rapport a révélé que ces examens, auxquels avaient recours nombre d'employeurs, pouvaient reposer sur des assises scientifiques douteuses[203] ; c'était le cas, par exemple, pour les épreuves visant à détecter l'anémie drépanocytaire[204]. Cette forme d'anémie est une maladie autosomique récessive potentiellement mortelle qui se retrouve fréquemment dans la population noire. Les porteurs d'un seul des deux allèles mutants sont dits porteurs du trait drépanocytaire. Même s'il n'existait alors, pas plus qu'aujourd'hui du reste, aucune preuve que la présence de ce trait nuise au rendement professionnel, les employeurs ont souvent fait passer le test aux Noirs et leur ont souvent refusé des emplois en cas de résultat positif.

On peut se demander si la protection de la Charte canadienne[205] ou des lois provinciales sur les droits de la personne[206] contre la discrimination fondée sur les déficiences mentales ou physiques serait assez large pour embrasser la discrimination génétique.

En attendant que l'éducation génétique se fasse à tous les niveaux de la société, l'équilibre à établir entre la sécurité au travail, les droits individuels et les coûts assumés par les employeurs ou par l'État en matière de santé est une opération délicate. Dans l'état actuel des choses, il est peut-être nécessaire que le législateur interdise spécifiquement toute discrimination génétique[207].

B. Examens exigés par les assureurs

La question des examens génétiques préalables à l'établissement d'une police d'assurance soulève des préoccupations similaires. Le régime canadien d'assurance-maladie, assumant l'universalité des frais médicaux, offre aux Canadiens une protection

---

202. *Ibid.* Voir particulièrement Thomas H. MURRAY, « Warning: Screening Workers for Genetic Risk » (1983), 13:1 *Hast. Cent. Rep.* 5.

203. OTA, *The role of Genetic Testing in the Prevention of Occupational Disease*, Washington (D.C.), OTA, 1983. L'OTA est à mettre cette évaluation à jour.

204. Voir également Daniel J. KEVLES, *In the Name of Eugenics: Genetics and the Uses of Human Heredity*, New York, Alfred A. Knopf, 1985, pp. 257 et 278. L'auteur a démontré que les examens volontaires, subventionnés par le Congrès, pour la détection de la maladie de Tay-Sachs chez les juifs ashkénazes, ont connu beaucoup plus de succès et ont été beaucoup moins stigmatisants que le dépistage obligatoire de l'anémie drépanocytaire.

205. Précitée, note 6, art. 15. Voir *supra*, chapitre quatre.

206. Par exemple, la *Charte des droits et libertés de la personne*, précitée, note 76, art. 10.

207. Voir le rapport du CONSEIL DES SCIENCES DU CANADA, *op. cit.* note 34.

plus grande que celle dont jouissent les Américains[208]. À l'égard des polices d'assurance-invalidité ou d'assurance-vie privées et des régimes financés par les employeurs, le Canada est néanmoins aux prises avec les mêmes problèmes que les États-Unis concernant la catégorisation des personnes « à risque ». Il est possible d'établir un parallèle avec la politique des assureurs vis-à-vis la séropositivité au VIH, suivant laquelle on demande de plus fortes primes aux personnes présentant un risque élevé, ou même on leur refuse toute couverture. Habituellement, les examens requis par la compagnie d'assurances, contrairement au dépistage en milieu de travail, ne sont pas directement utiles aux proposants, qui pourraient tout aussi bien apprendre de leur médecin ce qu'ils révèlent, sans encourir les conséquences susmentionnées[209].

Pour établir une police individuelle, la compagnie d'assurance doit être au courant de renseignements délicats concernant la santé d'une personne. Cependant, le législateur devra tenir compte, dans l'élaboration de sa politique en ce domaine, de la fiabilité et de la validité des tests et de l'injustice que représente l'exclusion discriminatoire des personnes présentant un risque élevé de maladie[210]. Certes, la nature même de l'assurance privée légitime la discrimination. Il serait tout de même possible d'offrir une couverture minimale à tous et d'éviter les problèmes de discrimination en émettant des polices d'assurance-vie ou d'assurance-invalidité de base sans examen. Toute protection supplémentaire pourrait alors dépendre du consentement du candidat à subir des examens génétiques.

C. Dépistage et procréation

Le droit et la religion ont toujours imposé certaines restrictions aux mariages consanguins. Cependant, la loi ne fait pas du dépistage génétique une condition au mariage[211]. À l'exception du test sanguin établissant la compatibilité des rhésus, les médecins ne recommandent pas, en général, d'autres tests de dépistage génétique aux

---

208. OTA, *Medical Testing and Health Insurance*, Washington (D.C.), OTA, 1988. À la page 7 de ce rapport récent, on apprend qu'aux États-Unis, 20 % de particuliers et 15 % de membres de groupes ont dû acquitter des primes plus élevées pour leur police d'assurance parce que le risque était jugé supérieur à la normale ; 8 % des demandes personnelles et 10 % des demandes collectives émanant de petits groupes ont été rejetées, le risque étant jugé non assurable.

209. L.D. JONES, « The Use of Genetic Information in Evaluating Insurability » (Allocution présentée devant l'American Society of Human Genetics, octobre 1986) [non publié].

210. B.M. KNOPPERS, *loc. cit.*, note 200.

211. Quatre États américains imposent le dépistage génétique avant le mariage. Voir L.B. ANDREWS, *op. cit.*, note 8, p. 233. Par ailleurs, certains pays ou États font subir les analyses sanguines habituelles (rhésus, toxoplasmose ou titre d'anticorps rubéoleux, maladies infectieuses, etc.) avant de délivrer un permis, ce qui est bien différent.

futurs époux[212]. Toutefois, avec le développement et l'expansion des études axées sur la liaison génétique familiale et avec la sensibilisation du public, on verra plus fréquemment les gens se soumettre volontairement à des tests de dépistage génétique avant de se marier ou d'avoir un enfant. Il n'en reste pas moins que l'État devrait, dans ce domaine, être tenu de justifier tout dépistage obligatoire, même si celui-ci vise des populations présentant un risque élevé d'affection génétique précise[213] : les décisions touchant le mariage ou la procréation sont extrêmement personnelles.

Dans le troisième chapitre, nous avons discuté la proposition de l'Assemblée parlementaire du Conseil de l'Europe visant à consacrer légalement le droit à un patrimoine génétique inaltéré. On pourrait considérer comme « altéré » un génome susceptible de causer une maladie inscrite dans une liste de maladies graves. Il a été proposé de n'autoriser les personnes dont le génome est ainsi « altéré » à procréer que si elles acceptent de subir une intervention relevant du génie génétique[214]. Sur le plan de la politique sanitaire, il serait plus efficace et moins attentatoire aux droits individuels d'offrir des examens génétiques et de les rendre accessibles à tous. Les porteurs demeureraient ainsi libres de leurs choix face à des risques identifiés, c'est-à-dire libres de décider s'ils se marieront, s'ils auront des enfants et s'ils auront recours aux tests prénatals possibles.

Dans le domaine des techniques de reproduction, on conseille aux médecins de proposer le recours à des donneurs de gamètes ou d'embryons aux couples présentant un risque génétique, ou de suivre les personnes à risque génétique (ou leurs enfants)[215]. Du reste, le risque de transmission de maladies génétiques graves constitue l'un des critères généralement acceptés pour le recours aux techniques de reproduction[216]. Les progrès de la science et la possibilité de sélectionner des gamètes et des embryons « sains » nous rapprocheront-ils encore plus de la poursuite de la perfection génétique ?

---

212. Voir toutefois la loi récemment adoptée par l'Illinois (*Loi publique 86-884 (Lois de 1989) relative aux maladies sexuellement transmissibles et aux maladies métaboliques héréditaires et modifiant les lois citées*, approuvée le 11 septembre 1989, citée dans (1990), 41:1 *Rec. int. Lég. sanit.* 51). En vertu de l'article 204, le secrétaire d'administration délivre à toutes les personnes sollicitant une dispense de bans une brochure sur les maladies sexuellement transmissibles et les maladies métaboliques héréditaires.

213. En raison de la fréquence élevée de la thalassémie à Chypre, l'Église orthodoxe grecque a exigé de tous les futurs mariés qu'ils subissent un examen pour établir s'ils en sont porteurs (communication personnelle avec Mme Nafsika Kronidou, Conseil de l'Europe, Chypre, 1989).

214. *Supra*, note 89 et suiv. et le texte auquel elles renvoient. Voir également D.J. KEVLES, *op. cit.*, note 204, p. 277, où l'on trouve cette citation de Paul Ramsey : [TRADUCTION] « La liberté de donner naissance est la liberté de le faire avec discernement et non celle de produire des êtres gravement déficients qui auront à porter leur propre fardeau ». Kevles mentionne aussi que le Barreau de Chicago approuve le dépistage et la thérapie génétiques obligatoires avant le mariage, lorsqu'ils sont accessibles.

215. Bartha M. KNOPPERS, « L'arbitrage du médecin face aux normes régissant la fécondation "in vitro" », dans Christian BYK (dir.), *Procréation artificielle : Où en sont l'éthique et le droit ?*, Lyon, Lacassagne, 1989, p. 49.

216. *Ibid.*

V. Perfectionnisme génétique

L'appréhension la plus commune est la crainte de la poursuite de la perfection génétique[217]. Nous avons déjà évoqué la politique de génocide appuyée sur le souci de garantir la « pureté de la race[218] ». La fausse corrélation entre race ou nation et fondements génétiques a connu son apogée avec les politiques nazies, pendant la Seconde Guerre mondiale. On aurait pu espérer que la fin de la guerre eût sonné le glas de l'idéal eugénique, vu les liens entre celui-ci et l'holocauste.

Pourtant, sept États américains ont adopté, pendant les années 1970, des lois imposant aux Noirs des tests de dépistage du trait drépanocytaire. Au moins cinq d'entre eux refusaient tout permis de mariage à ceux qui n'obtempéraient pas[219]. Dix ans plus tard, une banque de sperme était créée en Californie pour offrir des gamètes de qualité « supérieure[220] ». En outre, tant au Canada qu'aux États-Unis, il a fallu attendre les années 1970 pour que le législateur abroge certaines lois portant stérilisation obligatoire des personnes ayant des troubles mentaux[221].

Les États camouflent souvent leur politique eugénique en invoquant le bien commun, la rentabilité économique ou la santé publique. Et avec, d'une part la possibilité de recourir à l'amniocentèse pour le diagnostic prénatal de maladies comme le syndrome de Down, d'autre part l'inclusion de dispositions eugéniques dans les lois de certains pays concernant l'avortement[222], la détermination de ce qui est « normal » revêt un caractère davantage individuel. La science permettant de détecter, avant la naissance, de plus en plus de maladies (pas nécessairement graves), les décisions relatives à la procréation risquent de faire l'objet de pressions sociales plus appuyées, ce qui pourrait freiner la recherche d'une thérapie appropriée[223] ou l'amélioration de la condition sociale des individus [TRADUCTION] « non parfaits sur le plan génétique ». Faut-il intervenir dans ces choix ? Dans l'affirmative, qui doit le faire ?

---

217. K. BOONE, *loc. cit.*, note 2 ; voir également M. LAPPÉ, *loc. cit.*, note 7 et J. FRÉZAL, « Les problèmes éthiques en génétique humaine » (1985), 104 *Louvain Medical* 38.

218. Voir également Raphaël LEMKIN, *Axis Rule in Occupied Europe*, Washington (D.C.), Carnegie Endowment for International Peace, 1944, ch. 9 « Genocide », p. 79. Lemkin a créé le mot « génocide » dans cet ouvrage fondamental et a lutté sans répit pour que les Nations Unies reconnaissent le concept et pour qu'il soit ratifié par plus de cent nations (*Convention pour la prévention et la répression du crime de génocide* (1948), 78 R.T.N.U. 27).

219. Voir N.A. HOLTZMAN, *op. cit.*, note 8, p. 219.

220. Voir D.J. KEVLES, *op. cit.*, note 204. Voir également Gwen TERRENOIRE, « Conseil génétique et eugénisme : le passé du conseil génétique aux États-Unis » (1986), 11 *Cahiers Science, technologie et société* (Éthique et biologie), Paris, Éd. du C.N.R.S. 171.

221. Voir, par exemple, *The Sexual Sterilization Act*, S.A. 1928, ch. 37 et le *Sexual Sterilization Act*, S.B.C. 1933, ch. 59, abrogés au début des années 1970.

222. Voir *Les crimes contre le fœtus*, *op. cit.*, note 113, p. 69.

223. M. LAPPÉ, *loc. cit.*, note 7, p. 9. Voir également N.A. HOLTZMAN, *loc. cit.*, note 40, p. 628.

L'eugénisme revêt deux formes : l'eugénisme négatif et l'eugénisme positif. La première forme vise à faire diminuer la fréquence des gènes délétères, la seconde à faire augmenter celle des gènes favorables.

À l'égard des maladies que la médecine ne peut guérir complètement[224], la démarche retenue consiste à conseiller les personnes à risque. Celles-ci peuvent alors faire un choix éclairé relativement à la procréation. Il s'agit là d'eugénisme négatif[225]. Par ailleurs, les progrès techniques peuvent également permettre la sélection des embryons (ou, mais cela est moins sûr, de la lignée germinale) dans le but d'accroître la transmission de gènes jugés favorables : c'est l'eugénisme positif.

Ni l'une ni l'autre de ces formes ne peut cependant prétendre à la réalisation intégrale de l'objectif ultime de l'eugénisme : la modification du pool génique. C'est la nature elle-même qui dresse l'obstacle le plus puissant à la renaissance de la théorie eugénique[226], car seule une fraction des caractères et des désordres est rattachable à un gène unique sur lequel une sélection positive ou négative pourrait s'opérer ; les affections héréditaires les plus fréquentes sont en effet de nature polygénique. Cette restriction apaise les craintes exagérées qui accompagnent souvent les débats portant sur la génétique humaine[227]. Il n'en reste pas moins que les choix relatifs à la « normalité » doivent être faits non seulement dans le cadre de notre vie quotidienne, mais également pour les générations futures.

Il existe un domaine où il faut dès à présent établir les principes applicables à la sélection ou au perfectionnisme génétique ; c'est celui des techniques de reproduction. Ces techniques donnent accès à du matériel génétique humain, sous forme de gamètes (ovules ou spermatozoïdes) et d'embryons, dont elles permettent l'utilisation. À l'instar de tous les organismes internationaux qui se sont déjà prononcés[228], la Commission de réforme du droit du Canada a proposé, dans un récent document de travail, d'interdire les formes les plus extrêmes d'expérimentation génétique sur l'embryon humain[229].

---

224. Par exemple, la phénylcétonurie qui peut être détectée par des tests de dépistage sur les nouveau-nés et traitée au moyen d'une diète faible en protéines. Le fardeau imposé par la maladie est néanmoins tel que certains parents demandent un diagnostic prénatal.

225. On évite généralement d'employer le terme « eugénisme » dans le contexte du diagnostic prénatal, en insistant plutôt sur le fait qu'il permet aux couples à risque d'avoir des enfants normaux.

226. D.J. KEVLES, *op. cit.* note 204, p. 289.

227. *Ibid.* Voir également K. BOONE, *loc. cit.*, note 2.

228. Voir généralement B.M. KNOPPERS, *loc. cit.*, note 89, pp. 336-358 ainsi que le rapport complémentaire. Nous avons soutenu que les textes du droit international en matière de droits de l'homme sont insuffisants et n'ont pas la spécificité nécessaire pour protéger la personne humaine dans le contexte du progrès scientifique. Toutefois, en attendant une intervention législative, il pourrait être possible d'élargir, par interprétation, la portée des textes relatifs à l'expérimentation sur des sujets humains. Voir particulièrement FONDATION MARANGOPOULOS POUR LES DROITS DE L'HOMME, *op. cit.*, note 194, et COMMISSION DE RÉFORME DU DROIT DU CANADA, *L'expérimentation biomédicale sur l'être humain*, Document de travail n° 61, Ottawa, La Commission, 1989.

229. Voir *L'expérimentation biomédicale sur l'être humain*, *op. cit.*, note 228 (la thérapie et la modification géniques de la lignée germinale ou somatique n'y sont pas traitées) et *Les crimes contre le fœtus*, *op. cit.*, note 113, p. 60.

L'Assemblée parlementaire du Conseil de l'Europe a pour sa part recommandé dernièrement que l'expérimentation génétique ne puisse être utilisée qu'à des fins thérapeutiques. Elle interdirait ainsi les possibilités les plus extrêmes du génie génétique — notamment le clonage et la manipulation génétique non thérapeutique visant la sélection sexuelle ou raciale : « l'embryon et le fœtus humains doivent bénéficier en toutes circonstances du respect dû à la dignité humaine[230] ».

En dehors du secteur des techniques de reproduction, les recherches en matière génétique commencent à peine. Dans un document récent, le comité d'étude sur la thérapie génique du Conseil de recherches médicales du Canada a exprimé l'avis qu'il était peu probable que des manipulations génétiques se fassent à des fins perfectionnistes[231]. De surcroît, il n'existe aucune technique, scientifiquement applicable, qui permette d'améliorer des traits comme l'intelligence[232].

Le perfectionnisme génétique nous amène à mettre en balance, d'un côté les droits individuels et de l'autre les obligations sociales, d'un côté la liberté de procréation et de l'autre, les notions d'ordre, de santé et de bien-être publics. Le droit à un génome « sain » existe-t-il ? On pourra trouver des éléments de réponse en examinant brièvement les poursuites intentées par des parents ou par des enfants en raison de malformations prévisibles (*wrongful birth and wrongful life suits*), ainsi que l'évolution récente de la protection juridique du fœtus.

VI. Malformations congénitales et responsabilité civile

Au cours des cinquante dernières années, les connaissances relatives aux risques tératogènes de nature environnementale se sont accrues, de même que la capacité de diagnostiquer des maladies génétiques avant la naissance et avant la conception. Ces progrès médicaux ont pavé la voie à des poursuites judiciaires intentées après la naissance, par des parents imputant à la faute d'autrui le préjudice subi par leur enfant. Cette faute consistait soit en un acte dommageable affectant directement le fœtus dans l'utérus et entraînant l'anomalie, soit en un diagnostic erroné établi avant ou après la conception, à la suite duquel était né un enfant présentant une malformation[233].

---

230. Recommandation 1046, précitée, note 97, art. 10 ; voir aussi *supra*, notes 98 et 99. C'est également cette position qui est défendue dans un rapport du gouvernement québécois, intitulé *Rapport du comité de travail sur les nouvelles technologies de reproduction humaine*, Québec, Ministère de la Santé et des Services sociaux, 1988, p. 90 et dans un document du BARREAU DU QUÉBEC, « Rapport du comité sur les nouvelles technologies de reproduction » (1988), 48:2 suppl. *R. du B.* pp. 37-40.

231. Voir CONSEIL DE RECHERCHES MÉDICALES DU CANADA, *op. cit.*, note 30, p. 13. Le Conseil recommande de limiter l'objet de la recherche aux cellules somatiques, comme l'on fait d'autres comités à travers le monde. Voir généralement, le rapport Benda, *op. cit.*, note 39 ENQUETE COMMISSION, *op. cit.*, note 39 et COMMISSION D'EXPERTS, *op. cit.*, note 38.

232. Friedrich VOGEL et Arno G. MOTULSKY (dir.), *Human Genetics: Problems and Approaches*, 2e éd., Berlin, Springer-Verlag, 1986, particulièrement le chapitre 8 « Genetics and Human Behavior », p. 584, et Eve K. NICHOLS, *Human Gene Therapy*, Cambridge (Mass.), Harvard University Press, 1988, p. 166.

233. B.M. KNOPPERS, *loc. cit.*, note 111.

Dans le premier cas, les actions étaient fondées sur la fiction juridique assimilant l'enfant à naître à un enfant né, lorsqu'il y va de son intérêt. Une fois l'enfant né vivant et viable, les parents peuvent selon ce principe obtenir en son nom des dommages-intérêts en application des règles générales sur la responsabilité pour négligence, même si la faute a été commise avant la naissance.

Dans le second cas (diagnostic ou conseils erronés), les actions étaient fondées sur l'hypothèse selon laquelle les parents, n'eût été de la faute invoquée, n'auraient pas conçu d'enfant ou auraient eu recours à un avortement licite. Peu de temps après, on a aussi intenté des poursuites au nom des enfants eux-mêmes, en soutenant que si les parents avaient obtenu un diagnostic et des conseils adéquats, la conception n'aurait pas eu lieu.

Les tribunaux ont, à maintes reprises, accueilli les actions du premier type intentées par des parents, en appliquant les principes juridiques traditionnels relatifs à la négligence. Mais pour les actions du second type (diagnostic ou conseils erronés) intentées par les enfants, la situation est bien différente. À quelques exceptions près[234], tous les tribunaux saisis, estimant qu'on leur demandait d'apprécier le préjudice subi par une personne forcée de vivre avec une déficience par rapport à l'absence de vie, ont refusé de se livrer à un tel calcul, y voyant un affront à la dignité et au respect dûs à toute vie humaine. Cet obstacle d'ordre éthique, ainsi que la difficulté de déterminer le montant des dommages-intérêts susceptibles d'être attribués, vouaient ces poursuites à l'échec. Dans les cas exceptionnels où les demandeurs ont obtenu gain de cause, les tribunaux ont rejeté ces arguments et contourné le problème de la preuve du lien de causalité pour se concentrer sur les dommages incontestables subis par les enfants et sur le fait que les dommages-intérêts accordés aux parents ne représentaient une protection financière pour les enfants que jusqu'à leur majorité. Ils ont estimé qu'il n'était pas plus difficile de déterminer le montant des dommages-intérêts dans ce cas que dans celui des autres actions pour préjudice corporel[235].

Parallèlement à cette évolution du droit de la responsabilité à l'égard des enfants non encore nés, des mesures de protection du fœtus ont commencé à se faire jour : restrictions à l'avortement, lois visant à protéger le fœtus viable contre certains actes criminels, ordonnances judiciaires imposant certains comportements aux femmes

---

234. *Curlender* c. *Bio-Science Laboratories*, 165 Cal. Rptr. 477, 106 Cal. App. 3d 811 (1980) ; *Turpin* c. *Sortini*, 119 Cal. App. 3d 690, 174 Cal. Rptr. 128 (1981) révisée par 182 Cal. Rptr. 337, 643 P. 2d 954, 31 Cal. 3d 220 (C.S., 1982) ; *Harbeson* c. *Parke-Davis, Inc.*, 656 P. 2d 483, 98 Wash. 2d 460 (C.S., 1983) ; *Procanik* c. *Cillo*, 478 A. 2d 755, 97 N.J. 339 (1984) ; *Siemieniec* c. *Lutheran General Hospital*, 480 N.E. 2d 1227 (Ill. App. 1 Dist. 1985). Dans la dernière affaire, la Cour a jugé que la demande de l'enfant dérivait de la poursuite intentée par les parents.

235. Pour une décision récente d'un tribunal québécois refusant les dommages-intérêts demandés en s'appuyant sur la jurisprudence américaine, voir *Engstrom* c. *Courteau*, [1986] R.J.Q. 3048 (C.S.). Voir également, B.M. KNOPPERS, *loc. cit.*, note 111, sur l'applicabilité des règles de la responsabilité aux préjudices causés *in utero*, in vitro ou à la vie « en projet ».

pendant la grossesse ou l'accouchement[236]. Et il y a tout lieu de croire qu'au cours de la prochaine décennie, la vie embryonnaire in vitro ou « en stockage » sera protégée par la réglementation des techniques de reproduction[237].

Compte tenu de cette évolution du droit, l'obligation générale de ne pas causer de tort à « autrui » et l'obligation particulière des parents d'agir dans le meilleur intérêt de leurs enfants deviendront-elles le fondement d'actions en dommages-intérêts pour anomalies congénitales évitables ? Dans l'hypothèse où la modification des gènes serait possible, l'obligation d'y recourir pourrait être jugée raisonnable, comme c'est aujourd'hui le cas pour la thérapie prénatale ou post-natale. Un auteur affirme ainsi que des parents qui refuseraient des modifications génétiques porteraient atteinte au droit de leur enfant de naître avec un génome particulier, dans la mesure où il serait possible d'obtenir ce génome au moyen de la thérapie génique et d'éviter ainsi que l'enfant soit atteint d'une grave déficience[238].

Le même auteur soutient que la liberté de procréer doit :

> [TRADUCTION]
> Au minimum, inclure la liberté de prévenir, par avortement ou par traitement prénatal, la naissance d'un enfant porteur de gènes nuisibles. S'il est effectivement permis, ou même obligatoire, de traiter un enfant après ou avant sa naissance, il devrait être permis de le faire au stade embryonnaire ou avant la conception, car cela évitera à l'enfant ou à ses descendants le fardeau de le faire plus tard. En fait, l'enfant pourrait même ne pas naître, si les parents ne disposent que de la thérapie post-natale. [Ainsi], le droit de procréer comprend le droit de pratiquer l'eugénisme négatif, c'est-à-dire le droit de supprimer les caractéristiques préjudiciables chez les générations futures[239].

On peut convenir que la modification de la lignée germinale peut profiter aux générations futures et éviter des souffrances inutiles, ou estimer qu'une personne a le [TRADUCTION] « droit d'empêcher que sa progéniture et les descendants de celle-ci soient atteints d'affections génétiques[240] ». Mais de là à soutenir que cette [TRADUCTION] « progéniture a droit à ce qu'une intervention thérapeutique soit pratiquée sur les gamètes de ses parents lorsqu'elle est essentielle pour lui assurer un génome sain[241] », il y a de la marge.

---

236. S. RODGERS, *loc. cit.*, note 112. Voir également Bonnie STEINBOCK, « The Logical Case for "Wrongful Life" » (1986), 16:2 *Hast. Cent. Rep.* 15; M.W. SHAW, *loc. cit.*, note 110 et Margery W. SHAW, « Should Child Abuse Laws Be Extended to Include Fetal Abuse ? », dans Aubrey MILUNSKY et George J. ANNAS (dir.), *Genetics and the Law III*, New York, Plenum Press, 1985, p. 309 ; Bartha M. KNOPPERS, « Comparative Abortion Law: The Living Abortus », dans K. MASON (dir.), *Paediatric Medicine*, Londres, Chapman & Hall, 1989, p. 387 et B.M. KNOPPERS, *loc. cit.*, note 89. Voir en outre *Les crimes contre le fœtus*, *op. cit.* note 113.

237. B.M. KNOPPERS, *supra*, notes 89 et 111.

238. John A. ROBERTSON, « Genetic Alteration of Embryos : The Ethical Issues », dans A. MILUNSKY et G.J. ANNAS (dir.), *op. cit.*, note 236, p. 115.

239. *Id.*, p. 125.

240. *Ibid.*

241. *Ibid.*

Étant donné que la modification des gamètes ou de la lignée germinale n'en est qu'au stade expérimental, faut-il offrir aux parents potentiels la possibilité de recourir à des embryons génétiquement sains provenant de donneurs ? Est-il obligatoire de le faire ?

À moins que la liberté des choix de procréation comprenne la liberté de transmettre des gènes « malades », « a-normaux » ou non modifiés, la consécration juridique de l'obligation de ne pas causer de préjudice à ses descendants et d'agir au mieux de leurs intérêts pourrait impliquer l'obligation d'éliminer les gènes délétères et non pas seulement de traiter l'affection qui en découle[242]. Reconnaître le droit à un génome modifié pourrait se traduire par des avantages tant pour les individus (modification de la lignée somatique) que pour les générations futures (thérapie de la lignée germinale ou recours au don de gamètes ou d'embryons).

Les parents pourraient alors avoir de plus grandes obligations envers leurs enfants non encore conçus ou non encore nés qu'envers leurs enfants déjà nés.

Suivant un auteur,

> [TRADUCTION]
> La liberté de procréation embrasse la liberté de ne pas procréer et la liberté de procréer. Or celle-ci comporte nécessairement, dans une certaine mesure, la liberté de choisir ou de maîtriser les caractéristiques de la progéniture, de façon à lui éviter d'avoir à subir des préjudices[243].

Cela n'équivaut pas du tout à assujettir le droit de procréer à l'approbation ou à l'application de choix génétiques donnés. La notion de « droit » des parents à des enfants en santé risque d'inciter les médecins à recommander des avortements, ou encore à faire une sélection d'embryons et à éliminer ceux qui sont maladifs, pour éviter les risques de poursuites judiciaires. La défense de « droits » génétiques pour les fœtus ou pour les enfants aurait des conséquences similaires. Bien que [TRADUCTION] « [l]a limitation ou l'abolition du droit d'avoir des enfants atteints de maladies génétiques ou même du droit de transmettre des gènes défavorables aux générations futures ait un nombre considérable de partisans[244] », la solution de ces problèmes qui concernent la collectivité doit être axée sur [TRADUCTION] « l'acceptation par la société du coût social de la liberté individuelle[245] ». Il peut certes paraître anormal (voire odieux) qu'au nom de la liberté de religion ou de procréation, un couple engendre délibérément et en toute connaissance de cause un enfant destiné à une vie de souffrance[246]. Mais les rares cas où une telle décision serait prise ne pourraient-ils être

---

242. *Ibid.*

243. *Ibid.*

244. D.J. KEVLES, *op. cit.*, note 204, p. 300.

245. *Id.*, Daniel Callahan, cité dans D.J. KEVLES.

246. Joseph FLETCHER, *The Ethics of Genetic Control: Ending Reproductive Roulette*, New York, Anchor, 1974, p. 187 : [TRADUCTION] « Ceux qui savent qu'un enfant naîtra anormal — ou qui auraient pu le savoir s'ils l'avaient voulu — mais qui laissent néanmoins naître un tel enfant, commettent un acte aussi répréhensible que s'ils contribuaient de façon coupable à une mort injustifiable ».

considérés comme le risque que la société doit assumer en contrepartie d'une liberté de procréation accrue ? Il serait en effet tout aussi odieux d'imposer des choix de procréation au nom d'une « normalité » définie par la collectivité.

Le respect de la dignité inhérente à la personne humaine s'exprime notamment par le respect de décisions extrêmement personnelles et intimes, comme celle de mettre au monde un enfant, dans telles conditions, avec telle personne. Les droits légitimes auxquels peuvent prétendre les enfants ayant subi un préjudice corporel du fait de la négligence d'autrui ne sauraient avoir pour effet d'obliger les parents potentiels à éviter de donner naissance à un enfant génétiquement déficient. La possibilité de poursuites intentées par des enfants handicapés contre leurs parents fait peser de graves menaces sur la cellule familiale. [TRADUCTION] « Dans une société qui vénère et protège jalousement les valeurs et les mœurs individuelles, les poursuites judiciaires d'enfants handicapés contre leur mère sembleraient battre en brèche ce respect et saper la liberté de choix traditionnelle[247] ».

D'aucuns, avons-nous vu, forceraient les parents à prendre, en matière de procréation, les décisions propres à empêcher la mise au monde d'enfants atteints de troubles graves[248]. Mais en limitant l'accès aux techniques permettant la prévention de ces naissances et en restreignant les ressources médicales offertes à cet égard, on contribuerait aussi à la limitation du choix des parents. Nous avons vu que l'Enquete Commission bannirait carrément toute manipulation du génome (dans le cas où ces manipulations seraient techniquement possibles), de telles interventions bafouant à son avis la dignité humaine[249]. Or, restreindre l'accès au diagnostic prénatal limiterait encore davantage le choix des parents. Si l'objectif poursuivi consiste à maximiser la liberté de choix en matière de procréation, il faudra trouver un moyen pour que les politiques qui font obstacle à cette liberté fassent l'objet d'un débat public sérieux.

VII. Conclusion

Le recours au langage des droits dans le contexte génétique favorise les conflits et tient pour immuables les idéologies actuellement en présence (déterminisme, naturalisme, discrimination et perfectionnisme). Or, l'avenir de la génétique humaine ne se situe pas du côté des inévitables controverses touchant la manipulation ou

---

247. Catherine J. DAMME, « Controlling Genetic Disease Through Law » (1982), 15 *U.C. Davis L. Rev.* 801, p. 837. Voir particulièrement les arguments convaincants avancés dans THE LAW COMMISSION, *Report on Injuries to Unborn Children*, Londres, HMSO, 1974, pp. 23-26 et l'article de Alexander M. CAPRON, « Tort Liability in Genetic Counseling » (1979), 79 *Colum. L. Rev.* 618.

248. Voir les commentaires relatifs aux auditions du Conseil de l'Europe, *supra*, note 99 et suiv. Voir également D.J. KEVLES, citant Paul Ramsey, *op. cit.*, note 204 ; M.W. SHAW, *loc. cit.*, note 110 ; J. FLETCHER, *op. cit.*, note 246.

249. *Supra*, note 39 et le texte auquel elle renvoie.

l'élimination des gènes délétères. Il repose plutôt sur la nécessité d'expliquer et de communiquer l'information, sur l'éducation et sur la possibilité de faire des choix éclairés.

Actuellement, il existe des risques de discrimination génétique préjudiciable dans les trois secteurs où s'effectuent des examens génétiques (le travail, l'assurance, la procréation). Il n'en demeure pas moins que ces examens nous renseignent sur les causes et sur la prévention des affections génétiques. Il ne serait pas prématuré de commencer, sur le plan de la collectivité, à débattre de ces questions en vue d'élaborer une politique cohérente, qui respecte les droits et la dignité de la personne. L'élaboration de cette nouvelle politique devrait être fondée sur un programme d'éducation, de façon qu'elle soit le fait d'individus bien renseignés. Autrement dit, nous ne devrions pas attendre, avant d'agir, qu'apparaissent les manifestations concrètes de la discrimination génétique et des thèses « naturalistes ».

Si nous cessions d'invoquer le « droit à un génome particulier », sain ou non, inaltéré ou non, quelles sont les limites raisonnables qui pourraient être envisagées dans le cadre d'une société libre et démocratique — pour reprendre les termes de l'article premier de la Charte ? Quel contexte moral et juridique favoriserait au maximum l'information et la liberté de choix, tout en restreignant les abus possibles ? En quoi pourrait donc consister la « justice génétique » ?

CHAPITRE SIX

Vers une justice génétique

I. Introduction

Dans les précédents chapitres, nous avons décrit les possibilités techniques de la nouvelle génétique humaine ainsi que la complexité et la variabilité du patrimoine génétique individuel et collectif, et nous avons affirmé que la protection du patrimoine génétique humain est essentielle à la préservation des droits de la personne. Dans le présent chapitre, nous explorerons les préceptes normatifs et éthiques qui sous-tendent la législation sur les droits de la personne dans le contexte médical. Les problèmes particuliers de la génétique humaine nécessitent-ils que l'on élargisse la portée de ces principes ou que l'on en élabore de nouveaux ? La nouvelle ère scientifique qui s'ouvre exige-t-elle une nouvelle éthique ? Maintenant que la maîtrise commence à se substituer au hasard, que se termine l'époque de la [TRADUCTION] « roulette reproductive[250] », repartons-nous de zéro ? L'ancienne alliance entre l'humanité et la création s'est-elle réduite [TRADUCTION] « à un fil ténu et fragile[251] » ? Et s'il en est ainsi, quelles valeurs doivent former l'assise des nouvelles responsabilités que nous fait assumer le décryptage du langage génétique du « Livre de l'Homme » ?

Ces principes de base pourraient servir de pierre de touche, former la source « morale[252] » au regard de laquelle on apprécierait l'applicabilité des théories actuelles de la justice élaborées à partir de ces principes. On pourrait aussi chercher de nouvelles règles et de nouveaux systèmes de droit — tenter d'élaborer une nouvelle « justice génétique[253] ».

L'élaboration d'une théorie de la justice génétique doit certes reposer sur une éthique, mais nulle théorie viable ne saurait se développer en vase clos, sans la prise en compte d'éléments plus pragmatiques. Tout débat sur la politique sanitaire doit donc prendre en considération les coûts sociaux et économiques du respect ou de la

---

250. J. FLETCHER, *op. cit.*, note 246.

251. Kurt BAYERTZ, citant Jacques Monod dans « Increasing Responsibility as Technological Destiny? Human Reproductive Technology and the Problem of Meta-Responsibility », dans P.T. DURBIN (dir.), *op. cit.*, note 187, p. 135, aux pages 146-147.

252. Alexander M. CAPRON, « Legal Rights and Moral Rights », dans B. HILTON et autres (dir.), *op. cit.*, note 68, pp. 221-227.

253. C'est George J. AGICH qui a utilisé cette expression dans « Genetic Justice » (1986), 24 *U.W.O. L. Rev.* 39, un article où il discutait de l'application des théories de la justice au génie génétique.

restriction de certaines libertés. Il faut également tenir compte du contexte clinique ou du contexte de la recherche où, en dernier ressort, cette politique sera mise en œuvre. Et surtout, l'élaboration d'une théorie de la justice ne saurait avoir lieu sans que l'on pense aux personnes directement concernées.

II. Considérations éthiques

Les études les plus exhaustives des questions morales spécifiques que soulèvent le dépistage, le conseil et la thérapie génétiques se trouvent dans les rapports préparés en 1982[254] et en 1983[255] par la commission présidentielle américaine chargée d'étudier les problèmes éthiques posés par la recherche en matière médicale et biomédicale et en matière de comportement. Plus récemment, d'autres commissions, formées pour l'examen des techniques de reproduction, ont commencé à débattre des questions morales et juridiques que suscitent ces techniques au regard de la génétique humaine. Signalons notamment le rapport Benda de l'Allemagne de l'Ouest[256], le rapport du groupe d'experts formé par le ministère de la Justice de la Suisse[257] et les documents de travail préparés par le Conseil de recherches médicales[258] et le Conseil des sciences du Canada[259]. Il importe en outre de signaler que le Conseil de l'Europe qui, le premier, a recommandé l'interdiction ou la réglementation des applications les plus extrêmes du génie génétique, examine maintenant, par l'intermédiaire de son comité ad hoc d'experts, le dépistage, le conseil et la thérapie génétiques[260].

Les examens, le dépistage et le conseil génétiques comprennent la recherche, le diagnostic, la détection des prédispositions, la prédiction du risque, la détection de l'état de porteur, la mise en banque d'ADN, la thérapie génique, le conseil préalable à la conception, le diagnostic prénatal ainsi que l'offre de choix de procréation, y compris le don de gamètes ou d'embryons. Toutes ces activités soulèvent des problèmes moraux, dont certains sont nouveaux. C'est pourquoi nous examinerons quelques principes éthiques communs à la médecine et à la génétique humaine : les principes d'autonomie, de bienfaisance et de non-malfaisance.

---

254. *Splicing Life, op. cit.*, note 33.

255. *Screening and Counseling*, *op. cit.*, note 33. Voir également les excellents rapports de l'OTA sur le conseil et le dépistage en génétique humaine, *Human Gene Therapy*, *op. cit.*, note 26, et *New Developments in Biotechnology*, *op. cit.*, note 52.

256. *Op. cit.*, note 39 ; voir aussi ENQUETE COMMISSION, *op. cit.*, note 39.

257. COMMISSION D'EXPERTS, *op. cit.*, note 38.

258. *Op. cit.*, note 30.

259. *Op. cit.*, note 34.

260. CONSEIL DE L'EUROPE, COMITÉ AD HOC D'EXPERTS SUR LES PROGRÈS DES SCIENCES BIOMÉDICALES (CAHBI), *Le dépistage génétique prénatal, le diagnostic génétique prénatal et les conseils génétiques*, Strasbourg, Le Conseil, 1989.

A. Autonomie

L'autonomie (étymologiquement, le fait de se régir par ses propres lois) s'entend généralement de la perception que nous avons de nous-mêmes et d'autrui comme des êtres qui prennent eux-mêmes les décisions qui les concernent, tant sur le plan physique que sur le plan psychologique. Il a récemment été décidé en Californie que, sur le plan physique, ce pouvoir de décision s'étendait aux cellules et aux tissus corporels[261]. Les cellules du demandeur, John Moore, avaient servi à des fins de recherche scientifique et avaient été exploitées commercialement à cause de leurs propriétés uniques et précieuses et de l'intérêt des informations qu'elles renfermaient. La Cour d'appel de la Californie devait déterminer si le médecin pouvait utiliser les cellules sans le consentement du demandeur. Elle a déclaré : [TRADUCTION] « Pour le meilleur ou pour le pire, nous sommes irrémédiablement entrés dans une époque où il nous faut revoir notre conception des droits et des rapports juridiques relatifs au corps humain et aux cellules humaines[262]. » Selon la Cour, le patient devait [TRADUCTION] « avoir le pouvoir ultime de décider ce qu'il advient de ses tissus. Soutenir le contraire ouvrirait la porte à des atteintes importantes à la vie privée et à la dignité, accomplies au nom du progrès médical[263] ». Ainsi, le respect de la personne est souvent lié à l'autonomie. Dans le contexte de la génétique humaine, la mise en banque de l'ADN et l'échange d'information génétique mettent en péril le respect de l'action autonome et indépendante des individus.

Le principe de l'autonomie s'étend aussi à la liberté de choix et d'action[264]. Nous avons vu, dans le chapitre précédent, comment certaines idéologies ou croyances peuvent influer sur les choix. Si l'on estime, par exemple, que les caractéristiques d'une personne sont déterminées par son bagage génétique, on ne lui attribue pas une grande liberté de choix. Conséquence logique, on pourra alors refuser l'accès à certains milieux de travail à des personnes ayant un génotype particulier, en raison de leur constitution génétique. Par ailleurs, on assiste à l'émergence graduelle d'une éthique fondée sur la qualité de la vie, qui se manifeste de façon plus évidente aux points limites de la conception et de la mort. Elle est invoquée, pour ne citer que quelques exemples de son application, à l'égard des techniques de reproduction, des moyens artificiels pris pour maintenir en vie les mourants et de l'allocation des ressources médicales. Lorsque la qualité de vie de ceux qui sont destinés à hériter de certaines affections est considérée comme tellement accablante que la seule option envisageable

---

261. *Moore* c. *Regents of the University of California*, 249 Cal. Rptr 494 (App. 2 Dist. 1988), nouvelle audition accordée, 252 Cal. Rptr. 816 (1988). Pour des commentaires sur la réclamation du demandeur fondée sur le droit privé, voir L.B. ANDREWS, *op. cit.* note 8, et Marie-Angèle HERMITTE, « L'affaire Moore » (décembre 1988), 417 *Le Monde Diplomatique* 20, p. 21.

262. *Moore* c. *Regents of the University of California*, précité, note 261, p. 504.

263. *Id.*, p. 508.

264. John C. FLETCHER, « Ethical and Social Aspects of Risk Predictions » (1984), 25 *Clin. Genet.* 25, pp. 25-26.

est d'éviter de les faire naître, les parents perdent leur autonomie en matière de liberté de procréation[265].

D'un autre côté, si l'accessibilité au diagnostic prénatal est tenue pour un pas vers le perfectionnisme, il est possible que cela entraîne la restriction des options ouvertes aux parents en matière de reproduction. Nos idéologies ou nos conceptions morales peuvent donc porter atteinte de nombreuses façons à l'autonomie sociale et à l'autonomie de procréation.

Dès 1972, on a reconnu qu'il fallait, pour préserver l'autonomie, que le dépistage génétique soit volontaire. Pour garantir le caractère volontaire de l'opération, il est nécessaire d'obtenir un consentement éclairé. L'obligation d'informer les sujets procède donc du principe éthique de l'autonomie. Son objet n'est pas uniquement la protection contre les risques physiques, lesquels sont minimes, mais aussi la protection contre [TRADUCTION] « les atteintes sociales ou psychologiques[266] ». À cet égard, on a entre autres formulé la recommandation suivante :

> [TRADUCTION]
> Nous recommandons instamment que soit éliminée des programmes de dépistage toute mesure dont l'effet serait de restreindre l'autonomie de procréation en raison d'une constitution génétique quelconque ou de stigmatiser les couples qui, pleinement informés des risques génétiques, continuent à vouloir des enfants conçus par eux. La formulation de critères de normalité fondés sur la constitution génétique est injustifiable[267].

La commission présidentielle a considéré elle aussi que le dépistage obligatoire ne se justifiait pas, sauf pour éviter que des personnes sans défense (comme les enfants) ne subissent des préjudices sérieux. Même dans ce cas, elle estimait que le choix et la liberté des parents devaient primer.

Ces déclarations sur le principe de l'autonomie ont précédé la généralisation des examens génétiques *in utero*, les poursuites intentées par des enfants handicapés, la possibilité de recourir, pour des motifs génétiques, au don de gamètes et d'embryons et, bien entendu, la possibilité d'avoir recours aux examens ou aux thérapies génétiques expérimentales pré-implantation[268]. Les progrès réalisés mettent en lumière le fait que

---

265. *Screening and Counseling*, *op. cit.*, note 33, p. 44. Voir également, Robert M. VEATCH, *The Foundation of Justice: Why the Retarded and the Rest of Us Have Claims to Equality*, New York, Oxford University Press, 1986.

266. Article spécial, « Ethical and Social Issues in Screening for Genetic Disease » (1972), 286:21 *N. Engl. J. Med.* 1129, p. 1131. Voir également NATIONAL ACADEMY OF SCIENCE, *op. cit.*, note 166.

267. Article spécial, *loc. cit.*, note 266, pp. 1130-1131.

268. Voir, cependant, l'avertissement donné par la commission présidentielle, *Splicing Life*, *op. cit.*, note 33, p. 66 :

> [TRADUCTION]
> Si le génie génétique et les techniques de reproduction connexes permettent de réduire de façon marquée les défauts génétiques et le fardeau qu'ils représentent pour leurs victimes et pour les ressources de la collectivité, le traitement génétique obligatoire peut toutefois se défendre [. . .] Les progrès futurs de la chirurgie génétique ou de la thérapie génique peuvent nous amener à nous écarter encore une fois du principe voulant que les adultes

certaines affections sont évitables et, partant, la possibilité de conflit entre le principe d'autonomie et le principe de bienfaisance.

Le principe d'autonomie joue aussi un rôle important dans le maintien de la confidentialité, la protection des secrets partagés. Dans le contexte du dépistage génétique, c'est en effet lui [TRADUCTION] « qui sert à protéger le bien-être des sujets et à empêcher toute utilisation irrégulière des renseignements obtenus[269] ».

Cette question touchera pratiquement tout le monde au fur et à mesure que le dépistage des prédispositions génétiques à des affections courantes deviendra possible[270]. En effet, les maladies génétiques ne se limitent pas à des affections monogéniques rares, elles comprennent aussi les affections multifactorielles comme le cancer, les maladies cardiaques, le diabète, la schizophrénie, etc., dont beaucoup sont assez répandues. Cela signifie qu'un large segment de la population pourrait d'ici peu faire l'objet d'une surveillance génétique, ce qui accentue le problème de la confidentialité.

La commission présidentielle a affirmé qu'aucun tiers — employeur, assureur par exemple — ne devrait recevoir communication de renseignements génétiques sans le consentement exprès de la personne concernée[271]. Il est possible, toutefois, qu'on ne puisse pas interdire toute communication à des tiers. Ainsi, la nature même du contrat d'assurance requiert que l'assureur connaisse les risques touchant la santé de l'assuré, et l'employeur peut avoir besoin de tels renseignements pour protéger ses employés. Il faut donc formuler des lignes de conduite en matière de confidentialité, afin de garantir le respect de la dignité et de l'autonomie de la personne humaine ainsi que le droit de travailler ou d'être assuré[272].

> en pleine possession de leurs moyens peuvent toujours refuser une intervention médicale, hormis les cas d'urgence, et que la reproduction relève dans une large mesure du domaine des activités privées et autonomes.

Signalons également cet extrait de *Screening and Counseling*, *op. cit.*, note 33, pp. 55-56 :

> [TRADUCTION]
> Une telle réponse n'est pas défendable. L'accès des enfants handicapés aux ressources collectives ne saurait dépendre de la décision de leurs parents de se soumettre ou non au dépistage. Une telle réponse va également à l'encontre des efforts déployés à l'heure actuelle pour la garantie de droits et de chances aux personnes handicapées.

269. J. FLETCHER, *loc. cit.*, note 264, p. 27. Voir également *Screening and Counseling*, *op. cit.*, note 33.

270. Dorothy C. WERTZ et John C. FLETCHER (dir.), *Ethics and Human Genetics: A Cross-Cultural Perspective*, Berlin, Springer-Verlag, 1989.

271. *Screening and Counseling*, *op. cit.*, note 33.

272. Les employeurs devraient avoir l'obligation de prouver que l'exclusion d'employés potentiels découle d'une affection existante qui justifie la mesure. Toute discrimination fondée sur la seule prédisposition à des affections multifactorielles ou à des maladies à apparition tardive courantes devrait être interdite. Voir le chapitre cinq.

B. Bienfaisance

Le second principe éthique en jeu est le principe de bienfaisance, celui qui fait veiller au bien-être individuel ou collectif des autres, en servant leurs intérêts. Son application requiert que l'on soupèse les bienfaits et les préjudices que nos actions peuvent causer à autrui. Par exemple, nous avons vu que de façon générale le maintien de la confidentialité contribue au respect de l'autonomie. Toutefois, l'obligation d'assurer la confidentialité n'est pas absolue et peut souffrir des exceptions lorsque le fait de s'y conformer risque de causer un préjudice grave à autrui. À cet égard, la commission présidentielle a déclaré qu'on pouvait passer outre à cette obligation, dans certains cas, lorsque des personnes du même sang courent des risques graves[273]. La prolifération des examens génétiques et la nécessité d'inclure des membres de la famille dans les études de liaison génétique nous obligeront à réexaminer les situations dans lesquelles il peut être justifié de communiquer des renseignements génétiques à des parents qui risquent de subir un préjudice important.

C. Non-malfaisance

Le principe de non-malfaisance est le pendant du principe de bienfaisance[274]. Son objet, ne causer aucun mal, diffère de celui du principe de bienfaisance en ce qu'il peut exiger une obligation positive. Nous avons vu, par exemple, que l'application du principe de bienfaisance suppose, dans certaines circonstances, la restriction de l'autonomie individuelle dans le but d'éviter de causer un préjudice à autrui. Or l'application du principe de non-malfaisance peut exiger davantage — elle peut par exemple obliger la personne qui dispose de renseignements confidentiels à les divulguer à d'autres. Cette obligation peut se comparer à l'obligation de porter secours aux personnes en danger sans mettre sa propre sécurité en péril[275]. Il est donc permis de se demander s'il existe un devoir positif de connaître son propre bagage génétique et de révéler à des parents des renseignements génétiques susceptibles de revêtir une importance capitale dans l'adoption d'un mode de vie ou dans les choix de procréation ; ou encore, s'il existe un devoir positif d'éviter de concevoir un enfant susceptible d'être atteint d'une maladie génétique identifiée.

---

273. *Screening and Counseling*, *op. cit.*, note 33.

274. De façon générale, voir H. Tristram ENGELHARDT, *The Foundations of Bioethics*, New York, Oxford University Press, 1986 ; Robert M. VEATCH, *A Theory of Medical Ethics*, New York, Basic Books, 1981 ; Norman FOST, « Regulating Genetic Technology: Values in Conflict », dans A. MILUNSKY et G.J. ANNAS (dir.), *op. cit.*, note 236, p. 15.

275. Seul le droit civil prévoit l'obligation expresse de porter secours. Voir par exemple le *Code pénal* français, Paris, Dalloz, 1989 (art. 63) et la Charte québécoise, précitée, note 76, art. 2. Pour une étude de la common law à ce sujet, voir COMMISSION DE RÉFORME DU DROIT DU CANADA, *L'omission, la négligence et la mise en danger*, Document de travail n° 46, Ottawa, La Commission, 1985, p. 18.

III. Théories de la justice

Les principes de justice reposent non seulement sur des préceptes éthiques, mais encore sur des concepts sociaux d'équité. Lorsque les ressources sont limitées et les demandes nombreuses, il faut établir certains critères pour la répartition des biens parmi les membres de la collectivité. C'est l'origine de la notion de justice distributive[276]. La justice distributive requiert que les cas similaires soient traités de façon semblable, et les cas différents, de façon différente, dans la mesure de leurs différences. Il faudrait donc fournir les soins de santé sur la base de différences pertinentes entre individus[277]. Comment peut-on concilier ces préceptes éthiques avec les théories classiques de la justice, lorsque l'on sait que chaque personne est génétiquement différente et que nous partageons tous certaines [TRADUCTION] « vulnérabilités génétiques[278] » ?

Dans une étude mondiale réalisée récemment sur les perspectives transculturelles relatives à l'éthique et à la génétique humaine, on conclut que la distribution équitable des ressources constitue un problème aigu, particulièrement à une époque où les demandes augmentent[279]. En regard des dépenses globales relatives aux soins de santé, quelle priorité faut-il donner aux services génétiques, particulièrement dans les pays qui font de la prévention un objectif important mais dont les ressources sont limitées ?

Les auteurs d'une recherche internationale relative au système de santé des États-Unis recommandent que

> [TRADUCTION]
> [L]es services génétiques soient également accessibles à tous sans égard à la capacité de payer, à la situation géographique, aux opinions sur l'avortement, à l'éducation ou aux origines ethniques. Les personnes qui paient pour obtenir des services particuliers ne doivent pas avoir priorité sur les autres. L'État doit rembourser les laboratoires commerciaux et réglementer leur activité pour qu'ils servent également tout le monde et n'effectuent que des actes médicalement indiqués, conformément aux lignes directrices établies pour les établissements publics ou universitaires[280].

L'application de ce principe suppose que l'activité de réglementation et de surveillance de l'Administration en matière de services génétiques s'exerce non seulement à l'égard du secteur public de la santé, mais également à l'égard du secteur privé et commercial.

---

276. Dans son sens ordinaire, la justice distributive désigne un droit proportionnel aux besoins du titulaire. Voir *infra*, note 287.

277. Rebecca DRESSER, « Social Justice in New Reproductive Techniques », dans A. MILUNSKY et G.J. ANNAS (dir.), *op. cit.*, note 236, pp. 159-160.

278. K. NOLAN et S. SWENSON, *loc. cit.*, note 168, p. 42. Voir également W. SCHIRMACHER, dans P.T. DURBIN (dir.), *op. cit.*, note 187, p. 211 [TRADUCTION] « [. . .] nous devons apprendre à utiliser la variabilité de notre existence ».

279. D.C. WERTZ et J.C. FLETCHER, *op. cit.*, note 270.

280. John C. Fletcher et Dorothy C. Wertz, communication personnelle au Comité de l'étude sur la prédisposition génétique aux maladies, Conseil des sciences du Canada, 1988.

Les théories classiques de la justice où l'on tente de fonder la distribution des ressources peuvent être rangées dans l'une ou l'autre des écoles de pensée suivantes : utilitariste, libertarienne et égalitariste[281]. Dans le contexte des soins de santé, et encore plus s'il s'agit d'un système de médecine socialisée, il est possible d'ajouter une quatrième école de pensée, celle du contrat social de John Rawls[282].

A. Utilitarisme

L'utilitarisme mesure la justice en fonction du plus grand bien global. [TRADUCTION] « Dans cette perspective, l'inégalité de traitement est moralement acceptable si le préjudice global qui en résulte est moindre que l'ensemble des avantages qu'elle procure[283] ». Toutefois, l'application de cette théorie soulève des problèmes. Mis à part la difficulté d'évaluer le préjudice et les avantages dans le domaine de la santé (bienfaisance), l'utilitarisme place tous les biens ou les choix humains sur une seule échelle, plutôt que de reconnaître la diversité des comportements et des choix de l'être humain. Nous savons cependant que la vie et la santé ne sont pas de simples « marchandises[284] ». En outre, l'analyse coûts-avantages est une méthode hautement rationnelle ; or, nous savons que nos choix professionnels ou nos choix de carrière sont souvent considérés comme irrationnels par les autres[285], tout comme peuvent l'être les choix que font certaines personnes ou certains couples après des consultations génétiques[286]. L'application de la conception utilitariste au domaine de la

---

281. Voir Joel FEINBERG et Hyman GROSS (dir.), *Philosophy of Law*, 3e éd., Belmont (Calif.), Wadsworth Pub., 1986.

282. John RAWLS, *Théorie de la justice*, Paris, Seuil, 1987.

283. R. DRESSER, *loc. cit.*, note 277, p. 161.

284. Elizabeth ANDERSON, « Values, Risk, and Market Norms » (1988), 17 *Phil. Pub. Aff.* 54. Voir également Angus CLARKE, « Genetics, Ethics, and Audit » (1990), 335:8698 *Lancet* 1145, pp. 1146 et 1147 ; l'auteur décrit les dangers que présente [TRADUCTION] « l'application simpliste d'une analyse coûts-avantages à la fourniture de services génétiques. En particulier, il faut éviter d'utiliser cette analyse pour vérifier l'efficacité des différents services », car en procédant ainsi, [TRADUCTION] « on pousse les cliniciens à maximiser le rôle des interruptions de grossesse dans le cas de désordres ''coûteux'' ».

285. E. ANDERSON, *loc. cit.*, note 284, p. 59.

    [TRADUCTION]
    Ce qu'il faut, c'est une méthode interprétative qui tente de cerner les actions humaines dans les termes mêmes qu'emploient leurs auteurs pour les comprendre. Pour évaluer la pertinence des données utilisées dans l'analyse coûts-avantages, il faut donc découvrir comment les choix de marché relatifs aux risques menaçant la santé ou la vie sont compris par les personnes qui les font.

286. Selon Emery et autres, cité dans Sherman ELIAS et George J. ANNAS (dir.), *Reproductive Genetics and the Law*, New York, Yearbook Medical Publications, 1987, p. 51, [TRADUCTION] « le tiers des personnes informées qu'elles couraient le risque d'avoir un enfant atteint d'une maladie génétique grave n'ont pas été dissuadées et ont même planifié d'autres grossesses ». Pour une analyse des processus décisionnels des parents en matière de procréation, voir A. LIPPMAN-HAND et F. Clarke FRASER, « Genetic Counseling — The Postcounseling Period: II. Making Reproductive Choices » (1979), 4 *Am. J. Med. Genet.* 73.

génétique humaine restreindrait la liberté de choix (autonomie) et le respect de la dignité humaine.

B. École libertarienne

Pour les libertariens, l'autonomie revêt une importance primordiale. Les théories libertariennes procèdent de la philosophie de John Locke. Leur principe primordial est celui de la libre disposition de ses biens et de son corps. En matière politique, elles supposent l'intervention minimale de l'État et la prise de décisions libres et éclairées par les individus[287]. [TRADUCTION] « Cette liberté l'emporte sur tout intérêt collectif contradictoire relatif à l'égalité d'accès aux soins de santé. Pour les libertariens, le marché libre et les injustices qui l'accompagnent règnent d'une façon absolue dans un système de santé équitable[288] ».

En génétique humaine, les libertariens font grand cas de l'inégalité de la distribution génétique. Les gènes, considérés comme des objets de propriété privée, seraient dans leur optique soumis aux contraintes du marché libre [TRADUCTION] « dans lequel les forces et les faiblesses génétiquement déterminées peuvent évoluer[289] ». Cette forme de darwinisme social est incompatible avec le principe d'universalité du système de santé du Canada qui repose sur une conception égalitariste de la justice.

C. Égalitarisme

La conception égalitariste de la justice préconise le respect de la personne en tant qu'être égal du fait même de son humanité. S'inspirant de la tradition rousseauiste, elle pose que tous les êtres humains ont la même valeur morale et le même droit au bien-être et à la liberté. Les égalitaristes perçoivent [TRADUCTION] « l'inégalité de la distribution naturelle comme une calamité morale qu'il faut corriger au moyen d'une action sociale, [et] présupposent que tous les individus ont un droit égal sur la totalité

---

287. Pour une optique libertarienne de la justice en matière de soins de santé, voir H.T. ENGELHARDT, *op. cit.*, note 274, p. 85, et pour une critique de la conception de celui-ci, voir Robert M. VEATCH, « Compte rendu, *The Foundations of Bioethics* » (1986), 105:6 *Ann. Intern. Med.* 987, p. 988 :

> [TRADUCTION]
> La conception d'Engelhardt ne repose que sur les arrangements librement consentis dans lesquels les gens puissants peuvent obtenir ce qu'ils veulent. Il ne reste qu'à ceux que la loterie naturelle ou sociale n'a pas favorisés et qui ont besoin de soins médicaux par suite de privations génétiques ou sociales, à s'en remettre à la charité.

Voir également comment Engelhardt et Rie réfutent l'éthique de la justice distributive, H. Tristram ENGELHARDT et Michael A. RIE, « Morality for the Medical-Industrial Complex » (1988), 319:16 *N. Engl. J. Med.* 1086. Pour une critique plus approfondie de la position d'Engelhardt, voir R.M. VEATCH, *op. cit.*, note 265.

288. R. DRESSER, *loc. cit.*, note 277, p. 161 et *New Developments in Biotechnology*, *op. cit.*, note 52.

289. G.J. AGICH, *loc. cit.*, note 253, p. 43.

de l'actif et du passif du pool génique[290] ». L'égalitarisme prône la modification des institutions sociales de façon à réduire au minimum ou à compenser l'inégalité des chances.

Le problème de cette doctrine réside dans ses possibilités de conflit avec le principe de liberté. Comme nous l'avons vu[291], la liberté ou le libre choix constitue un élément important de la protection de la dignité inhérente à la personne, elle-même à la base du droit international et du droit constitutionnel canadien. Peu de gens, certes, nieraient qu'un minimum de justice distributive soit nécessaire pour compenser les inégalités sociales[292]. Toutefois, [TRADUCTION] « [i]l en est qui iraient probablement plus loin et soutiendraient que l'égalité substantielle est une condition essentielle du respect de la valeur intrinsèque de la personne humaine[293] ». Et c'est là que surgit le conflit, car [TRADUCTION] « il n'est pas possible d'atteindre de tels objectifs égalitaires sans coercition et sans restreindre considérablement la liberté individuelle[294] ». C'est pourquoi il faut recourir à une autre théorie de la justice.

D. Contrat social

Dans sa *Théorie de la justice*[295], John Rawls dit de la distribution des dons naturels qu'elle n'est ni juste ni injuste ; il s'agit simplement de faits. Selon lui, c'est plutôt la façon dont les institutions traitent ces faits qui est la cause de la justice ou de l'injustice. Sa théorie de la justice, fondée sur la notion de contrat social, est axée sur ce qu'une société formée d'individus rationnels qui ne sauraient pas ce que la vie leur a donné en partage comme talent ou statut social tiendrait pour juste ou injuste. Il présume donc qu'un « voile d'ignorance » cache l'avenir, et suppose qu'à partir de cette « position originelle », les participants au contrat social élaboreront un système de justice conforme à leurs intérêts. Il en résulterait tout d'abord, et nécessairement, que chacun jouirait du plus haut degré de liberté compatible avec la liberté analogue d'autrui. Deuxièmement, l'égalité des chances serait un fait accompli. Et troisièmement, toute inégalité découlant de différences dans les aptitudes ou la valeur naturelles serait redressée de façon que les plus défavorisés jouissent du maximum d'avantages. Il nomme cela le « principe de différence ». Comment est-il possible d'appliquer cette conception du contrat social dans le contexte de la génétique humaine ?

---

290. *Ibid.*

291. *Supra*, chapitres deux et quatre.

292. O. SCHACHTER, *loc. cit.*, note 116, p. 851.

293. *Ibid.*

294. *Ibid.*

295. *Op. cit.*, note 282.

La commission présidentielle susmentionnée[296] a examiné la théorie de Rawls dans le contexte des soins de santé. Elle a entrevu la possibilité de substituer la notion de loterie des avantages sociaux ou naturels décrite dans la théorie du contrat social de Rawls à celle de l'actif génétique initial. Il serait alors possible de réduire l'inégalité des chances découlant des constitutions génétiques individuelles en intervenant dans la loterie biologique naturelle, et de parvenir à l'égalité et à la liberté par la participation de citoyens « raisonnables[297] » qui élaboreraient un système de coopération à leur avantage mutuel[298].

George Agich a eu recours à la théorie de la justice de Rawls pour élaborer sa théorie de la justice génétique[299]. Dans le système de Rawls, on s'attaquerait au problème des inégalités génétiques en les corrigeant de façon bénéfique pour les moins favorisés sur le plan génétique. Agich soutient que les attributs génétiques doivent être inclus dans la position originelle, car il est nécessaire de connaître les possibilités d'intervention génétique pour décider de ce qui est juste[300]. Il estime également que les décisions sur l'opportunité de traiter ou de prévenir les maladies génétiques nécessiteraient certaines modifications à la théorie de Rawls, pour permettre à ceux qui se trouvent dans la position originelle de penser aux générations futures. Au surplus, souligne-t-il, aucune maladie n'est purement génétique ; les seules connaissances génétiques ne suffisent donc pas, il faut également connaître le milieu et les possibilités d'action sociale réparatrice. C'est pourquoi [TRADUCTION] « [l]'incertitude des prévisions que permet la génétique humaine et l'ampleur des répercussions que peuvent avoir ses applications, jointes au caractère potentiellement réductionniste de ses explications, pèsent lourdement dans la justification du dépistage et des traitements génétiques, particulièrement au regard du principe de justice[301] ».

Nous souscrivons à l'opinion d'Agich selon laquelle il faut modifier la théorie de Rawls pour que les personnes placées dans la position originelle (un voile d'ignorance) disposent de données génétiques. Cette modification doit cependant s'effectuer d'une façon qui, non seulement favorise l'individu, mais assure une participation éclairée au

---

296. *Splicing Life*, *op. cit.*, note 33, p. 68. Voir également *New Developments in Biotechnology*, *op. cit.*, note 52.

297. John RAWLS, « La théorie de la justice comme équité : une théorie politique et non pas métaphysique », dans Catherine AUDARD et autres (dir.), *Individu et justice sociale : autour de John Rawls*, Paris, Seuil, 1988, p. 279 (trad. C. Audard). L'auteur explique à la p. 313 (n. 20) de son article que cela avait été une erreur « de décrire la théorie de la justice comme une partie de la théorie du choix rationnel », dans son ouvrage original précité (note 282).

298. Pour une excellente critique des idées de Rawls, voir C. AUDARD et autres (dir.), *op. cit.*, note 297. Voir également Marie-Angèle HERMITTE, « Le droit civil du contrat d'expérimentation », dans FONDATION MARANGOPOULOS POUR LES DROITS DE L'HOMME, *op. cit.*, note 194, p. 38, à la page 39 :

> Les tendances actuelles de l'expérimentation sur l'homme répondent donc assez exactement à la philosophie de John Rawls, mélange d'utilitarisme et de respect des droits de l'homme ; l'utilitarisme fournit la base de raisonnements que la philosophie des droits de l'homme et du contrat social vient réorganiser plus ou moins profondément.

299. *Loc. cit.*, note 253.

300. *Id.*, p. 47.

301. *Id.*, p. 42.

nouveau contrat social. Il s'agirait de se fonder sur cette conception lumineuse selon laquelle [TRADUCTION] « le pool génique humain ne connaît aucune frontière nationale, il est le patrimoine biologique de toute l'espèce humaine[302] ». Il sera alors possible de réexaminer le contrat social à l'aune du principe de l'égalité éclairée.

Il ne faut pas non plus considérer que la loterie génétique nous fait inégaux. Nous savons maintenant que chaque personne est génétiquement unique[303]. Pourquoi alors ne pas voir dans les différences individuelles le fondement du principe d'égalité[304] ?

IV. Nouveaux préceptes éthiques

Si, comme nous l'avons fait valoir, la connaissance des différences génétiques permet l'élaboration du contrat social à partir d'une position d'« égalité génétique » éclairée, quels autres préceptes éthiques peuvent contribuer à cette élaboration ? Nous voyons deux principes de base, celui de la réciprocité[305] ou de l'échange et celui de la mutualité ou de la responsabilité civique. Ces deux principes peuvent former l'assise morale d'un système de freins et de contrepoids établi par des citoyens éclairés et non imposé par l'ignorance ou la prérogative de l'État.

A. Réciprocité

Le premier principe de base du nouveau contrat social est le principe de la réciprocité ou de l'échange. Il est fondé sur la reconnaissance d'une « différence », c'est-à-dire d'une inégalité entre les connaissances que détiennent les professionnels de la génétique médicale et les citoyens ordinaires. La justice requiert la redistribution de ces connaissances d'une façon qui profite aux personnes les moins biens informées, c'est-à-dire aux citoyens ordinaires. Cela est essentiel si l'on veut que l'État ne soit pas en mesure d'utiliser le savoir génétique pour imposer des décisions aux individus et pour vérifier s'ils s'y conforment. Afin de garantir que ce soient les plus défavorisés qui bénéficient de l'échange de connaissances, il vaut mieux s'en remettre à la relation médecin-patient qui, traditionnellement, a permis la protection du patient[306]. Cette

302. Clifford GROBSTEIN et Michael FLOWER, « Gene Therapy: Proceed with Caution » (1984), 14:2 *Hast. Cent. Rep.* 13, p. 16.

303. Voir *supra*, note 140.

304. Bartha M. KNOPPERS, « Human Genetics, Predisposition and the New Social Contract », dans INTERNATIONAL CONFERENCE ON BIOETHICS, *op. cit.*, note 29, p. 168.

305. J. RAWLS, *op. cit.*, note 282. L'auteur emploie ce terme pour parler de la coopération, une notion qui ne correspond pas à notre interprétation de la réciprocité comme « échange » ou « transfert ». Le mot « coopération » toutefois, est celui qui est traditionnellement employé pour désigner la réciprocité. Voir J. FEINBERG et H. GROSS, *op. cit.*, note 281, p. 416.

306. B.M. KNOPPERS et C.M. LABERGE, *loc. cit.*, note 91, p. 1024.

protection prend la forme de la doctrine du consentement éclairé, fondée sur le principe d'autonomie. Dans sa formulation classique, cette doctrine supposait l'obligation de faire part des risques de préjudice corporel. Aujourd'hui, elle englobe la prévention des préjudices sociaux et psychologiques, non seulement à l'égard du patient, mais également à l'égard de la famille de celui-ci et de la société en général. En plus de donner aux patients le pouvoir d'utiliser l'information reçue de la façon qu'ils jugent la meilleure pour eux, la doctrine du consentement éclairé leur permet de décider s'ils souhaitent même être mis au courant de certains risques.

L'exercice de ce pouvoir de décision individuel de même que

> [TRADUCTION]
> [L]a protection du libre choix [sont] lié[s] à l'existence d'une population éduquée, consciente des buts visés par les examens génétiques ainsi que des avantages, des coûts et des risques. D'une façon générale, il faut bien sûr dans cette optique veiller à mieux éduquer la population ; mais on peut, plus spécifiquement, veiller à ce que les examens génétiques ne soient effectués que lorsque les sujets visés en comprennent l'objet et ne risquent pas d'être pénalisés en raison de leur décision, quelle qu'elle soit. Voilà le consentement éclairé[307].

Le consentement véritablement éclairé suppose également l'existence d'un corps médical compétent et bien informé ; il s'agit là d'une nécessité pressante[308], qui requiert un échange de connaissances entre l'expert en biologie moléculaire ou en génétique et l'omnipraticien. Si l'on vise la véritable réciprocité dans la relation patient-médecin, la réalisation de l'objectif fondamental — mutualité, communauté, responsabilité civique — deviendra possible.

B. Mutualité

Le deuxième principe de base est celui de la mutualité ou de la responsabilité civique. Ce principe reconnaît que les maladies génétiques n'atteignent pas uniquement les individus, mais aussi les familles et les collectivités, d'où la nécessité du partage responsable de l'information génétique. La mutualité relève donc du principe de bienfaisance et est compatible avec le principe de liberté ou de libre choix, lequel [TRADUCTION] « suppose que l'on accorde le respect qui convient à la responsabilité individuelle[309] ».

---

307. N.A. HOLTZMAN, *loc. cit.*, note 40, p. 629. Voir également David ROY et Maurice DE WACHTER, *The Life Technologies and Public Policy*, Montréal, Institut de recherches politiques, 1986, pp. 148-149.

308. N.A. HOLTZMAN, *loc. cit.*, note 40, pp. 626-628. Sans cette réciprocité et sans cet échange ouvert et franc sur ce que comporte le prélèvement d'ADN et la recherche de marqueurs et de gènes, nous risquons d'assister à l'élaboration de politiques juridiques protectionnistes fondées sur des concepts empruntés au droit des biens ou au droit de la propriété intellectuelle ou industrielle, plutôt qu'à la conception de l'information génétique comme un attribut de la personne.

309. O. SCHACHTER, *loc. cit.*, note 116, p. 850.

Selon le principe de mutualité, l'individu reçoit des renseignements génétiques et est libre d'agir ou non à leur égard. Ceux qui n'entreprennent aucune action demeurent liés par le contrat social classique aux termes duquel l'État continue à imposer des restrictions à la liberté individuelle en fonction de la notion de « bien commun ». Il est possible que pour l'État, le « bien commun » suppose la mise en œuvre de programmes eugéniques obligatoires. Le maintien et la survie de la liberté individuelle résident par conséquent dans la participation civique.

Au niveau familial, chacun assumerait l'obligation sociale de ne pas garder pour soi des renseignements pouvant bénéficier à d'autres membres de la famille, lorsqu'une telle omission risquerait de leur porter préjudice. Sous cet angle, la mutualité relève du principe de non-malfaisance. Si un patient persistait dans son refus d'avertir les membres de sa famille, les exposant ainsi à des risques génétiques graves, le médecin pourrait exceptionnellement passer outre à ce refus et divulguer des renseignements relatifs à la planification des naissances ou au mode de vie[310].

Au niveau communautaire, chacun pourrait consentir librement au prélèvement ou à la mise en banque d'ADN et à l'utilisation de marqueurs dans le but de dresser des cartes de liaison[311]. Ce type de participation constitue la première étape de la mise sur pied de programmes de prévention médicale. Par ailleurs, il faudra bien entendu respecter, dans l'application de ces programmes, les différences génétiques individuelles et la liberté de choix dans la prise de décision.

Il incomberait à l'État, en contrepartie du consentement du patient à la participation et à la divulgation, de fournir les ressources nécessaires, non seulement au diagnostic, mais également à l'éducation, à la recherche, au traitement et aux soins. Le projet éducatif doit être vaste. Il doit viser à atteindre un degré de compréhension qui nous permettra à la fois de protéger ce qui est humain dans la nature génétique et de soulager la souffrance, de faire progresser l'espèce.

En conséquence, il nous faut explorer la signification de la dignité humaine dans le contexte de la génétique humaine. Nous devons nous méfier de la tendance à [TRADUCTION] « considérer comme contraire à la dignité humaine tout ce que l'on déteste intensément, et parfois irrationnellement. En invoquant l'atteinte à la dignité humaine, on introduit ainsi, par la bande, des idéologies personnelles dans le droit positif, sous forme de règles liant la législature[312] ».

---

310. Cette position s'accorde avec celle qu'exprime la commission présidentielle dans *Screening and Counseling*, *op. cit.*, note 33, p. 44. Pour l'auteur, la « famille » comprend les personnes avec lesquelles on entretient des rapports sociaux ou personnels, et non seulement celles avec lesquelles on a des rapports consacrés par le droit.

311. Voir *supra*, pp. 11-12, le texte sous la rubrique « V. Évolution de la génétique médicale ».

312. Jan STEPAN, « State Intervention in Family Procreation Decisions » (1988), Reports II (VIIIe Congrès mondial de droit médical) 233, p. 237.

Il serait ironique que le respect de la dignité inhérente à la personne humaine devienne la source d'un impérialisme génétique que nous nous imposerions à nous-mêmes, et qui pourrait prendre la forme de programmes visant à faire disparaître des gènes « nuisibles » au nom des droits génétiques des générations à venir ou celle de l'interdiction systématique des thérapies touchant le patrimoine génétique.

Il faut dépolariser le débat, car les débats polarisés font appel à des [TRADUCTION] « axiomes erronés » qui [TRADUCTION] « peuvent convaincre le lecteur qu'une intuition partielle représente toute la vérité[313] ». L'argument de la « pente glissante » est un de ces axiomes. Freiner le génie génétique par peur de « s'engager sur une pente glissante » équivaut à refuser un traitement à des malades [TRADUCTION] « parce que nous sommes incapables de distinguer les modifications correctives de la lignée germinale des améliorations eugéniques ; cet argument dénote un manque de confiance en l'aptitude humaine à agir judicieusement sur la base d'une classification éthique distinctive[314] ».

V. Conclusion

Devant les problèmes que soulève la nouvelle génétique humaine à l'égard du respect de la vie privée et du libre choix, le modèle de système de santé publique reposant sur la morale utilitariste et son calcul coûts-avantages se révèle inadéquat[315]. La théorie de la justice fondée sur le contrat social est plus prometteuse, car elle donne une signification à la dignité inhérente à la personne humaine dans le contexte génétique[316]. Nous proposons l'élaboration, sur la base de l'égalité génétique éclairée, d'un nouveau contrat social fondé sur les principes de réciprocité et de mutualité.

L'actualisation de la réciprocité ou de l'échange de connaissances se ferait au sein de la relation protégée entre le médecin et son patient, de sorte que l'individualité, la confidentialité et la liberté de choix seraient préservées.

La maladie génétique n'est pas qu'une affaire individuelle. Elle touche également la famille, la collectivité et les générations futures. L'individu a de ce fait l'obligation de contribuer à la détection et à la compréhension des maladies génétiques, d'où

---

313. K. BOONE, *loc. cit.*, note 2, p. 10.

314. *Id.*, p. 11. Voir également J. FLETCHER, *op. cit.*, note 246, p. 5 et suiv. concernant les failles des fallacieux arguments de la capacité (nous pouvons faire quelque chose, donc nous devons le faire) et de la nécessité (nous pouvons faire quelque chose, donc nous le ferons).

315. Ruth MACKLIN, « Mapping the Human Genome », dans A. MILUNSKY et G.J. ANNAS (dir.), *op. cit.*, note 236, pp. 107-111.

316. M.-A. HERMITTE, *loc. cit.*, note 298, p. 43 :

> Il faut suivre pas à pas la théorie générale des obligations ; elle est probablement plus liée qu'on ne l'imagine généralement à la protection des droits de l'homme, ou du moins à un type de protection, empirique certes, mais relativement proche, finalement, du message des droits de l'homme.

l'existence du principe de mutualité ou de responsabilité civique. Il est possible d'assumer cette responsabilité en participant volontairement à certains programmes, comme la mise en banque d'ADN. L'État, en contrepartie, fournit les ressources nécessaires à la recherche, à l'éducation, au diagnostic, au traitement et aux soins.

Les principes de réciprocité et de mutualité donneraient une assise solide au partage de la responsabilité et à la participation du patient à l'exercice de la médecine génétique, l'objectif consistant dans une justice génétique fondée sur la responsabilité individuelle.

Conclusion

Nous avons vu que la génétique humaine porte la promesse de la capacité de prédire de nombreuses maladies, rares ou répandues, laquelle touchera bientôt, directement ou indirectement, toute la population du globe. Dans le passé, beaucoup de couples ignoraient qu'ils étaient porteurs d'un gène récessif pathogène jusqu'à ce qu'ils aient un enfant atteint. À l'avenir, bien des gens se découvriront porteurs d'allèles responsables d'affections auxquelles ils ne comprennent rien. Jusqu'à récemment, une personne qui, en raison de ses antécédents familiaux, savait avoir cinquante pour cent de chances d'être atteinte d'une maladie à manifestation tardive, vivait en ignorant si elle était porteuse du gène et si elle aurait un jour la maladie. Maintenant, ces personnes peuvent disposer de plus de renseignements pour fonder leurs choix. Dans le cas des maladies multifactorielles courantes, des marqueurs génétiques spécifiques peuvent maintenant signaler à quelqu'un qu'il court un risque plus élevé que le reste de la population d'avoir une maladie particulière.

Nous aurons un jour la capacité technique de « traiter » le gène lui-même. Cela pourra se faire, pour certaines affections monogéniques, en traitant des cellules somatiques, mais il est probable que le traitement des cellules de la lignée germinale, même s'il devient techniquement possible, demeurera irréalisable dans la pratique. Pour l'heure, cependant, il y a un large écart entre notre capacité d'identifier des gènes particuliers et notre capacité de les traiter. Un couple dont les deux partenaires sont porteurs du gène d'une affection récessive peut donc se voir dans l'obligation de décider s'il prendra le risque d'avoir des enfants ou s'il l'évitera en ayant recours au diagnostic prénatal et à l'avortement sélectif ou aux techniques de reproduction. Notre perception des personnes handicapées influencera ces décisions, et celles-ci influenceront probablement à leur tour cette perception. Il est possible que des pressions sociales et médicales s'exercent sur les personnes susceptibles d'avoir hérité d'un gène pathogène, pour qu'elles vérifient si elles sont porteuses du gène et, le cas échéant, qu'elles en avisent les membres de leur famille sur la vie desquels ce renseignement peut avoir des répercussions. Les employeurs et les assureurs peuvent également avoir intérêt à posséder de tels renseignements. Une surveillance étroite peut s'exercer sur les personnes risquant de souffrir d'une maladie multifactorielle, pour qu'elles s'efforcent d'éviter la maladie en agissant sur leur milieu et sur leur mode de vie. Tous ces changements vont avoir des répercussions sur notre vie quotidienne et sur notre avenir comme société.

En 1982, le Conseil de l'Europe a recommandé l'établissement du droit à un patrimoine génétique inaltéré, fondé sur la notion de dignité humaine. Nous avons donc examiné les notions de patrimoine génétique et de dignité humaine.

Nous avons vu que les phénomènes biologiques de la mutation et de la méiose font de chacun de nous un être unique, mais que nous sommes liés temporellement et spatialement les uns aux autres par le pool génique. Nous avons vu que la thérapie génique de la lignée somatique aurait des incidences mineures et indirectes sur le pool génique, comme en ont les traitements médicaux conventionnels. Nous avons vu également que la thérapie génique de la lignée germinale, si elle était réalisable, aurait quant à elle un effet direct mais mineur sur le pool génique. Toutefois, il existe une différence d'ordre moral entre les deux thérapies. En effet, la thérapie de la lignée somatique porte sur un seul génome et peut être considérée comme une affaire privée, tandis que la thérapie de la lignée germinale, qui modifie directement le pool génique, peut être perçue comme relevant de l'intérêt public. La seconde évoque l'histoire politique trouble du mouvement eugénique, une histoire qui ne touche pas seulement les manipulations de la lignée germinale, lesquelles sont peu probables, mais qui s'applique également aux manipulations de la personne au moyen d'outils sociaux plus conventionnels, comme la discrimination.

Bien que l'être humain ne se réduise pas à sa simple constitution génétique, celle-ci est néanmoins considérée comme un élément important de la personne et, par conséquent, de la dignité humaine. Le droit international n'a pas défini de manière précise cette dignité mais elle en constitue le thème sous-jacent, et l'on considère que tous les droits de l'homme en découlent. Et si l'expression « dignité humaine » n'est pas expressément utilisée dans la *Charte canadienne des droits et libertés*, diverses dispositions de ce texte ressortissent à deux principes, l'autonomie et l'égalité, qui sont des composantes importantes de la dignité. Nous avons mentionné que ces garanties peuvent avoir une application directe sur la génétique, en matière de dépistage et d'utilisation d'échantillons d'ADN.

La façon de procéder pour protéger notre patrimoine génétique n'est pas claire. Il existe un consensus international sur la nécessité d'interdire les possibilités les plus extrêmes de la génétique humaine. Il nous faut toutefois apprendre à faire preuve de prudence sans s'opposer a priori à toute recherche sur le gène. Comme pour toute autre technologie, nous devons nous assurer que la génétique augmente l'éventail des choix possibles et non l'inverse. Non seulement il nous faut réprimer les abus, mais nous devons aussi nous interroger sur l'orientation des recherches génétiques. Nous devons déterminer les limites du libre choix à ce chapitre, et trouver une formule qui respecte la complexité, la variabilité et l'unicité de la personne humaine.

Nous avons fait état des dangers associés à la création, proposée par le Conseil de l'Europe en 1982, du droit à un patrimoine génétique inaltéré. Une semblable interprétation pourrait, sous le couvert de la protection, mener à la présélection génétique, aux examens de compatibilité génétique et, ultimement, aux poursuites judiciaires entre membres d'une même famille et entre générations. Les êtres humains sont des êtres complexes ; notre unicité génétique n'est qu'un des facteurs de notre humanité. Nous avons la capacité d'entrer en interaction avec l'environnement et de recréer celui-ci. Pourtant, des conceptions de l'être humain plus réductionnistes que celle-là peuvent influer sur nos lois et nos politiques sociales. Le déterminisme génétique, par exemple, voit dans l'être humain un produit déterminé par ses gènes, incapable, en conséquence, de créer un environnement social qui tienne compte des différences biologiques. Une telle conception peut avoir des répercussions importantes. Elle peut être à la source de politiques qui ont pour effet d'exclure des personnes de certains milieux (par exemple le lieu de travail) plutôt que d'intervenir sur la structure et l'environnement sociaux pour les adapter à ces personnes. Elle peut être évidente aussi dans certaines attitudes relatives au diagnostic prénatal. D'aucuns prétendront en effet qu'il est plus simple et moins coûteux d'éliminer les fœtus présentant des imperfections biologiques que d'élaborer un système social et un système d'éducation adaptés à ces enfants. Dans sa forme extrémiste, le déterminisme génétique a donné lieu à l'affirmation voulant que les enfants susceptibles d'hériter de certaines affections génétiques aient le droit de ne pas naître et que, conséquemment, les parents potentiels aient l'obligation de veiller à ce qu'ils ne naissent pas.

Les « naturalistes » proposent une vision tout aussi réductionniste de la nature humaine. Pour eux, la diversité aléatoire de notre constitution génétique constitue l'essence de l'humanité. Ils voient donc toute tentative de modification de cette constitution comme un affront à la dignité humaine. Une telle position interdit toute discussion visant à établir quand il peut être moralement acceptable de procéder à des modifications génétiques et réduit les possibilités de progrès de l'humanité comme espèce. Suivant la conception naturaliste, il est possible de voir dans toute forme de prévention de la souffrance par le biais de la thérapie génique un affront à la nature humaine, parce que la diversité biologique due au hasard en constitue un élément important. Les tenants de cette conception pourraient donc vouloir réduire les fonds affectés aux techniques génétiques et aux services médicaux.

Comment réconcilier ces visions polarisées de façon que notre unicité nourrisse le respect de l'humanité dans sa composante individuelle et collective ? Quel cadre juridique et éthique pouvons-nous élaborer pour préserver la liberté de choix tout en réprimant les abus et en limitant les effets secondaires sociaux indésirables ?

Ces questions nous ont amenés à explorer une théorie de la justice génétique susceptible de permettre la réalisation de ces objectifs. Nous nous sommes aperçus que des conflits pouvaient surgir entre le principe éthique d'autonomie et les principes de bienfaisance et de non-malfaisance et, partant, que ces principes ne nous offrent pas de solution. Les principes de justice et d'équité, de portée plus large, tiennent compte des moyens de répartir équitablement les ressources. Cependant, les théories utilitaristes de la justice soulèvent des problèmes sérieux, car elles font de l'individu le moyen de réaliser un objectif d'efficacité, habituellement d'ordre économique. Dans cette perspective, les personnes handicapées risquent de devenir des « coûts évitables ».

La théorie de la justice issue de l'école libertarienne peut, en matière de santé, prendre la forme du darwinisme social ; l'égalitarisme peut quant à lui entrer en conflit avec notre conception de la liberté ou du libre choix qui, comme l'égalité, constitue un élément important de la protection de notre dignité inhérente.

La théorie de la justice fondée sur le contrat social pourrait à la fois permettre la protection des droits individuels et favoriser la responsabilité collective en matière génétique. Elle repose sur un engagement social en faveur de la vulgarisation du savoir génétique et de son langage de probabilités, de sondes et de prédictions, et suppose l'éducation du public à tous les niveaux ainsi que le maintien du contrat de services médicaux comme lieu privilégié et confidentiel de l'individualisation de ce savoir. Le principe du respect de l'autonomie réside dans le consentement éclairé et dans la volonté de l'individu en tant que membre d'une société qui procure les bases des connaissances et de la compréhension collectives des différences et de la vulnérabilité génétiques.

La reconnaissance du fait que le pool génique ne connaît pas de frontières politiques, sociales ou raciales est indispensable à l'incontournable débat international. La définition et la protection de la dignité inhérente à la personne humaine intéressent l'humanité dans son ensemble ; il s'agit donc nécessairement d'une entreprise de portée internationale.

La nouvelle génétique humaine exige un examen plus approfondi des questions relatives aux droits de la personne qu'elle soulève. Nous n'avons fait qu'évoquer les problèmes reliés à la discrimination, à l'assurance, à l'emploi, aux règles de preuve, au partage ou au vol de renseignements et, en particulier, aux répercussions possibles de la génétique sur la politique et la législation sanitaires. Il est nécessaire de poursuivre les recherches concernant les effets qu'aura la génétique humaine sur la société canadienne et, plus spécialement, la pertinence des concepts actuels de droit public et privé. Il faut examiner les incidences de cette discipline sur la common law et sur le droit civil du Québec, relativement aux contrats, aux biens, à la propriété intellectuelle, au droit de la famille, au droit des personnes et au droit de la responsabilité civile.

La protection des droits de la personne dans le contexte génétique s'avérera onéreuse, non pas tant en raison du coût des techniques qu'en raison de celui de l'éducation et de la fourniture des services génétiques. Il nous faudra déterminer quelle part des ressources sociales nous sommes prêts à affecter à ce secteur et quelle importance nous accordons à la génétique par rapport à d'autres interventions également coûteuses.

Chaque être humain, comme agent moral, est responsable de ses choix génétiques et de la gestion qu'il fait de son « capital » ou de ses « investissements » génétiques. Ses choix doivent être éclairés et être faits à la lumière du contexte social et des répercussions sur la collectivité. En effet, le développement des possibilités techniques ne crée pas d'impératifs. Au contraire, il commande la responsabilité sur le plan collectif. Nous nous retrouvons donc en présence de la notion de patrimoine génétique prise dans son sens individuel, mais également dans son sens collectif de patrimoine commun de l'humanité conservé en fiducie pour le bien de tous.

Glossaire

ABERRATION CHROMOSOMIQUE : Anomalie résultant de l'addition ou de la soustraction de chromosomes entiers ou de certaines parties d'entre eux.

ACIDE DÉSOXYRIBONUCLÉIQUE (ADN) : Molécule formée de deux brins dans lesquels des paires de bases, dont l'agencement est responsable de l'information génétique, sont reliées entre elles par des liens faibles. L'ADN renferme quatre nucléotides : l'adénosine (A), la guanosine (G), la cytidine (C) et la thymidine (T). Les paires ne se forment qu'entre A et T et entre G et C, de sorte que la séquence d'un des brins nous permet de déduire celle de l'autre. Cette complémentarité est la clé du pouvoir de transmission de l'information de l'ADN. L'information codée dans l'ADN du gène détermine la structure et donc la fonction de la protéine correspondante.

ACIDE RIBONUCLÉIQUE MESSAGER (ARNm) : Molécule complémentaire de l'ADN d'un gène qui migre dans le cytoplasme pour servir de matrice lors de l'assemblage des acides aminés en protéines, dont certaines sont des unités structurales importantes des cellules et d'autres agissent comme enzymes.

AFFECTION MONOGÉNIQUE : Voir CARACTÈRE OU AFFECTION MENDÉLIEN.

ALLÈLE : Se dit de chacune des formes différentes d'un gène occupant un locus déterminé sur un chromosome.

AMNIOCENTÈSE : Épreuve médicale dans laquelle on effectue une ponction d'une petite quantité du liquide amniotique entourant le fœtus dans l'utérus. Ce liquide renferme des cellules fœtales qui sont mises en culture pour faire ensuite l'objet d'un dépistage de diverses aberrations chromosomiques ou troubles biochimiques.

AUTONOMIE : En éthique, principe en vertu duquel un individu ne doit être contraint par personne à faire certains gestes ou certains choix.

AUTOSOME : Tout chromosome ne participant pas à la détermination du sexe.

BIENFAISANCE : Bonté, bienveillance, charité. En éthique, principe en vertu duquel on doit faire le bien ou aider les autres à combler leurs aspirations légitimes.

CARACTÈRE OU AFFECTION MENDÉLIEN : Caractère ou affection dépendant d'un seul gène et associé à un mode simple de transmission héréditaire (dominant ou récessif, autosomique ou lié au chromosome X). Terme formé d'après le nom du moine autrichien Gregor Mendel qui a été le premier à observer de tels caractères chez les pois et qui a jeté les bases de la génétique moderne.

CARTE DE LIAISON : Carte chromosomique montrant la position relative de certains gènes.

CARTE GÉNIQUE : voir CARTE DE LIAISON.

CELLULE : Unité fondamentale de la structure des organismes vivants. La plus petite masse de protoplasme limitée par une membrane, constituée d'un noyau et du cytoplasme qui l'entoure, et capable d'autoreproduction.

CELLULE SOMATIQUE : Toute cellule de l'organisme n'ayant pas la capacité de devenir une cellule germinale (ovule ou spermatozoïde).

CHORÉE DE HUNTINGTON : Maladie héréditaire à transmission dominante qui se manifeste habituellement entre les âges de 30 et de 50 ans. Elle produit une dégénérescence lente et progressive de certains tissus cérébraux, et finalement la mort. Les principales manifestations sont les mouvements désordonnés (chorée) et la démence. On sait maintenant sur quel chromosome est situé le gène responsable.

CHROMOSOME : Élément filamenteux au sein du noyau d'une cellule, renfermant l'ADN, le matériel génétique (c.-à-d. les gènes). Une cellule humaine normale renferme 46 chromosomes, soit deux paires de 22 autosomes et 2 chromosomes sexuels (XX ou XY).

CHROMOSOMES SEXUELS : Les chromosomes X et Y qui sont responsables de la détermination du sexe. La combinaison XY donne des individus mâles et la combinaison XX, des individus femelles.

CLONAGE : Processus par lequel on produit un groupe de cellules (clones) ayant un patrimoine génétique identique à celui de la cellule originale. Dans le cadre des techniques de modification de l'ADN, le clonage regroupe les méthodes servant à produire plusieurs copies d'un gène ou d'un segment d'ADN.

DÉTERMINISME : Théorie selon laquelle toute action humaine est motivée par des mécanismes immuables.

DOMINANT : Chaque cellule somatique (du corps) renferme deux copies (allèles) d'un gène au niveau d'un site déterminé. On qualifie de dominant un allèle qui s'exprime peu importe l'allèle correspondant. (antonyme : récessif).

DOUBLE HÉLICE : Forme adoptée par les deux brins d'ADN reliés entre eux, évoquant une échelle tordue.

EMPREINTES GÉNÉTIQUES D'ADN : Analyse en laboratoire de l'ADN d'un individu ; comme les empreintes digitales, l'ADN d'un individu est unique.

ENZYME DE RESTRICTION : Enzyme ayant la propriété de reconnaître une séquence nucléotidique particulière et de couper l'ADN au niveau de cette séquence.

EUGÉNISME : Ensemble des tentatives visant à améliorer le patrimoine héréditaire d'une population en facilitant la transmission de caractères jugés souhaitables (eugénisme positif) et en décourageant la transmission des caractères jugés non souhaitables (eugénisme négatif).

EXPRESSION : voir EXPRESSION GÉNÉTIQUE.

EXPRESSION GÉNÉTIQUE : Processus par lequel une séquence d'ADN d'un gène produit le caractère dont elle est responsable.

EXPRESSIVITÉ : Manifestation variable de l'expression d'un gène, qui se traduit par des signes extérieurs chez différents individus porteurs du gène.

FIBROSE KYSTIQUE (mucoviscidose) : Maladie autosomique récessive à incidence élevée chez la race blanche. Les principaux problèmes cliniques proviennent de l'obstruction des canaux d'organes comme les poumons et le pancréas par des sécrétions anormalement épaisses. On connaît maintenant l'emplacement du gène de cette maladie sur le chromosome.

GAMÈTE : Spermatozoïde ou ovule. Cellule reproductrice mâle ou femelle parvenue à maturité renfermant un seul jeu de chromosomes et non les deux comme dans les cellules somatiques.

GÈNE : Unité physique et fonctionnelle fondamentale de l'hérédité. Un gène est constitué d'une séquence ordonnée de nucléotides qui forment l'ADN situé à un emplacement particulier sur un chromosome déterminé.

GÉNOME : Matériel génétique total que renferment les chromosomes des cellules d'un individu.

GÉNOTYPE : Matériel génétique porté par un individu au niveau d'un site génique particulier ou de l'ensemble des gènes, par opposition au phénotype qui désigne les caractères apparents.

HÉMOPHILIE : Groupe d'affections congénitales se traduisant par un temps de coagulation du sang anormalement long. L'hémophilie classique est liée au chromosome X. Cela signifie que la maladie frappe habituellement les sujets mâles et qu'elle se transmet aux enfants d'une femme asymptomatique, ou à toutes les filles d'un homme porteur de la maladie.

IN VITRO : Manipulations effectuées sur des systèmes biologiques à l'extérieur d'un organisme inaltéré.

JUSTICE : Correspond habituellement à un traitement égal et équitable. En éthique, principe selon lequel nos actes ne doivent pas se traduire par des avantages ou des torts disproportionnés à autrui.

LIAISON GÉNÉTIQUE : Tendance qu'ont des gènes situés à des emplacements différents d'être transmis ensemble. Plus les sites sont voisins sur le chromosome, plus la liaison est forte. Plus ils sont éloignés, plus ils sont susceptibles d'être transmis de façon indépendante par suite du phénomène de recombinaison au cours de la méiose.

LIÉ AU CHROMOSOME X : Qualifie un gène situé sur le chromosome X, ou un caractère déterminé par un tel gène.

LIGNÉE GERMINALE : Lignée cellulaire qui produit les gamètes (spermatozoïde ou ovule) nécessaires à la reproduction. Toute modification de la lignée germinale peut se transmettre à la génération suivante.

LOCUS : Emplacement particulier d'un gène sur un chromosome.

MALADIE DE TAY-SACHS : Affection autosomique récessive se manifestant par des troubles mentaux, la paralysie, la démence et la cécité ; la mort survient habituellement avant la fin de la troisième année de vie. Le gène en cause code pour une enzyme qui dégrade certaines substances chimiques du cerveau. Lorsque le gène est défectueux, ces substances ne sont pas dégradées et s'accumulent dans le cerveau et le tissu nerveux. Le gène se retrouve plus fréquemment chez les juifs ashkénazes originaires d'Europe de l'Est. On connaît maintenant l'emplacement du gène.

MARQUEUR : Voir MARQUEUR GÉNÉTIQUE.

MARQUEUR GÉNÉTIQUE : Différence génétique facilement repérable dont la fréquence est suffisante pour être utile dans les études des familles et des populations.

MÉIOSE : Division cellulaire se produisant uniquement dans les cellules germinales au cours de la formation de l'ovule et du spermatozoïde. Il en résulte une cellule dont le nombre de chromosomes est réduit de moitié.

MULTIFACTORIEL : Qualifie un caractère ou une affection dont l'expression résulte de plusieurs gènes et de plusieurs facteurs environnementaux agissant de concert.

MUTATION : Modification du matériel génétique produisant une nouvelle caractéristique. Lorsqu'elle se produit dans une cellule germinale, elle peut être transmise aux générations suivantes.

NATURALISME : Théorie selon laquelle l'une des caractéristiques essentielles de l'être humain tient à ce qu'il est le produit du hasard.

NON-MALFAISANCE : Terme généralement associé à la maxime « primum non nocere » qui signifie « avant tout, ne pas nuire ». En éthique, principe qui veut que l'on a l'obligation de ne pas faire de mal, de ne pas nuire et de ne pas risquer de nuire.

NUCLÉOTIDE : Sous-unité d'ADN ou d'ARN constituée d'une base azotée (adénine, guanine, thymine ou cytosine dans l'ADN ; dans l'ARN, l'uracile remplace la thymine). L'ADN et l'ARN sont formés de milliers de nucléotides reliés entre eux.

PÉNÉTRANCE : Fréquence avec laquelle des porteurs de deux allèles récessifs ou d'un allèle dominant responsables d'une maladie manifestent les symptômes de la maladie. On dit que la pénétrance est réduite lorsqu'elle est inférieure à 100%.

PHÉNOTYPE : Apparence d'un individu résultant de l'interaction des gènes et de l'environnement. Terme utilisé également de façon plus précise pour désigner les caractères apparents produits par un génotype particulier.

PHÉNYLCÉTONURIE : Erreur innée du métabolisme caractérisée par l'incapacité de l'organisme à transformer la phénylalanine alimentaire en tyrosine par suite d'un déficit en une enzyme hépatique (la phénylalanine hydroxylase). L'accumulation de phénylalanine qui s'ensuit est responsable de troubles mentaux. Une simple épreuve chez le nouveau-né permet de diagnostiquer la maladie. La maladie se traite grâce à un régime alimentaire pauvre en phénylalanine.

POLYGÉNIQUE : Qualifie un caractère dépendant de plusieurs gènes agissant de concert.

POLYMORPHISME : Présence dans une population de plusieurs formes génétiques différentes d'un caractère, dont aucune n'est rare. Les polymorphismes, utiles dans les analyses de liaison génétique, peuvent provenir de modifications au sein d'un gène ou de modifications de l'ADN entre deux gènes.

POLYMORPHISME DES SITES DE RESTRICTION (RFLP) : Fragment d'ADN résultant d'une coupure par une enzyme de restriction. Le fragment est plus ou moins long selon le nombre de sites de restriction présents. Le polymorphisme de ces sites (présents sous plusieurs formes dans la population, et non rares) les rend utiles comme marqueurs génétiques dans les études de liaison servant à cartographier le génome.

POOL GÉNIQUE : Tous les allèles de tous les individus dans une population.

PORTEUR : Individu ne possédant que l'un des deux allèles nécessaires pour l'expression d'une maladie récessive, ou individu possédant un gène responsable d'une maladie dominante qui ne s'est pas encore manifestée.

PROTÉINE : Molécule composée d'une chaîne d'acides aminés réunis en une séquence selon la séquence des paires de base de l'ADN. Ces molécules participent à la structure et à la fonction des organismes vivants.

RÉCESSIF : Qualifie un allèle qui ne s'exprime que lorsque les deux allèles identiques sont présents sur les deux chromosomes (antonyme : dominant).

RECOMBINAISON : Échange, au cours de la méiose, de segments de chromosomes homologues, dont l'un provient de la mère et l'autre du père. Ce processus permet une plus grande variabilité que si les chromosomes étaient transmis tels quels.

RES NULLIUS : N'appartient à personne. Chose n'ayant pas de propriétaire, soit parce que l'ancien propriétaire l'a abandonnée, soit qu'elle n'a jamais eu de propriétaire, soit qu'elle n'est pas susceptible d'appropriation.

SÉQUENCE D'ADN : Ordre dans lequel sont disposées les paires de base dans une molécule d'ADN, un gène ou un chromosome.

SONDE : voir SONDE GÉNIQUE.

SONDE D'ADN : voir SONDE GÉNIQUE.

SONDE GÉNIQUE : Segment d'un ADN à simple brin marqué par une molécule radioactive ou un groupement chimique et servant à identifier une région spécifique du génome.

SPINA-BIFIDA : Ouverture dans le canal rachidien due à une affection multifactorielle du développement.

SYNDROME DE DOWN (mongolisme, trisomie 21) : Aberration chromosomique causée par la présence d'un chromosome 21 supplémentaire (trisomie 21). Les symptômes sont les troubles mentaux, les malformations cardiaques congénitales, un faciès typique et une espérance de vie réduite. La fréquence du syndrome de Down augmente avec l'âge de la mère.

THALASSÉMIE : Groupe de plusieurs anomalies héréditaires de l'hémoglobine résultant de gènes défectueux responsables d'une production réduite de la globine, protéine entrant dans la composition de la molécule d'hémoglobine.

THÉRAPIE GÉNIQUE : Insertion d'un ADN normal directement dans les cellules dans le but de corriger une anomalie génétique.

TRAIT DRÉPANOCYTAIRE : Correspond au phénotype d'une personne porteuse d'un allèle anormal causant la drépanocytose. Une épreuve sanguine simple permet de le dépister. La mutation responsable de la drépanocytose est très fréquente chez certaines populations qui ont été en contact avec le paludisme, telle la population noire d'Afrique. On pense que le gène défectueux s'est maintenu dans la population parce qu'il confère aux porteurs une résistance accrue au paludisme, même s'il tue ceux qui portent les deux copies du gène. On connaît maintenant le site et la séquence d'ADN du gène.

Table des arrêts

Canada

Andrews c. *Law Society of British Columbia*, [1989] 1 R.C.S. 151.
Attorney-General of British Columbia and Astaroff (1983), 6 C.C.C. (3d) 498 (C.A. C.-B.).
Borowski c. *Attorney General of Canada*, [1987] 4 W.W.R. 385 (C.A. Sask.).
Dion c. *Procureur général du Canada*, [1986] D.L.Q. 353 (C.S.).
Engstrom c. *Courteau*, [1986] R.J.Q. 3048 (C.S.).
Hunter c. *Southam Inc.*, [1984] 2 R.C.S. 145.
Mills c. *La Reine* [1986], 1 R.C.S. 863.
Ministre du Revenu national c. *Kruger Inc.*, [1984] 2 C.F. 535 (C.A.).
R. c. *Amway du Canada Ltée.*, [1986] 2 C.F. 312 (Div. 1re inst.).
R. c. *Beare* ; *R.* c. *Higgins*, [1988] 2 R.C.S. 387.
R. c. *Big M. Drug Mart Ltd.*, [1985] 1 R.C.S. 295.
R. c. *Dyment*, [1988] 2 R.C.S. 417.
R. c. *Edwards Books*, [1986] 2 R.C.S. 713.
R. c. *Esposito* (1985), 24 C.C.C. (3d) 88 (C.A. Ont.).
R. c. *Jones*, [1986] 2 R.C.S. 284.
R. c. *Legere* (1989), 5 W.C.B. (2d) 384 (C.A. N.-B.).
R. c. *Morgentaler*, [1988] 1 R.C.S. 30.
R. c. *Oakes*, [1986] 1 R.C.S. 103.
R. c. *Parent* (1989), 65 A.R. 307 (B.R.).
R. c. *Pohoretsky*, [1987] 1 R.C.S. 945.
R. c. *Therrien* (1982), 67 C.C.C. (2d) 31 (C. comté Ont.).
Re Jamieson and The Queen (1982), 70 C.C.C. (2d) 430 (C.S. Qc).
Renvoi relatif à la Public Service Employee Relations Act (Alb.), [1987] 1 R.C.S. 313.
Renvoi relatif au par. 92(2) de la B.C. Motor Vehicle Act, R.S.B.C. 1979, chap. 288, [1985] 2 R.C.S. 486.
SDGMR c. *Dolphin Delivery Ltd.*, [1986] 2 R.C.S. 573.
Singh c. *Ministre de l'Emploi et de l'Immigration*, [1985] 1 R.C.S. 177.
Tremblay c. *Daigle*, [1989] 2 R.C.S. 530.

États-Unis

Curlender c. *Bio-Science Laboratories*, 165 Cal. Rptr. 477, 106 Cal. App. 3d 811 (1980).
Harbeson c. *Parke-Davis, Inc.*, 656 P. 2d 483, 98 Wash. 2d 460 (C.S. 1983).

Moore c. *Regents of the University of California*, 249 Cal. Rptr. 494 (App. 2 Dist. 1988) nouvelle audition accordée 252 Cal. Rptr. 816 (1988).
Procanik c. *Cillo*, 478 A. 2d 755, 97 N.J. 339 (1984).
Siemieniec c. *Lutheran General Hospital*, 480 N.E. 2d 1227 (Ill. App. 1 Dist. 1985).
State c. *Castro* 545 N.Y.S. 2d 985 (1989) (Bronx Cty).
Turpin c. *Sortini*, 119 Cal. App. 3d 690, 174 Cal. Rptr. 128 (1981), 182 Cal. Rptr. 337, 643 P. 2d 954, 31 Cal. 3d 220 (C.S. 1982).

Table des lois

Canada

Charte canadienne des droits et libertés, partie I de la *Loi constitutionnelle de 1982* [annexe B de la *Loi de 1982 sur le Canada* (1982, R.U., ch. 11)].
Charte des droits et libertés de la personne, L.R.Q., ch. C-12.
Loi sur la qualité de l'environnement, L.R.Q., ch. Q-2.
Loi sur les biens culturels, L.R.Q., ch. B-4.
Sexual Sterilization Act, S.B.C. 1933, ch. 59.
The Sexual Sterilization Act, S.A. 1928, ch. 37.

États-Unis

Loi publique 86-884 (Lois de 1989) relative aux maladies sexuellement transmissibles et aux maladies métaboliques héréditaires et modifiant les lois citées, approuvée le 11 septembre 1989.

France

Code pénal, art. 63.

Traités et accords internationaux

Charte africaine des droits de l'homme et des peuples (1981).
Convention américaine relative aux droits de l'homme (1969).
Convention de sauvegarde des droits de l'homme et des libertés fondamentales (1950).
Convention des Nations Unies sur le droit de la mer (1982).
Convention pour la prévention et la répression du crime de génocide (1948).
Convention pour la protection des biens culturels en cas de conflit armé (1954).
Déclaration d'Helsinki (1964), Recommandations destinées à guider les médecins dans les recherches biomédicales (modifiée à Tokyo en 1975 ; à Venise en 1983 et à Hong Kong en 1989).
Déclaration de Genève (1948).
Déclaration de Lisbonne (1981).
Déclaration universelle des droits de l'homme (1948).
Pacte international relatif aux droits économiques, sociaux et culturels (1966).
Pacte international relatif aux droits civils et politiques (1966).

Conseil de l'Europe (Assemblée parlementaire)

Recommandation 934 (1982) relative à l'ingénierie génétique.
Résolution 808 (1983) relative au retour des objets d'art.
Recommandation 1100 (1989) sur l'utilisation des embryons et fœtus humains dans la recherche scientifique.
Recommandation 1046 (1986) relative à l'utilisation d'embryons et fœtus humains à des fins diagnostiques, thérapeutiques, scientifiques, industrielles et commerciales.

Bibliographie

A., J.-G., « Chorée de Huntington : test prédictif offert » (1989), 24:7 *Le Médecin du Québec* 87.

AD HOC COMMITTEE ON DNA TECHNOLOGY, AMERICAN SOCIETY OF HUMAN GENETICS, « DNA Banking and DNA Analysis: Points to Consider » (1988), 42:5 *Am. J. Hum. Genet.* 781.

AGICH, George J., « Genetic Justice » (1986), 24 *U.W.O. L. Rev.* 39.

ANDERSON, Alun, « Judge Backs Technique » (1989), 340:6235 *Nature* 582.

———, « New Technique on Trial » (1989), 339:6224 *Nature* 408.

ANDERSON, Elizabeth, « Values, Risks, and Market Norms » (1988), 17 *Phil. Pub. Aff.* 54.

ANDREWS, Lori B., *Medical Genetics: A Legal Frontier*, Chicago, American Bar Foundation, 1987.

ANNAS, George. J., « Crack, Symbolism, and the Constitution » (1989), 19:3 *Hast. Cent. Rep.* 35.

AUDARD, Catherine et autres (dir.), *Individu et justice sociale : autour de John Rawls*, Paris, Seuil, 1988.

BARREAU DU QUÉBEC, « Rapport du comité sur les nouvelles technologies de reproduction » (1988), 48:2 suppl. *R. du B.*

BAUDOUIN, Jean-Louis et Catherine LABRUSSE-RIOU, *Produire l'homme : de quel droit ?*, Paris, P.U.F., 1987.

BENYEKHLEF, Karim, « Réflexions sur la légalité des tests de dépistage de drogues dans l'emploi » (1988), 48 *R. du B.* 315.

BLAKESLEE, S., « New Techniques Help Researchers Track Gene Defects » (14 septembre 1989), *International Herald Tribune* 7.

BOONE, Keith, « Bad Axioms in Genetic Engineering » (1988), 18:4 *Hast. Cent. Rep.* 9.

BRISSON, Jean-Maurice, *Texte annoté de la Charte des droits et libertés de la personne du Québec*, Montréal, SOQUIJ, 1986.

CALLAHAN, Daniel, « Ethical Responsibility in Science in the Face of Uncertain Consequences » (1976), 265 *Annals N.Y. Acad. Sci.* 1.

CANTER, Edith F., « Employment Discrimination Implications of Genetic Screening in the Workplace under Title VII and the Rehabilitation Act » (1984-1985), 10 *Am. J. L. Med.* 323.

CAPRON, Alexander M., « The Rome Bioethics Summit » (1988), 18:4 *Hast. Cent. Rep.* 11.

———, « Tort Liability in Genetic Counseling » (1979), 79 *Colum. L. Rev.* 618.

CLARKE, Angus, « Genetics, Ethics, and Audit » (1990), 335:8698 *Lancet* 1145.

COMMISSION D'EXPERTS POUR LA GÉNÉTIQUE HUMAINE ET LA MÉDECINE DE LA REPRODUCTION, *Rapport au Département fédéral de l'intérieur et au Département de la justice et police* (Berne, 19 août 1988).

COMMISSION DE RÉFORME DU DROIT DU CANADA, *Les crimes contre le fœtus*, Document de travail n° 58, Ottawa, La Commission, 1989.

———, *L'expérimentation biomédicale sur l'être humain*, Document de travail n° 61, Ottawa, La Commission, 1989.

———, *L'omission, la négligence et la mise en danger*, Document de travail n° 46, Ottawa, La Commission, 1985.

———, *Les techniques d'investigation policière et les droits de la personne*, Rapport n° 25, Ottawa, La Commission, 1985.

CONGRÉGATION POUR LA DOCTRINE DE LA FOI, *Instruction sur le respect de la vie humaine naissante et la dignité de la procréation,* Cité du Vatican, Typographie Polyglotte Vaticane, 1987.

CONSEIL D'ÉTAT, *Sciences de la vie : de l'éthique au droit,* 2e éd. Paris, La Documentation française, 1988.

CONSEIL DE L'EUROPE, A.P, *Genetic Engineering: Risks and Chances for Human Rights*, European Parliamentary Hearing, Copenhague, 25 et 26 mai 1981, Strasbourg, Le Conseil, 1981.

CONSEIL DE L'EUROPE, COMITÉ AD HOC D'EXPERTS SUR LES PROGRÈS DES SCIENCES BIOMÉDICALES (CAHBI), *Le dépistage génétique prénatal, le diagnostic génétique prénatal et les conseils génétiques*, Strasbourg, Le Conseil, 1989.

CONSEIL DE RECHERCHES MÉDICALES DU CANADA, *Lignes directrices concernant la recherche sur la thérapie génique somatique chez les humains*, Ottawa, Approvisionnements et Services Canada, 1990.

———, *Pour une éthique internationale en recherche sur des sujets humains*, Ottawa, Approvisionnements et Services Canada, 1988.

CONSEIL DES SCIENCES du CANADA, *La génétique et les services de santé au Canada*, Ottawa, Approvisionnements et Services Canada, 1990.

DAMME, Catherine J., « Controlling Genetic Disease Through Law » (1982), 15 *U.C. Davis L. Rev.* 801.

DE JAGER, K., « Claims to Cultural Property Under International Law » (1988), 1 *Leiden J. Int'l L.* 183.

DE MONTIGNY, Yves, « La protection contre les fouilles, les perquisitions et les saisies abusives : un premier bilan » (1989), 49 *R. du B.* 53.

DELMAS-MARTY, Mireille, « Un nouvel usage des droits de l'homme », dans *Éthique médicale et droits de l'homme*, Paris, Actes Sud/INSERM, 1988, p. 313.

DURBIN, Paul T. (dir.), *Technology and Responsibility*, Dordrecht, D. Reidel, 1987.

EDELMAN, Bernard et Marie-Angèle HERMITTE (dir.), *L'homme, la nature et le droit*, Paris, Christian Bourgois, 1988.

EDWARDS, R.G., « Diagnostic Methods for Human Gametes and Embryos » (1987), 2:5 *Human Reprod.* 415.

ELIAS, Sherman et George J. ANNAS, *Reproductive Genetics and the Law*, New York, Yearbook Medical Publications, 1987.

EMERY, Alan E.H. et David L. RIMOIN, « Nature and Incidence of Genetic Disease », dans Alan E.H. EMERY et David L. RIMOIN (dir.), *Principles and Practice of Medical Genetics*, vol. 1, Edimbourg, Churchill Livingstone, 1983.

ENGELHARDT, H. Tristram, *The Foundations of Bioethics,* New York, Oxford University Press, 1986.

ENGELHARDT, H. Tristram et Michael A. RIE, « Morality for the Medical-Industrial Complex (1988), 319:16 *N. Engl. J. Med.* 1086.

Fécondation in vitro, analyse du génome et thérapie génétique (rapport Benda), Paris, La Documentation française, 1987.

FEINBERG, Joel et Hyman GROSS (dir.), *Philosophy of Law*, 3e éd., Belmont (Calif.), Wadsworth Pub., 1986.

FLETCHER, John C., « Ethical and Social Aspects of Risk Predictions » (1984), 25 *Clin. Genet.* 25.

FLETCHER, Joseph, *The Ethics of Genetic Control: Ending Reproductive Roulette*, New York, Anchor, 1974.

FONDATION MARANGOPOULOS POUR LES DROITS DE L'HOMME, *Expérimentation biomédicale et Droits de l'Homme*, Paris, P.U.F., 1988.

FRÉZAL, J., « Les problèmes éthiques en génétique humaine » (1985), 104 *Louvain Medical* 38.

GELEHRTER, Thomas D. et Francis S. COLLINS, *Principles of Medical Genetics,* Baltimore, Williams & Wilkins, 1990.

« Gene Therapy in Man: Recommendations of the European Medical Research Councils » (1988), 11:8597 *Lancet* 1271.

GOODFELLOW, P.N., « Cystic Fibrosis: Steady Steps Lead to the Gene » (1989), 341:6238 *Nature* 102.

GOUVERNEMENT DU CANADA, *Nouvelle perspective de la santé des Canadiens* (rapport Lalonde), Ottawa, 1974.

GROBSTEIN, Clifford et Michael FLOWER, « Gene Therapy: Proceed with Caution » (1984), 14:2 *Hast. Cent. Rep.* 13.

HERMITTE, Marie-Angèle, « L'affaire Moore » (décembre 1988), 417 *Le Monde Diplomatique* 20.

———, *Le droit du génie génétique végétal*, Paris, Librairies Techniques, 1987.

HOLTZMAN, Neil A., *Proceed with Caution: Predicting Genetic Risks in the Recombinant DNA Era*, Baltimore, Johns Hopkins University Press, 1989.

———, « Recombinant DNA Technology, Genetic Tests, and Public Policy » (1988), 42:4 *Am. J. Hum. Genet.* 624.

HUPPÉ, Luc, « La dignité humaine comme fondement des droits et libertés garantis par la Charte » (1988), 48 *R. du B.* 724.

JACOB, François, *La logique du vivant : une histoire de l'hérédité*, Paris, Gallimard, 1970.

———, *La statue intérieure*, Paris, Seuil, 1987.

JACQUARD, Albert, *L'héritage de la liberté : de l'animalité à l'humanitude*, Paris, Seuil, 1986.

KEVLES, Daniel J., *In the Name of Eugenics: Genetics and the Uses of Human Heredity*, New York, Alfred A. Knopf, 1985.

KEYSERLINGK, Edward W., « Non-Treatment in the Best Interests of the Child: A Case Commentary of *Couture-Jacquet* v. *Montreal Children's Hospital* » (1987), 32 *R.D. McGill* 413.

KING, M.C., « Genetic Testing of Identity and Relationship » (1989), 44:2 *Am. J. Hum. Genet.* 178.

KISS, Alexandre-Charles, « La notion de patrimoine commun de l'humanité » (1982) II, 175 *RCADI* 99.

KNOPPERS, Bartha M., « L'adoption d'un code de conduite international en matière de technologies de la reproduction », dans ASSOCIATION DE DROIT INTERNATIONAL, *Report of the Sixty-Third Conference*, Varsovie (Pologne), L'Association, 1988, p. 879.

———, « L'arbitrage du médecin face aux normes régissant la fécondation 'in vitro' », dans Christian BYK (dir.), *Procréation artificielle : où en sont l'éthique et le droit ?*, Lyon, Lacassagne, 1989, p. 49.

———, « Comparative Abortion Law: The Living Abortus », dans K. MASON (dir.), *Paediatric Medicine*, Londres, Chapman & Hall, 1989, p. 387.

———, *Conception artificielle et responsabilité médicale : une étude de droit comparé*, Cowansville (Qc), Yvon Blais, 1986.

———, « Genetic Screening and Genetic Information in the Workplace » (Allocution prononcée devant l'American Society of Human Genetics, octobre 1986) [non publié].

———, « Human Genetics, Predisposition and the New Social Contract », dans INTERNATIONAL CONFERENCE ON BIOETHICS, *The Human Genome Sequencing: Ethical Issues*, Brescia, (Italie), Clas International, 1989, p. 168.

———, « Modern Birth Technology and Human Rights » (1985), 33 *Am. J. Comp. Law* 1.

———, « Reproductive Technology and International Mechanisms of Protection of the Human Person » (1987), 32 *R.D. McGill* 336.

KNOPPERS, Bartha M. et Claude M. LABERGE, « DNA Sampling and Informed Consent » (1989), 140:9 *Journal de l'Association médicale canadienne* 1023.

LABERGE, Claude, « La révolution biologique », dans Jacques DUFRESNE, Fernand DUMONT et Yves MARTIN (dir.), *Traité d'anthropologie médicale*, Québec, Presses de l'Université du Québec, 1985.

LANGANEY, André, « La diversité génétique humaine : considérable et mal connue », dans *Génétique, procréation et droit*, Paris, Actes Sud, 1985, p. 349.

LAPPÉ, Marc, « The Limits of Genetic Inquiry » (1987), 17:4 *Hast. Cent. Rep.* 5.

LAW COMMISSION, THE, *Report on Injuries to Unborn Children*, Londres, HMSO, 1974.

LEMKIN, Raphaël, *Axis Rule in Occupied Europe*, Washington (D.C.), Carnegie Endowment for International Peace, 1944.

LEPAGE, Henri, « Destins du droit de propriété » (1985), *Droits (Revue française de théorie juridique)* Paris, P.U.F., 1985.

———, *Pourquoi la propriété ?*, Paris, Hachette, 1985.

LEWIN, Roger, « DNA Typing on the Witness Stand » (1989), 244:4908 *Science* 1033.

LEWONTIN, Richard C., Steven ROSE et Leon J. KAMIN, *Nous ne sommes pas programmés : Génétique, hérédité, idéologie*, Paris, La Découverte, 1985.
LIPPMAN-HAND, A. et F. Clarke FRASER, « Genetic Counseling — The Postcounseling Period: II. Making Reproductive Choices » (1979), 4 *Am. J. Med. Genet.* 73.
MALHERBE, Jean-François, *Pour une éthique de la médecine*, Paris, Larousse, 1987.
MANNING, Morris, « Proof of Facts in Constitutional Cases », dans Gérald-A. BEAUDOIN (dir.), *Causes invoquant la Charte 1986-1987*, Cowansville (Qc), Yvon Blais, 1987, p. 271.
MARX, Jean L., « DNA Fingerprinting Takes the Witness Stand » (1988), 240:4859 *Science* 1616.
———, « Gene Transfer is Coming on Target » (1988), 242:4876 *Science* 191.
MCDOUGAL, Myres S., Harold D. LASSWELL et Lung-Chu CHEN, *Human Rights and World Public Order: The Basic Policies of an International Law of Human Dignity*, New Haven (Conn.), Yale University Press, 1980.
MCKUSICK, Victor A., *Mendelian Inheritance in Man: Catalogs of Autosomal Dominant, Autosomal Recessive, and X-linked Phenotypes*, 9e éd., Baltimore, Johns Hopkins University Press, 1990.
MILUNSKY, Aubrey et George J. ANNAS (dir.), *Genetics and the Law III*, New York, Plenum Press, 1985.
MOTULSKY, Arno G., « Medical Genetics » (1989), 261:19 *JAMA* 2855.
MURRAY, Thomas H., « Warning: Screening Workers for Genetic Risk » (1983), 13:1 *Hast. Cent. Rep.* 5.
NEEL, James V., « Social and Scientific Priorities in the Use of Genetic Knowledge », dans Bruce HILTON, Daniel CALLAHAN, Maureen HARRIS, Peter CONDLIFFE et Burton BERKLEY, *Ethical Issues in Human Genetics, Genetic Counseling and the Use of Genetic Knowledge*, New York, Plenum Press, 1973, p. 353.
« New Tools for Genome Study Being Made » (1988), 24:32 *Medical Post* 28.
NICHOLS, Eve K., *Human Gene Therapy*, Cambridge (Mass.), Harvard University Press, 1988.
NOLAN, Kathleen et Sara SWENSON, « New Tools, New Dilemmas: Genetic Frontiers » (1988), 18:5 *Hast. Cent. Rep.* 40.
NORA, James J. et F. Clarke FRASER, *Medical Genetics: Principles and Practice*, 3e éd., Philadelphie, Lea & Febiger, 1989.
ORGANISATION MONDIALE DE LA SANTÉ et CONSEIL DES ORGANISATIONS INTERNATIONALES DES SCIENCES MÉDICALES, *Directives internationales proposées pour la recheche biomédicale impliquant des sujets humains*, Genève, CIOMS, 1982.
PALCA, Joseph, « Gene Transfer to Humans Approved in the Face of Advice » (1988), 335:6191 *Nature* 577.
———, « Human Genome Organization is Launched with a Flourish » (1988), 335:6188 *Nature* 286.
———, « National Research Council Endorses Genome Project » (1988), 331:6156 *Nature* 467.
« Preimplantation and Early Post-Implantation Diagnosis » (1987), 2:5 *Human Reprod.* 399.
Rapport du comité de travail sur les nouvelles technologies de reproduction humaine, Québec, Ministère de la Santé et des Services sociaux, 1988.
RAWLS, John, *Théorie de la Justice*, Paris, Seuil, 1987.
« A Report from Germany » (1988), 2:3 *Bioethics* 254.
RODGERS, Sanda, « Fetal Rights and Maternal Rights: Is There a Conflict? » (1986), 1 *R.J.F.D.* 456.
ROY, David et Maurice DE WACHTER, *The Life Technologies and Public Policy*, Montréal, Institut de recherches politiques, 1986.
SASS, Hans-Martin, « A Critique of the Enquete Commission's Report on Gene Technology » (1988), 2:3 *Bioethics* 264.
SCHACHTER, Oscar, « Human Dignity as a Normative Concept » (1983), 77 *Am. J. Int'l L.* 848.
SCHMITZ, Cristin, « DNA Fingerprinting » (1989), 48:8 *Lawyer's Weekly* 1.
SÈVE, Lucien, *Recherche biomédicale et respect de la personne humaine : Explication d'une démarche*, Paris, La Documentation française, 1987.
SHAW, Margery W., « Conditional Prospective Rights of the Fetus » (1984), 5 *J. Legal Med.* 63.

SHORT, Elizabeth M., « Proposed ASHG Position on Mapping/Sequencing the Human Genome » (1988), 43:1 *Am. J. Hum. Genet.* 101.
SIEGHART, Paul, *The International Law of Human Rights*, Oxford, Clarendon Press, 1983.
SILBERNER, Joanne, « Finally, Putting Genes Into Humans » (17 octobre 1988), *US News and World Report* 66.
Special article, « Ethical and Social Issues in Screening for Genetic Disease » (1972), 286:21 *N. Engl. J. Med.* 1129.
STEINBOCK, Bonnie, « The Logical Case for 'Wrongful Life' » (1986), 16:2 *Hast. Cent. Rep.* 15.
STEINBROOK, Robert, « In California, Voluntary Mass Prenatal Screening » (1986), 16:5 *Hast. Cent. Rep.* 5.
STRINGER, C.B. et P. ANDREWS, « Genetic and Fossil Evidence for the Origin of Modern Humans » (1988), 239:4845 *Science* 1263.
SUZUKI, David et Peter KNUDTSON, *Genethics: The Ethics of Engineering Life*, Toronto, Stoddart, 1988.
TERRENOIRE, Gwen, « Conseil génétique et eugénisme : le passé du conseil génétique aux États-Unis » (1986), 11 *Cahiers Science, technologie et société* (Éthique et Biologie) Paris, Éd. du C.N.R.S. 171.
U.S. CONGRESS, OFFICE OF TECHNOLOGY ASSESSMENT, *Human Gene Therapy: Background Paper*, Washington (D.C.), OTA, 1984.
———, *Mapping Our Genes: Genome Projects — How Big, How Fast?*, Baltimore, Johns Hopkins University Press, 1988.
———, *Medical Testing and Health Insurance*, Washington (D.C.), OTA, 1988.
———, *New Developments in Biotechnology: Ownership of Human Tissues and Cells*, Washington (D.C.), U.S. Government Printing Office, 1987.
———, *The Role of Genetic Testing in the Prevention of Occupational Disease*, Washington (D.C.), OTA, 1983.
U.S. NATIONAL ACADEMY OF SCIENCE, *Genetic Screening: Programs, Principles, and Research*, Washington (D.C.), U.S. Government Printing Office, 1975.
U.S. NATIONAL RESEARCH COUNCIL, *Mapping and Sequencing the Human Genome*, Washington (D.C.), National Academy Press, 1988.
U.S. PRESIDENT'S COMMISSION FOR THE STUDY OF ETHICAL PROBLEMS IN MEDICINE AND BIOMEDICAL AND BEHAVIORAL RESEARCH, *Screening and Counseling for Genetic Conditions*, Washington (D.C.), La Commission, 1983.
———, *Splicing Life*, Washington (D.C.), La Commission, 1982.
VEATCH, Robert, Compte rendu, *The Foundations of Bioethics* (1986), 105:6 *Ann. Intern. Med.* 987.
———, *The Foundation of Justice: Why the Retarded and the Rest of Us Have Claims to Equality*, New York, Oxford University Press, 1986.
———, *A Theory of Medical Ethics*, New York, Basic Books, 1981.
VOGEL, Friedrich et Arno G. MOTULSKY (dir.), *Human Genetics: Problems and Approaches*, 2e éd., Berlin, Springer-Verlag, 1986.
WARNOCK, Mary, « Do Human Cells Have Rights? » (1987), 1:1 *Bioethics* 1.
WERTZ, Dorothy C. et John C. FLETCHER (dir.), *Ethics and Human Genetics: A Cross-Cultural Perspective*, Berlin, Springer-Verlag, 1989.